AF560300

TRANSGENIC CROPS

ENCYCLOPEDIA OF AGRICULTURE V

TRANSGENIC CROPS

By

Renuka Sharma

DISCOVERY PUBLISHING HOUSE PVT. LTD.
INDIA

Published by:
Tilak Wasan
DISCOVERY PUBLISHING HOUSE PVT. LTD.
4383/4B, Ansari Road, Darya Ganj
New Delhi-110 002 (India)
Phone : +91-11-23279245; 23253475; 43596065
E-mail: discoverybooksindia@gmail.com
discoverypublishinghouse@gmail.com
namitwasan9@gmail.com
web : www.discoverypublishinggroup.com

First Edition: **2013**

Reprinted: **2019**

ISBN: 978-93-5056-020-4 (Set)
ISBN: 978-93-5056-025-9

Transgenic Crops

Printed at:
Infinity Imaging Systems
Delhi

Preface

The breakthrough in science that permitted genes to be identified and manipulated as molecular ushered in the agricultural technology era, which is now more than a decade old. The new tools of agricultural technology are changing the way scientists can address problems in the life sciences; agriculture is one area facing major changes as a result of this new technology. The unanticipated rapid ratio at which discoveries and their applications in technology have unfolded has stored the capacity of society – more specifically, our agricultural research and educational institutions to absorb and adjust to change. We are challenged by pressing decisions opportunities, and problems that we face now and will continue to face in the future. Competition from abroad impels us to devise and use new technologies that can improve the efficiency and quality of agricultural production. These concerns led to this study – an overview of how the agricultural research system is responding to the latest technology and how it might prepare for future opportunities. Agricultural technology is moving in many directions with positive results – crop improvement, production of transgenic plants, vaccine development and diagnostic methods are some impending applications – but the development of genetic engineering's tools can be found in almost every agricultural discipline. The exception is that, through lessions learned, adequate food will be made available to the whole world in the future. The present title **"Endcyclopedia of Agriculture"** has been planned, written, and edited with the intention of being useful for the beginners, researchers and scientists involved in the field of agricultural genetic transformation.

I would like to express my sincere thanks to Dr. M.P. Arora, whose continuous inspiration and encouragement initiated me in bringing out this title.

I am specially indebted to my husband Mr. Rajeev Sharma for his enthusiastic support, constant helpfulness and good spirit during the writing of this title.

Quite frankly, this book would not have been written without the aid of my daughter Shreya, who co-operated patiently during periods of neglect.

Special and sincere thanks to my parents and in laws for their blessings and continuous encouragement in bringing out this title.

To make the work more comprehensive and informative, I have consulted many authoritative books, research journals, abstracts, monographs etc., so there can be no claim to originality except in the manner of treatment.

I also express thanks to my friends and colleagues whose continuous inspirations have initiated me to bring out this title.

I express my gratitude to Mr. Wasan and staff of M/s Discovery Publishing House Pvt. Ltd. for their whole hearted co-operation in the publication of this title.

I acknowledge the fact that the development and publication of this book would not have been possible without the assistance and encouragement of colleagues, research scholars and students. They are so numerous to mention. I thank all of them most warmly for helping to create the present title.

Any worthwhile criticism and suggestions for improvement would be thankfully acknowledged.

Renuka Sharma

CONTENTS

Chapter 1

TRANSGENIC PLANTS

Carbohydrates are a ubiquitous part of human and animal diets. Their *abundance* and omnipresence are difficult to overestimate. Carbohydrates provide clothing and shelter as the cellulose of cotton and wood, a means of *communications* as the cellulose of paper, dietary nutrients and fiber as starch and b-glucans, and the basis for most beverages ranging from fruit juice and soft drinks to cognac.

The starch of most plant-derived foods and beverages is derived from either seeds or tubers. The properties of these are determined largely by their carbohydrate and protein components. Humans throughout time, from the earliest hunter-gatherers to today's consumer, have chosen specific foodstuffs and processed them for consumption, generally unknowingly, in a way reflecting the *functionality* of their carbohydrate components.

Starch, as the major edible carbohydrate component of foods, a major industrial feedstock, and the most abundant edible biopolymer, attracts the greatest attention as well regarding its functional properties and the possibilities for their modification.

Besides their importance for food and beverage, plant carbohydrates are *increasingly* used in many industrial sectors including the production of *biodegradable* plastics. They can be seen as a "green" alternative to hydrocarbon-based polymers.

Carbohydrates contribute to many of the properties of novel "functional foods," ranging from *sweetening* to flavor *enhancement*, fat replacement, dietary fiber *supplementation*, texture *preservation*, and edible packaging. This chapter will concentrate on the synthesis and transgenic modification of α–glucans, in *particular* starch, and fructans in plants and leave aside the β-glucans including cellulose.

APPROACHES TO STARCH AND CARBOHYDRATE MODIFICATION

The various applications require starches with different *properties*, whether as raw starch granules, as gelatinized (cooked) starch, or as various hydrosylates. Suitable *starches* can be found by selecting either the appropriate plant source (tuber vs. grain), the particular plant variety, or the specific *postharvest* treatment.

Postharvest, chemical or *enzymatic* alteration ("modification") of starch structure and hence properties has begun to be replaced with alternative strategies. *Conventional* breeding is one approach. If germplasm with the desired properties exists, easily scored and closely linked markers are needed for *introgression* of the requisite genes into a breeding line with good agronomic *characteristics*.

Furthermore, a rapid screening method is needed for the trait. Often, insufficient variation in storage *carbohydrate* properties can be found in the existing germplasm pool for a given crop. In this case, another option is to create the exotic germplasm by transgenic methods. There are basically four *approaches* to *transgenic modification*.

The first is to change the quantity of *carbohydrates* in a seed or storage organ. Altering the relationship between the export strength of the carbohydrate source (generally, leaves) and the import strength of the carbohydrate sink (tubers, seeds) not only generally affects carbohydrate quantity and *ultimately* harvest yield but also may affect quality and *downstream* applications.

Modulation of the expression levels or *introduction* of the biosynthetic enzymes, or introduction of novel forms with different catalytic properties, for an existing pathway such as starch biosynthesis is a broad second category of approaches. Another is the *expression* of *degradative*, glucolytic or glycolytic *activities* to alter the structure of a native *carbohydrate*.

Lastly, an entirely novel pathway of branch can be introduced based on the metabolites present in the target tissue. These approaches will be *examined* in turn. Because starch is the major storage *carbohydrate* in plants, we shall concentrate on its biosynthesis, properties, and their *modification*.

STARCH STRUCTURE

Amylose and Amylopectin, the Two Components of Starch

Virtually all of the starch used by humans is storage starch, that which *accumulates* in seeds and tubers, and our knowledge of starch *structure* is mainly based on studies of this. Starch consists of two components, amylose and amylopectin, both of which are largely α–1,4-linked glucan polymers. Starch *structure* has been subject to many general reviews.

Generally, amylose constitutes 20-30% of the total and contains rare, α–1,6 branches, whereas amylopectin, which has frequent α–1,6 branches, makes up the rest. *Amylopectin* consists of linear, α–1,4-linked glucan chains *frequently* branched by α–1,6 bonds.

The average chain length (degree of polymerization, DP) in amylopectin is on average 21-25 *glucoses* which, because of the frequent branching, yields a weight-average *molecular* weight

Table 1.1: Starch Components and Their Properties

Property	*Amylose*	*Amylopectin*	*Phytoglycogen*
Degree of branching	Branches rare	Branched	Highly branched
Solubility in water	Insoluble	Insoluble	Soluble
Limiting viscosity number mL $(mg)^{-1}$	240-390	185-188	
Iodine affinity, mg I_2 (100 mg)$^{-1}$ starch	19-19.9	0.33-1.5	
Molecular size	10^5-10^6	10^7-10^8	10^7
Glucose residues (DP)	~103	~105-106	~10^5
Average chain length (CL)	100-1800	18-25	10-14
A-chains/B-chains		1.0-1.5	0.6-1.1
Iodine colouration (λ_{max})	660	530-550	430-450
β-amylolysis limit (%)	~70	~55	~30-45
α-amylolysis limit (%)	~100	~90	~80

(M_W) for amylopectin about 300 times larger than that of amylose. The branch points are not randomly *distributed* within amylopectin but rather are clustered. The chains of amylopectin are classified as the C-chain, the "core" chain *containing* the only reducing glucose in the molecule; the B-chains, which branch from the C-chain; and the A–chains, which are defined as the *outermost* branches of the molecule.

Progressive amylolytic digestion followed by *chromatography* has shown that the *B-chains* are *distributed* in several size classes. Chains of DP 15-20 are found in the linear portions of clusters, whereas chains of DP 45-60 extend between clusters.

A third form of starch, the highly branched "phytoglycogen," appears in certain mutants and is now thought to be an *intermediate* in the *biosynthesis* of amylopectin. The general properties of these *components* are *presented* in table elsewhere in this chapter.

Starch Granules

Starch is packed into granules whose shape and size are characteristic of each plant species. Starch granules in potato tubers, for example, are smooth, irregular, and 15-75 μm in diameter, whereas those from maize are *polyhedral* and 5-20 μm. The starches of the Triticeae cereals including barley and wheat are present in a bimodal *distribution* of large A-granules (15-30 μm) and small B-granules (2-5 μm). Starch granule form confers properties to the starches that are *important* in various *applications*, from paper coating to brewing.

In malting, the A- and *B-granules* are amylolytically digested in different manners, the A-granules by pinholing followed by internal *digestion* and the B-granules by surface erosion. This

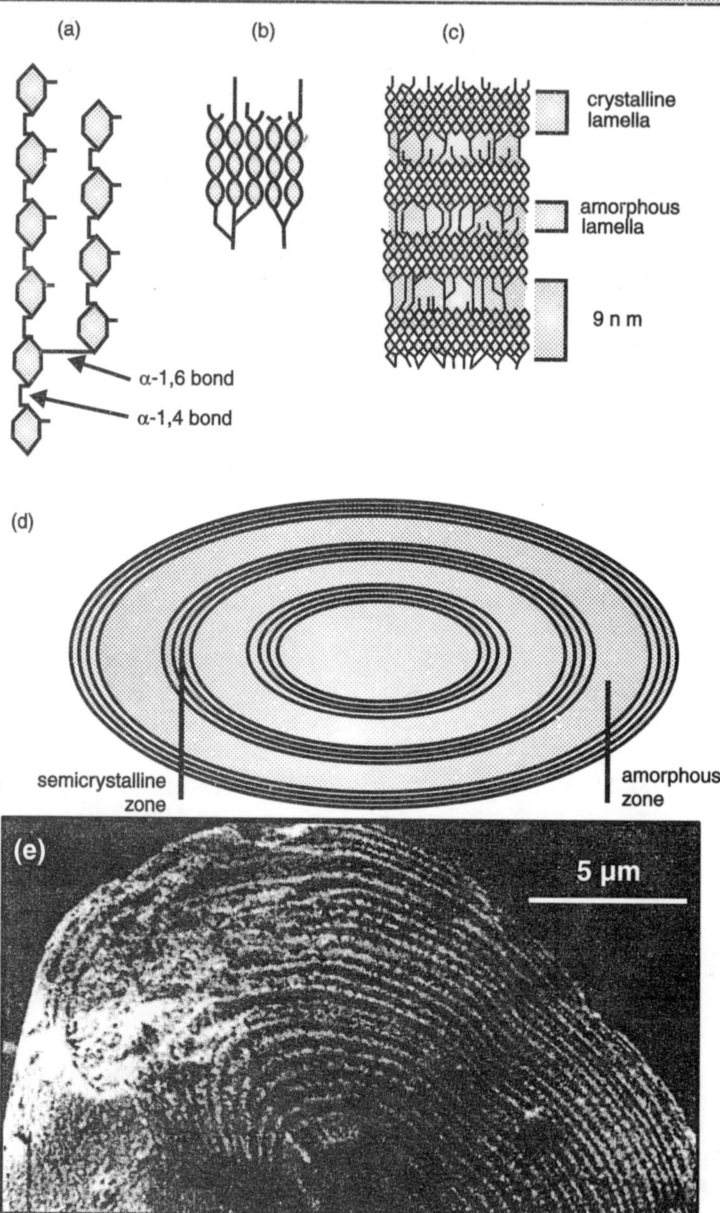

Figure 1.1: Current view of starch structure and its successive stages of organization within the granule, (a) Segment of amylopectin indicating the two bond types, (b) An amylopectin cluster showing the double helices formed between adjacent chains, (c) Helices are packed into crystalline lamellae spaced at intervals of 9 nm, interspersed with amorphous regions containing the parallel branch points, (d) The interspersed crystalline and amorphous lamellae form concentric semicrystalline zones several hundreds of nanometers wide. These zones are separated by amorphous zones lacking orderly packing of amylopectin helices. A pair of semicrystalline and amorphous zones form a growth ring in the granule, (e) Scanning electron micrograph of a potato starch granule showing the growth rings. The granule has been digested with α–amylase to remove partially the amorphous zones, which are more easily hydrolyzed.

leads to uneven *conversion* during malting, a problem in brewing. The existence of mutants affecting starch granule size distribution or *morphology* in various plants including barley and pea indicates that *engineering* of crops for specific granule size *distributions* is in principle possible.

The properties of starch, and the ultimate effects of biotechnologically induced changes in starch *biosynthesis*, largely reside in the organization of the starch granule. Work with advanced physical *techniques* and biochemical studies *extending* back almost 20 years have produced much insight into granule structure, the generally accepted view of which is *presented* in figure elsewhere in this chapter.

At the lowest level of *organization*, paired, adjacent amylopectin chains form double helices. The helices are *arranged* as clusters, and the clusters in turn form *crystallites*. The linear, helical regions of the α–1,4 glucan chains form, in a radial direction, crystalline lamellae.

These alternate at a *periodicity* of 9 nm with amorphous regions containing the α–1,6 branch points. Sets of these *alternating* crystalline and amorphous regions form semicrystalline zones hundreds of nanometers wide that alternate with broad amorphous zones.

Together, the *semicrystalline* and amorphous bands form concentric shells termed growth rings. Interspersed within the amylopectin structure is the amylose *component* of the granule. In addition, lipids are tightly associated with the helix cores and proteins, in particular granule-bound starch *synthase* (GBSS), are tightly bound to the starch.

The emergent properties of starch *granules* when treated with *enzymes*, solvents, or heat are greatly affected by the *organization* of the granule and by the bound lipids. These properties are related to the activities of the starch synthetic enzymes in complex ways, *complicating* rational approaches to specific targets in starch *functionality*. The genetic, developmental, and biochemical variations among plants *producing* storage starch result in a wide range of final properties of the starch.

STARCH DEPOSITION

In storage tissues, starch is *synthesized* within amyloplasts, which are derived as are chloroplasts from proplastids. Starch is also *synthesized* diurnally for *transient* assimilate storage in leaf chloroplasts. Starch biosynthesis is part of the complex process of *tuberization*, conversion of a stem into storage tissue, in potato and other crops *producing* storage tubers.

In the cereals, starch is deposited in the starchy endosperm, whereas in most dicotyledonous plants it *accumulates* in fleshy cotyledons. Within developing endosperm, starch granules appear *within* a day of the onset of *cellularization* and continue until the grain dries. Tubers, however, have no sharp end point for starch *biosynthesis*.

Source of Photosynthate for Starch Biosynthesis

Starch biosynthesis with its key *enzymes* and metabolites is *diagrammed* in figure elsewhere in this chapter. Photosynthate is generally supplied as sucrose via the phloem of the *maternal* tissues. Both source and sink strength are critical to starch yield in storage organs.

In some plants, breakdown and resynthesis of sucrose appear necessary to maintain a sucrose gradient and thus sink strength, although this is not the case in others such as barley. The sucrose taken into the endosperm is *subsequently* converted into *UDPglucose* by sucrose *synthase* (UDPglucose:D-fructose-2-*glucosyltransferase*, EC 2.4.1.13):

sucrose + UDP → UDPglucose + D-fructose

This is a reversible reaction but, under the conditions found in storage tissues, the breakdown of sucrose is favoured. In many plants, sucrose synthase activity appears to be important to overall sink *strength* and hence yield. Antisense-mediated *reductions* in sucrose synthase levels in *transgenic* tomato and potato reduce overall starch biosynthesis, as do mutations to the sucrose synthase genes such as found in the maize *shl* and *sus1* mutants.

The UDPglucose product of sucrose synthase is then converted to glucose- l-phosphate by UDPglucose pyrophosphorylase (UTPglucose- l -phosphate uridylyltransferase, EC 2.7. 7.9). The UDPglucose pyrophosphorylase enzyme has been purified and the gene encoding it cloned from barley as well as from other plants. Glucose- l-phosphate is further processed to ADPglucose, the specific nucleotide sugar that serves as the substrate for the starch synthases. This is catalyzed

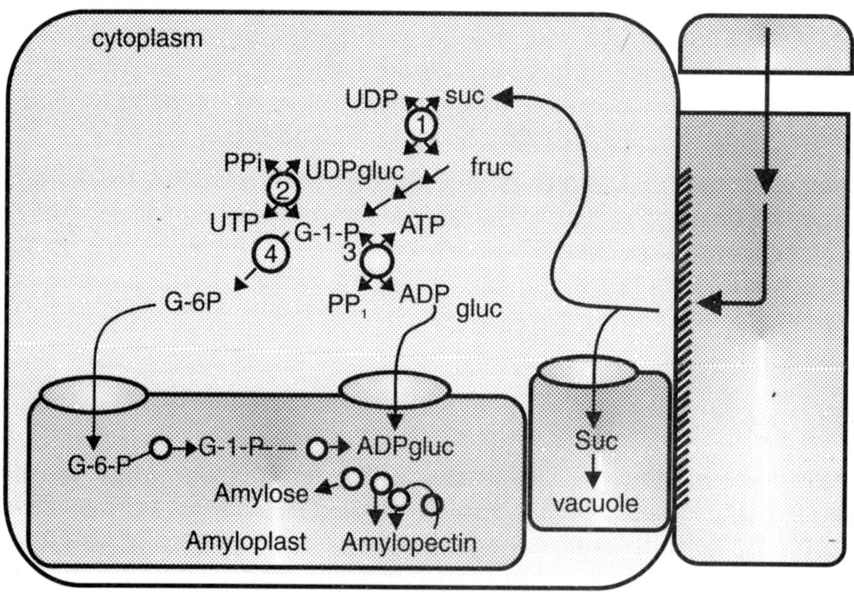

Figure 1.2: Schematic diagram of the currently accepted pathway for starch biosynthesis in storage organs. Photosynthate is transported as sucrose from source leaves through the phloem to the storage organ. It is then moved as sucrose into the storage tissues or cleaved in some plants by a cell wall invertase to glucose and fructose (not shown) to be resynthesized as sucrose by sucrose phosphate synthase in the cytoplasm. Storage as fructans in the vacuole represents an alternative to starch biosynthesis in temperate grasses. The key enzymes of starch biosynthesis are (1) sucrose synthase (SucSyn), (2) UDPglucose pyrophosphorylase (UGP), (3) ADPglucose pyrophosphorylase (AGP), (4) phosphoglucomutase (PGM), (5) granule-bound starch synthase (GBSS), (6) soluble starch synthase (SS), (7) starch branching enzyme (SBE), and (8) debranching enzyme (DBE). Not all alternative shunts in the pathway are shown. Fructose can be converted to glucose-1-phosphate via fructokinase (FK), phosphoglucoisomerase (PGI), and phosphoglucomutase (PGM). The relative proportions of ADPglucose synthesized in the cytoplasm and amyloplast vary from species to species. Translocators are shown as ovals on the organelle membranes.

by the enzyme ADPglucose pyrophosphorylase (AGP, glucose-Iphosphate adenylyltransferase, EC 2.7.7.27) in the reaction

$$\text{ATP} + \alpha\text{–D-glucose-I-phosphate} \rightarrow \text{pyrophosphate} + \text{ADPglucose}$$

The Committed Pathway of Starch Biosynthesis

The conversion of glucose- I -phosphate to ADPglucose by AGP is considered the first specific, or committed, step in starch biosynthesis. The AGP enzyme has been extensively studied and reviewed since the 1960s and also is the target for engineering of the pathway as discussed in the following. The enzyme in all tissues is a heterotretramer of two regulatory (small) and two catalytic (large) subunits.

In most tissues, it is allosterically regulated, activated by 3-phosphoglycerate but inhibited by orthophosphate. Due in part to its regulation and also to the severely shrunken phenotypes of mutants of AGP, it has been seen as the major control point for the flow of carbon into starch. Flux analyses, however, contradict this interpretation. Until recently, it was universally held that AGP is nuclear encoded but localized in the plastids in all tissues, photosynthetic and storage.

However, at least for maize and barley *endosperm*, a combination of investigations on the *bt-1* mutant, studies of isolated amyloplasts, and messenger RNA (mRNA) *transcriptional* analyses has shown that up to 95% of the cereal AGP is cytosolic.

A reasonable explanation for the difference between *chloroplasts* and amyloplasts regarding AGP *localization* rests on *chloroplasts* being sources of energy whereas *amyloplasts* are sinks. If AGP were restricted to amyloplasts, the ATP would have to be imported and then converted to PPi and AGPglucose. This is *energetically* less favourable than movement of *ADPglucose* into the plastid and transport of ADP outward in return.

Nevertheless, some AGP is plastidic even in the cereals, where the majority is cytoplasmic; the relative roles of the two forms remain to be established. Furthermore, in potato tubers it appears that the majority of the carbon moves as *glucose-6-phosphate* into the amyloplasts, where it is *subsequently* converted to glucose- I-phosphate and then to starch.

The details of the pathway in any particular plant are important regarding the *possibilities* of modifying starch quantity or quality. Starch content as well as starch quality can be affected by modulating the activity and properties of the AGP present in storage tissues.

Synthesis of Amylose

Amylose consists of glucose subunits linked by α–1,4 bonds into linear chains, with occasional α–1,6 branch points connecting additional α–1,4linked chains onto a backbone. In barley, the average chain length is 1800 glucose units, but it may vary in the cereals between 1000 and 4400 glucose moieties, yielding a molecular weight of between 1.6 × 105 and 7.1 × 105. In most normal starches, amylose makes up 20-30% of the total by weight.

This is reduced to virtually none in the waxy mutants. The general features of amylose and the other main *component* of starch, amylopectin, are well established. The α–1,4 links in both amylose and amylopectin are made by the starch synthases (EC 2.4.1.21). The enzyme occurs in multiple forms, but all forms use ADPglucose as the glucose donor to the growing chain.

In the storage organs, namely *endosperm*, cotyledons, and tubers, amylose is synthesized by the form called granule-bound starch synthase I (GBSS or GBSSI). The "waxy" starches, perhaps the most common example of a modified *carbohydrate* created through both breeding and transgenic *biotechnology*, virtually completely lack amylose because of the absence of the GBSSI.

The other forms of starch synthase are unable to *compensate* in such mutants, called waxy ("glutinous" in rice) because of the *resulting* property of the starch (the gene for GBSSI thereby being wx). In nonstorage tissues, however, amylose continues to be synthesized in waxy mutants, a form of the starch synthase called GBSSII carrying out the task in the cases examined.

The gene or transcript for GBSSI has been cloned from many sources; alignments of these sequences revealed that these are highly conserved. The α–1,6 branch points in amylose are not synthesized by GBSSI or GBSSII but may derive from the action of a starch branching enzyme (SBE, see next for amylopectin) or from a branched oligosaccharide as the starch-synthetic substrate, with the poorly branched product *subsequently* elongated by GBSS. The substrate for amylose biosynthesis remains *controversial* and in vivo may be either amylopectin chains or soluble *maltooligosaccharides*, both, or neither.

Synthesis of Amylopectin

Amylopectin is considerably more complex as a molecule, and its biosynthesis is commensurately more intriguing. The linear, α–1,4-linked portion of the polymer is produced by the soluble starch synthases (EC 2.4.1.21), which catalyze growth of the α–1,4 glucan chain by addition of glucose residues from ADPglucose. Historically, these enzyme forms received their name because they are not bound tightly to the starch granule, in contrast to the granule-bound starch synthase or GBSS.

More recently, it has become clear that all forms of starch *synthase* are to some extent partitioned onto the starch granules or somehow become trapped in the growing, insoluble granule, so the *original* distinction is not very useful.

The amylopectin-synthesizing starch synthases are found in multiple forms in virtually all plants examined. Alignment of the proteins encoded by the sequenced soluble synthase form divides them into three main groups: SSI, SSII, and SSIII. Investigations of mutants and transgenics lacking or reduced in the activity of one of the SS forms indicate that each plays a specific, or at least preferential, role in amylopectin synthesis.

These efforts have been complemented by expression of specific forms in *E. coli* and analyses of the α-glucan products made in the bacteria. From such experiments, SSII appears to synthesize α–1,4 chains of intermediate length, whereas the SSI form in barley appears to be involved in initiation of new chains. Potatoes expressing antisense to SSII, *consistent* with this view, have reduced relative *abundance* of chains of DP 18-50.

The complexity of amylose *biosynthesis* from the perspective of *engineering* the pathway lies not only in the multiplicity of forms but also in their overlapping roles. Although one form may, because of its kinetics, be responsible for producing chains of a certain size class, in a mutant or transgenic plant where this form is absent another form may substitute but only partially or with *identical* results.

The combination of *overlapping* roles and *pleiotropism* can lead to novel or *unpredicted* amylopectin structures in engineered starches. The soluble synthases cover half of the story of amylopectin biosynthesis, however. The starch branching enzymes (SBEs, α–1,4-glucan, α–1,4glucan-6-glucosyl transferase, EC 2.4.1.18, Q-enzyme) are responsible for producing the α– 1,6 branches on the amylopectin molecule, which can then be further extended by the soluble starch synthases.

Because it is the branching of amylopectin that confers its specific functional properties and behaviour in food and beverage production, the SBEs have attracted *considerable* interest for the genetic tailoring of starch. The SBEs are transferases rather than synthases, detaching an α–1,4 -linked *oligoglucan* from the end of an amylopectin chain and moving it into an α–1,6 position elsewhere in the molecule.

Nevertheless, they stimulate soluble starch synthases by *increasing* the effective substrate concentration determined by the number of nonreducing α–glucan ends in the amylopectin. As with the starch synthases, multiple isoforms have been identified that show organ (usually leaf or storage tissue) or temporal *specificity* in their *expression* patterns. The various forms show differences as well in the length of chains transferred, which has implications for engineering of starch.

These forms have been characterized as A or B types by their distinct properties. Antisense work in potato indicates that SBE A is responsible for *transferring* shorter chains than SBE B because average chain length increases in its absence. The well-known *amylose-extender* (*ae*) mutants illustrate the profound effect SBE has on starch properties.

Rather than containing an increased amount of amylose as would be produced by the GBSS enzyme, these plants are in fact defective in amylopectin *branching*. Over the last several years, a revolution in thinking about amylopectin biosynthesis has taken place with the introduction of the *preamylopectin trimming* model. The model addresses the question of how the nonrandom distribution of branch points typical of amylopectin may arise.

It also helps to explain why mutants lacking a debranching enzyme such as the *sugaryl* of maize or a similar one in the alga *Chlamydomonas* and *Arabidopsis* contain a highly branched α–glucan referred to as phytoglycogen. In the model, SBEs and debranching enzymes (DBEs) carry out *discontinuous* steps of synthesis and amylolysis so that excess branches added by the SBE are removed.

Crystallization of the product removes it from the cycle and fixes the structure as, in essence, a partially debranched glycogen. An alternative, the *soluble glucan recycling* model, has been proposed. In this hypothesis, DBE plays only a subsidiary role in forming amylopectin, helping to turn over branched, soluble oligoglucans. This *hypothesis* explains the occurrence of *phytoglycogen* in DBE mutants but does not take the clustered branching of amylopectin into account.

The validity of the two models is currently difficult to test. Furthermore, the actual in vivo functions of the soluble starch synthases, SBEs, and debranching enzymes still remain to be disentangled from the pleiotropic effects seen in mutants and antisense experiments.

TRANSGENIC MODIFICAITION OF CARBOHYDRATE BIOSYNTHESIS

Efforts to alter carbohydrate biosynthesis extend back to about 1990 and have *proceeded* hand in hand with the use of *overexpression* and antisense inhibition to unravel *carbohydrate* biosynthesis in plants. The approaches can be divided into those that seek to alter starch quantity through affecting the strength of the carbon source or sink, those that attempt to convert starch to simple sugars, those with the goal of altering the amylose/amylopectinratio, those trying to alter amylopectin structure, and lastly those that seek to produce novel carbohydrates through the introduction of new *biosynthetic* activities.

Overviews of these efforts have been made several times from various perspectives. The key point is that grain or tuber quality and end use are related to the structures of the starch and protein components. These structures can be modified *transgenically* if suitable natural mutants are not available.

Alteration of Starch Quantity

Storage organs constitute net consumers or sinks for *photosynthetically* produced carbon, whereas leaves are the sources. Generally, source-sink balances are regulated by sugar levels (hexoses as well as sucrose) and by stress.

Willmitzer and his colleagues *demonstrated* that source strength in tobacco is inhibited by accumulation of sugar in the leaves. Expression of a yeast invertase in the cell wall of tobacco cleaved the sucrose normally loaded into the phloem and blocked its export, mimicking a very weak sink. This work was repeated later in transgenic potato plants, and photosynthesis was shown to be inhibited by sugar accumulation in the leaves.

Using a parallel approach, sink strength was investigated by the same team. Sucrose synthase was *demonstrated*, through its removal in plants expressing sucrose synthase antisense under the strong 35S CaMV promoter, to play a crucial role in *determining* the sink strength of a potato tuber. Similar results were obtained by inhibiting the next step on the starch biosynthetic pathway, glucose- l-phosphate synthesis, through the expression of *pyrophosphatase* and concomitant reduction in pyrophosphate (PPi) content. Following the pathway further, the *accumulation* of both starch and protein was inhibited by antisense *knockdown* of AGPase levels in potato tubers.

Instead, the tubers *accumulated* up to 30% of their dry weight as sucrose and 8% as glucose, resulting in their increased fresh weight but decreased dry weight as well as pleiotropic effects on the *transcription* of other genes on the starch synthetic pathway. Generally, the practical goal is to increase the *accumulation* of starch in tubers or grains rather than to block it.

Low-starch, high-sugar potatoes would be quite poor for a major market sector, chips, crisps, and fries, because sugar accumulation results in discolouration of chips or slices during frying. The postharvest *accumulation* of sugar in tubers has been limited by transgenic inhibition of UDPglucose *pyrophosphorylase* activity.

An alternative, more effective approach was taken more recently by the expression of a tobacco invertase inhibitor in tubers. This reduced conversion of starch to soluble sugars by up to 75%, which appears to be at levels sufficient for the practical improvement of potato processing. Increased sink strength has been engineered through expression of a yeast invertase in the tuber, promoting cleavage of sucrose and hence a stronger translocation gradient to the tuber.

One strategy to improve potato tubers is to increase starch levels. Besides increasing total yield in dry weight, a higher starch content is correlated with a decrease in fat uptake during frying and therefore a more healthful product. In an attempt to do this, a mutant *E. coli* AGP form has been expressed in tubers as a *translational* fusion to a ribulose bisphosphate carboxylase transit peptide and driven by a patatin promoter.

Other efforts using the same AGP form failed to increase starch content because of associated higher turnover of starch into sugars. As reviewed elsewhere, efforts to date to increase yield and hence starch biosynthesis through the *manipulation* of single enzyme levels have not been very predictable.

An example of the capacity of carbohydrate metabolism to yield surprising results is the effect of expressing viral movement proteins in tobacco and potato. The protein MP17 of potato leaf roll virus increased soluble sugar and starch amounts in source leaves but did not affect *photosynthesis* in the leaf blade because of *sequestration* of the sugars in the vacuole.

Although such experiments do not provide a ready recipe for engineering sugar or starch accumulation in plants, much can be learned about carbohydrate metabolism in the meantime, and in the end, effective quantitative manipulations may become straightforward.

Production of Simple Sugars in Storage Organs

As an outcome of analyses of sugar and starch metabolism and source-sink interactions, know-how has developed on the *manipulation* or production of simple sugars in storage organs. Work on cold sweetening of potatoes, a problem discussed in the previous section, examined the role of acid invertase in the process. Although the *experiments* showed that invertases do not control the *conversion* of starch to sugars during storage, they do determine the hexose-to-sucrose ratios.

Transgenic *expression* of soluble invertase could thus be used as a strategy to produce hexoses in vivo. Tomatoes and most fruits, in contrast to potato tubers, accumulate sugar rather than starch. In experiments with goals opposite to what was *attempted* in potato, natural invertase levels in tomato fruits were reduced by an *antisense* strategy.

Sucrose levels increased and hexose levels decreased in the antisense fruits, *accompanied* by a 30% reduction in *fruit* size. In very promising newer work, an alternative approach to the production of hexose, in this case fructose, in potato tubers has been taken. Rather than introduce single enzymatic activities or reduce existing ones, a fusion coding for α–amylase from *Bacillus stearothermophilus* and glucose isomerase from *Thermus thermophilus*, both thermostable, was expressed in transgenic tubers under control of the GBSS promoter.

The complex was not *enzymatically* active during tuber development. Instead, production of fructose and glucose was achieved by crushing the tubers and heating for 45 minutes to 65°C. A parallel approach, demonstrated in transgenic tobacco, was reported by a different group slightly thereafter. In related work, a heat-toleran *β-glucanase* has been transferred to two malting varieties of barley.

This approach should improve malting quality through reduction of the content of 6-glucans in wort, the source of filtration problems and of cloudiness in beer. The native β-glucanases do not withstand well the heating of the mashing process.

These experiments clearly demonstrate the potential of in planta starch *modification* and of transferring an industrial process into the farmer's field to create a novel product. An example of an unexpected effect on carbohydrate synthesis or turnover from a transgene was shown through overexpression of wheat thioredoxin *h* in barley endosperm.

Thioredoxin *h* has been known to be important in *germination* for mobilization of storage protein in the endosperm. The thioredoxin must first be reduced, and the NADPH needed for this can be produced through hydrolysis of starch in the endosperm. Thus, it is perhaps satisfying but *nonetheless* surprising that overexpressed thioredoxin *h* should lead to a fourfold increase in α–1,6-debranching (*pullulanase*) activity in *germinating* grains.

Although the authors do not present the glucan profile, this approach should greatly alter the limit dextrin profile of germinating grain and have an impact on malting. The disaccharide trehalose, known for many years to be produced primarily by fungi and some insects, attracted interest because of its potential use as an osmoprotectant or stress-mitigating agent.

Efforts were therefore made to engineer its expression in tobacco and potato through the introduction of trehalose-6-phosphate synthase (*otsA*) and trehalose-6-phosphate phosphatase (*otsB*) genes from *E. coli*.

Although only very low levels of trehalose (0.11 mg g^{-1} fresh weight) could be obtained in this way, it was discovered that this poor yield is due at least in part to the presence of native trehalase activity not only in the transgenic regenerants but also in the control plants.

It later became clear that the enzymatic machinery for synthesizing trehalose is in fact universal among the angiosperms, although in most plants trehalase blocks the *accumulation* of the sugar.

This would not have been realized if control *experiments* with the trehalase inhibitor validamycin A had not been carried out, and it illustrates that metabolic *engineering* in plants is still very much of an adventure.

Alteration of the Amylose Complement in Starch

Some of the earliest efforts at qualitatively altering starch biosynthesis were directed at the amylose-to-amylopectin ratio. This was because the abundance of natural waxy mutants showed that amylose could be *eliminated* by suppression of GBSS activity and because low-amylose starches had certain processing advantages.

The first successful creation of a low-amylose (*amf*) potato was achieved in the group of Jacobsen and Visser through mutagenesis rather than transformation. This was followed by antisense expression of GBSS by the same group. Often, antisense suppression of endogenous genes succeeds even without full sequence identity in the transgene.

In other experiments, the GBSS of cassava, bearing only 74% identity to potato GBSS, was able in some *regenerant* lines to inhibit native GBSS synthesis completely. *Glutinous*, or amylose-deficient, rice is important in the diet of Japan, but a range of amylose contents may offer broader uses in foods.

An antisense approach to GBSS *suppression* in rice yielded transgenic lines varying in their amylose content from slight reduction to complete absence. In plants more *recalcitrant* to *transformation* such as wheat, the more traditional approach of *combining* mutants by crossing has so far been more effective in achieving low-amylose lines.

Alteration of Amylopectin Structure

A major goal in many laboratories has been the transgenic tailoring of amylopectin structure. The reason for this is that much of starch *functionality* in cooking, baking, and extrusion is determined by the degree and pattern of *branching* in amylopectin.

Linear chains readily form *interchain* hydrogen bonds, producing crystalline regions in starch granules and falling out of solution in the process called retrogradation in *gelatinized*, cooked starch. Lower levels of *crystallinity* result in more stable, but more wettable, gels. In malting and *fermentation*, digestibility by amylase is also directly linked to amylopectin structure.

Exoglucanases, in particular β-amylase, digest inward from the *nonreducing* ends of α–1,4-glucan chains in starch. These enzymes are blocked by α–1,6 bonds, yielding a "limit" dextrin. In malting, the *endoglucanase* α–amylase is also present, breaking the α–1,4 bonds within the glucan chain.

Because α–amylase does not cleave terminal α–1,4 bonds or those near α–1,6 bonds, α–limit dextrins remain after digestion. Hence, the processing benefits of increased yield of monosaccharides and disaccharides in starch hydrolysis and of tailoring of starch behaviour during cooking have driven interest in using transgenic approaches. One of the first efforts in which starch structure was altered in a *transgenic* plant involved expression of the *E. coli* glycogen synthase (*glgA*) in potato.

Glycogen synthase carries out the same reaction as plant starch synthases, *transferring* glucoses into α–1,4 glucan chains. Total starch content in the tubers declined, and amylose was reduced from 23% to 8-9%. The short chains (A + B1) in the amylopectin increased from 66% of the total chains detectable following hydrolysis to 85%, while the long (B2 + B3) chains decreased from 33% to 15%.

In a complementary effort, the *amf* low-amylose potato, which had been developed earlier by mutation breeding, was transformed with the gene for the *E. coli* glycogen branching enzyme (*glgB*). As in the previous example, this enzyme carries out the same reaction as the *corresponding* starch branching enzyme of the plant, although the final product in bacteria is highly branched glycogen.

Up to 25% more branches were made in the transgenic amylopectin and average chain length dropped, associated with more short chains of DP < 16. For certain applications, it would be highly useful to obtain virtually pure amylose directly from the plant rather than through chemical *fractionation* of starch.

So-called high-amylose or amylose-extender cereals have long been known, but, as described earlier, this is due not to synthesis of more of the product of GBSS ("true" amylose) but rather to less SBE activity and hence a less branched, more amylosic, amylopectin.

Taking a cue from these mutants, a group at Unilever was able to produce potato tubers virtually lacking normal amylopectin but containing apparent amylose levels as high as found in any commercial cereal.

Potato starch is phosphorylated in the amylose fraction, the phosphorylation conferring increased solubility, and this transgenic starch contained fivefold higher *phosphorus* contents than normal.

Rather than knocking out the branching enzyme activity to alter *amylopectin* structure, the Kossmann laboratory expressed a chimeric antisense construct against the genes of both major soluble starch synthases, SSIII and SSII, in potato. Total starch synthase activity was reduced up to 90%, but amylose production was normal and amylopectin not eliminated.

Instead, the amylopectin contained more chains of DP < 15, fewer of 15 to 80 glucose units, and more very long chains. The effect of removing one or the other SS form was not consistent with *eliminating* both *simultaneously*, indicating a complex interaction between the SS forms during amylopectin biosynthesis. In a more direct approach, the Kossmann group was able to modify the amount of starch phosphorylation in a transgenic tuber.

The group began by *isolating* proteins bound to starch and raising *antibodies* to them, with the expectation that starch-bound proteins would in some way be involved in starch biosynthesis. A gene for one of these, a protein of -160 kDa, was cloned by screening a complementary DNA (cDNA) expression library with the antiserum. This protein, named Rl, bears no resemblance to any previously *characterized* enzyme of starch *biosynthesis*.

When the level of this protein is reduced in antisense-transformed potatoes, the level of starch phosphorylation is likewise lowered to 10-50% of normal. Glucose-6-phosphate was *commensurately* reduced, and the effect on starch phosphorus levels was seen at both C-3 and C-6 positions to an equal degree. When R1 was expressed in *E. coli*, it led to phosphorylation of the bacterial glycogen.

Coincidentally, cold-induced *sweetening*, discussed earlier, was decreased through a secondary effect on starch digestibility. Curiously, in the antisense transgenic plants, leaves accumulated starch in excess of normal.

It remains to be seen whether the gene can be used to phosphorylate starch in plants particularly. The authors reported that similar sequences are expressed in rice and *Arabidopsis*, yet these starches are not normally phosphorylated. If activation of phosphorylation becomes possible in the cereals, an important new class of starches will be available to the marketplace.

Production of Nonstarch Carbohydrates

The interconvertibility of many of the sugar metabolites on the starch biosynthetic pathway in leaves and storage organs by native and *exogenous* enzymes indicates that, in principle, many new carbohydrates could be synthesized in transgenic plants.

An early attempt at this was the production of cyclodextrins in potato tubers. Cyclodextrins are rings comprising six to eight glucose units produced by bacterial cyclodextrin glucosyltransferases from a starch substrate. This group at Calgene expressed a *Klebsiella* cyclodextrin *glucosyltransferase* in potato tubers driven by a patatin promoter.

They were able to produce both six-unit (α-) and seven-unit *β-cyclodextrins* by this approach, although the yield was exceptionally low, 0.001-0.01% of the starch being converted to cyclodextrins. A more promising effort was made to produce mannitol in transgenic tobacco.

Sugar alcohols or polyols such as mannitol and sorbitol are found in diverse plant species, where they are believed to confer osmoregulatory and stress-ameliorating functions, as well as in bacterial, fungi, and mammals.

An *E. coli* gene for mannitol-l-phosphate dehydrogenase (*mtlD*) was expressed in tobacco and drove production of mannitol in excess of 6 μmol $(g)^{-1}$ of fresh weight in the leaves and in roots. In further work by the same group, specific targeting of this enzyme to tobacco chloroplasts led to *accumulation* of up to 100 mM mannitol in the plastids of one *transgenic* line, which was otherwise *phenotypically normal*.

The mannitol increased resistance to oxidative stress induced by methyl viologen, apparently through improved scavenging of hydroxyl radicals. Useful as this may be for plant improvement, no one has yet attempted commercial production and harvesting of mannitol in this manner. Perhaps the greatest attention has been paid to the *biosynthesis* of fructans in transgenic plants.

Fructans are fructose polymers localized, unlike starch, in vacuoles rather than plastids. They are synthesized by disproportionation, whereby a fructosyl residue is first *transferred* from one sucrose to another to make the shortest fructan, gluc-fruc-fruc. The process *proceeds* by further fructosyl *transfers* from sucrose as well as by transfers between fructans.

Mature fructans are found with a wide variety of branching patterns. In temperate grasses such as barley, fructans are an alternative to starch for carbon storage. This *accumulation* of fructans appears to contribute to yield stability under conditions unfavourable for starch biosynthesis because the fructans can later be converted to starch when *conditions* improve.

They also accumulate early in *endosperm development* but are turned over to support synthesis of starch as the grain matures. If starch biosynthesis is reduced by cold temperatures or blocked such as in the *shx* mutant of barley, fructans rather than starch may persist or accumulate. Aspects of fructan biosynthesis have been *summarized*. The focus on fructan engineering derives from its use as a potential pro- or prebiotic, *antitumorigenic* component of the human diet.

The most common sources of fructans, in particular inulin, have been the Jerusalem artichoke (*Helianthus tuberosus*) and chicory. However, initial efforts at engineering production of fructans in transgenic tobacco employed the bacterial *SacB* gene, encoding levan sucrase, from *Bacillus subtilis*. The transformed plants *accumulated* 3-8% fructan of the levan type found in the bacterium.

In a second effort with a bacterial transgene, the Willmitzer group *expressed* levan sucrase from *Erwinia amylovora* in the transgenic potato line *previously* engineered to be starch free with an antisense AGP. When the levan sucrase was targeted to the vacuole, 12 to 19% of the tuber dry weight was present as levan. However, yield was not increased relative to the parent line lacking starch. The first fructan synthetic enzyme to be cloned from a plant was sucrose-fructan *6-fructosyltransferase* (6-SFT) from barley. The group then expressed this clone in tobacco and in chicory.

Chicory normally produces fructan of a different type than those, the *graminans* and phleins, found in barley. The transgenic tobacco was able to synthesize the trisaccharide kestose as well as *unbranched* fructans of the phlein type. Chicory, normally making inulin, gained the ability to make graminan fructans, in *particular* the tetrasaccharide bifurcose, which is the main form in barley leaves.

In further experiments, chicory was transformed with a gene for an enzyme from onion, fructan:fructan 6G-*fructosyltransferase* (6GFFT), a key enzyme in the synthesis of the inulins found in the Liliales, which had been cloned by screening with a 6-SFT probe from barley.

Expression of the onion gene in chicory led to synthesis of the expected oniontype branched fructans as well as of linear inulin. Following similar lines with potatoes, a clone encoding a 6-SFT-like enzyme was first isolated from a cDNA library of the globe artichoke (*Cynara scolymus*).

When transformed into potato, the transgenic tubers produced high levels of 1-kestose along with nystose and traces of *fructosylnystose*. In subsequent work, the same group expressed both the sucrose: sucrose 1-fructosyltransferase (1-SST) and the fructan:fructan *1fructosyltransferase* from *C. scolymus* in transgenic potatoes.

The tubers produced up to 5% of their dry weight as high-molecular-weight inulins of a range identical to those found in the native artichoke, and some fructan was also detected in leaves. The tuber fructans were synthesized partly at the expense of starch production. An obvious choice as the transgene host for fructan biosynthesis is the sugar beet, which stores sucrose, the very substrate needed, rather than starch, for fructans.

When the gene for 1-SST, cloned from *H. tuberosus* together with that for 1-fructan:fructan fructosyl transferase (1-FFT), was transferred into sugar beet, the expected small fructans up to DP 4 were obtained. Remarkably, more than 90% of the sucrose of the beet was converted into fructans, and no deleterious effects on plant growth were observed under greenhouse conditions.

CONCLUSIONS

Plants are well suited as producers of modified starch and novel *carbohydrates*. Photosynthesis supplies a sucrose feedstock to carbohydrate storage organs, and the many intermediate steps in the conversion of sucrose to starch represent potential branch points at which the sugar may be shunted to new products. Storage starch, being insoluble, is not *physiologically* active, and the many *mutations* affecting starch synthesis *demonstrate* that a wide variety of structures can be tolerated by the plant.

Tubers and storage roots (beets) are not required for propagation, so the storage starch in these organs need not be accessible to the plant for turnover. Cereal grain starch is, however, important in *germination*; therefore, modification or *replacement* of this carbon source must take physiological needs into account.

To date, the main efforts in carbohydrate engineering in plants have been directed to alterations in starch yield, to increasing or decreasing the effective amylose content, and to changing the degree of branching in amylopectin.

Antisense approaches have been highly effective in bringing about *qualitative* changes in starch, although the type of starch produced has not been fully predictable. Great progress has been made over the last several years in *understanding* amylopectin *biosynthesis*.

However, the intricacies of the interactions between the various isoforms of starch synthase, starch *branching* enzyme, and debranching *enzymes* continue to dog attempts at rational starch design based on the functional properties desired in the final product.

Part of the difficulty lies as well in the elaborate nature of the starch structure itself, our limited ability to determine the structure fully as can be done for proteins or nucleic acids, and the complex relationship between gelatinization and *retrogradation* thermodynamics and rheology and starch structure.

The most success in producing novel carbohydrates has been achieved by the transfer of fructan *biosynthesis* from plants where it is common to other crops, *particularly* sugar beet and potato, where these carbohydrates are not normally found.

Fructans attract increasing interest as functional foods. Ultimately, the position of starch and other plant carbohydrates as "green," greenhouse-neutral replacements for petrochemicals offers great potential for the farming of crops containing *specialized* storage products.

In addition to nonfood uses, applications ranging from fat substitutes to fiber (as "resistant starch") in novel foods promise to create new markets for plant carbohydrates and new demand for their creation.

At present, however, the rejection by the public of genetic engineering in general, widespread in Europe and growing in North America and elsewhere despite the *environmental* benefits it can bring to agriculture, is *discouraging* growth in the production of transgenic carbohydrates.

It remains to be seen whether modified starch and *carbohydrates* produced in transgenic plants but destined for nonfood products can escape such pressures.

Chapter 2

TRANSGENE TECHNOLOGY

Two fertilisation events occur in angiosperm species. During these processes one sperm fuses with the egg and the *resulting* zygote *subsequently* develops into an embryo. The other sperm fuses with the secondary nucleus in the central cell forming a *primary* endosperm cell which develops into endosperm. Now these two *fertilisation* events can be *accomplished in vitro.*

As has been possible for a long time with animal and lower plant gametes, *in vitro* fertilisation (IVF) can be performed with single higher plant gametes. It has been performed mainly with maize. The *application* of single cell culture techniques allows single zygotes to develop into embryos and fertile plants, as well as single *in vitro* fertilised central cells to develop into endosperm. In culture, the zygote without an *endosperm* and the primary *endosperm* cell without an embryo are able to develop in a manner similar to that *in vivo.*

They are able to self-organise without mother tissue. Thus, *an in vitro* model system for investigations of zygotic *embryogenesis* and endosperm development is now available to dissect more precisely the early processes which are developmentally important.

To date *comprehensive cytological* and *ultrastructural in vivo* data on *double fertilisation* in maize are available, but there is a lack of molecular information on gamete *interactions* and only few data exist on fertilisation-induced molecular events after zygote formation.

Therefore, cDNA libraries of egg cells and zygotes were *generated* to explore gene *expression* after *fertilisation.* Analyses of these libraries showed that *expression* of several genes is up- or downregulated after in vitro gamete fusion.

Expression of some cell cycle genes was investigated in single gametes and zygotes of maize to follow the re-entering of the gametes into the cell cycle between *in vitro fertilisation* and first cell division. This is possible, because the gene *expression* status of single cells can be *investigated* by the use of reverse *transcriptase* polymerase chain reaction (RT-PCR) methods.

This article is focused on advances in zygote and primary endosperm cell *development in vitro* and describes the application of transgene *technology* to study early developmental processes.

IN VITRO FERTILISATION

Whereas animal and lower plant IVF-systems can easily make use of naturally free-living gametes, sperm, egg and central cells of angiosperms presuppose their isolation, because the embryo sac is generally deeply embedded in the ovule, and the sperm cells are enclosed in pollen grains or tubes.

Micromanipulation techniques and skills are prerequisites for the isolation, fusion and culture of single cells. These methods were developed *originally* for *experiments* with somatic cells. They were adapted and improved for investigations with gametic cells.

By use of these methods, *experimental* access to single gametes, *fertilisation* and *postfertilisation* events under continuous microscopic observation with defined conditions are possible, for example, isolation, selection and fusion of pairs of gametic protoplasts.

Also, this allows to design detailed *experiments* to follow precisely timed early events of zygote, embryo and endosperm formation after gamete fusion. Isolated gametes are *protoplasts* and therefore can be fused by techniques that have proved to be *successful* in the fusion of somatic protoplasts.

These are *electrofusion* and the fusion methods using *polyethylene* glycol or calcium to induce cell fusion. Sperm and egg cell fusion are *electrically* induced in maize and in wheat. Using maize, the same method was applied to central cell fertilisation.

Calcium mediated cell fusion of sperm and egg cells and of sperm and central cells were also performed in maize. Possibly attributed to the large *differences* between the cell sizes isolated sperm cells fuse fast, generally in less than one second with egg and central cells.

EMBRYO AND ENDOSPERM DEVELOPMENT

Development of a single isolated egg cell to the zygote, embryo and finally to a fertile hybrid plant or from an isolated central cell to endosperm after IVF have *exclusively* been reported in maize. Embryo and endosperm *development* occurs in culture *independently* from each other and without female tissue.

Sustained growth of *in vitro* fertilised egg cells or isolated *zygotes* has been achieved by co-cultivation of zygotes and feeder cells. The feeder effect depends on the medium *composition* which must fulfil the demands of both, the zygote and the feeder cells for optimal growth. *In vitro* development of maize *zygotes* turned out to be genotype-independent.

The generally high developmental *capacity* may be attributed to the natural *predestination* of the zygote to form an embryo. Originating from a single *in vitro* zygote, *transition* stage embryos, consisting of a *meristematic* region and a suspensor form a scutellum-like compact white tissue, and *subsequently*, a *coleoptile* and a plantlet.

Clearly, the plant formation occurs without a *maturation* period, as seed *formation* is circumvented. Seeds which are obtained from regenerated plants are of the F_2 generation. The maize *in vitro* zygote is *metabolically* highly active.

Newly formed cell wall material can be detected as early as 30 sec after *in vitro* gamete fusion. After IVF, karyogamy was observed as early as 35 min to 45 min in egg cells and 1 h in central cells. It is completed both in the egg and in the central cell within 2 h after fertilisation *in vitro* (HAF).

The time course of karyogamy was determined by using isolated, DAPI-stained nuclei of fertilised egg and central cells. Two types of *karyogamy* were observed in *in vitro* fertilised central cells. The sperm nucleus fuses either with one of the two polar nuclei or with the *secondary* nucleus which can be formed prior to pollination and fertilisation.

This was also found in maize. *In vitro* produced maize *zygotes* and *in vitro* produced wheat zygotes divide in culture. Depending on culture *conditions*, in maize it occurs as early as 29 HAF (E. Kranz, *unpublished* data), but generally 42-46 HAF. Maize zygotes divide in plants about 16 h after *karyogamy*. Zygotic polarity is mostly of maternal origin.

The distinct polarity of *in vitro and in vivo* maize zygotes may mainly derive from the uneven *distribution* of cytoplasm within the egg. Comparable to the situation in the embryo sac in plants, where the cell wall generally surrounds the egg only at the *micropylar* region, the isolated and cultured egg restores its polarity by forming new cell wall material in a polar fashion.

Maize eggs fused either with barley, *Coix* or *Sorghum* sperm cells divide asymmetrically, just as the maize egg divides after homologous fusion. The maize egg also divides *asymmetrically* after fusion with a wheat sperm. However, when a wheat egg is fused with a maize sperm, the plane of the dividing zygote is rather symmetrical and characteristic to the situation in the wheat egg fused previously with a wheat sperm.

Thus, the underlying processes performing the plane of the first cell division asymmetrically are also of maternal origin. In higher plants, the function of cell cycle regulatory genes during the first zygotic cell cycle remains to be investigated.

In maize, cyclin genes are differentially expressed during the first embryonic cell division cycle which is regulated zygotically rather than maternally as in many animal zygotes. Maize sperm cells express the cell division cycle-specific genes *cdc2ZmA/B and* the mitotic cyclin Zeama; CycA1; 1. However, the other mitotic cyclins Zeama; CycB1; 2 and Zeama; CycB2; 1 are not *expressed* in the male gametes.

What is generally the contribution of the sperm cell in egg cell division? Isolated egg cells of maize and fusion products of two maize egg cells do not divide. However, as in somatic cell culture, a short treatment of high amounts of 2,4-D can trigger cell division in cultured isolated egg and central cells.

Also, in mutants of *Arabidopsis, unfertilised* central cells can develop into endosperm. In animal and lower plant systems, egg activation and fertilisation-induced signalling events have been widely studied. *Investigations* like these are now also feasible in *angiosperms* by using single gametes.

In maize egg cells *and in vitro* zygotes, membrane Ca^{2+} and the calcium receptor protein calmodulin are mainly localised in the vicinity of their nuclei. It is well known that calcium ions play a central role in the regulation of metabolic processes and signal transduction.

A localised elevation to micromolar Ca^{2+} levels from the increased Ca^{2+} influx across the plasma membrane is needed for early fertilisation events, for example, the generation of the fertilisation potential and cell wall secretion in the brown alga *Fucus serratus.*

In maize, a transient elevation of free cytosolic Ca^{2+} in egg cells after fertilisation was reported. An influx of extracellular Ca^{2+} induced by gamete fusion was measured by the use of an extracellular Ca^{2+} selective *vibrating* probe. The Ca^{2+} influx spread subsequently through the whole egg cell plasma membrane as a wave front, starting in the vicinity of the sperm cell fusion side. In maize, central cell *fertilisation* can also be performed.

The isolated maize central cell does not divide without fertilisation, as the egg cell *generally* does not divide in culture. However, single fertilised central cells develop into a characteristic tissue, comparable to the *in vivo* situation.

The transition from the syncytium to the stage of cellularisation of *in vitro* endosperm occurs within 3-5 days after fertilisation. As found in plants, cell divisions are highly frequent and synchronised after cellularisation. In maize endosperm develops initially more rapidly in the micropylar than in the antipodal area of the fertilised embryo sac.

It is characterised by densely cytoplasmic cells *predominately* located at the base of the suspensor and larger vacuolated cells in other regions near the embryo. *In vitro* produced endosperm consists of one globular part containing small cells with dense *cytoplasm* and one oblong part with more large cells. Compared to the oblong part, the globular part develops more rapidly in culture.

The similarity in *morphological* polarisation both of the embryo and the endosperm might indicate underlying similar developmental *processes* and might have a common origin. The central cell might be regarded as a modified egg cell and early endosperm, evolved from a second embryo, develops as a special kind of *embryogenesis.* In plants, endosperm development is *terminated.*

Plant regeneration from *in vitro* produced endosperm has not been observed. However, shoot bud development from isolated and cultured endosperm of several species was reported. Also, plant *regeneration* was achieved from callus cultures which originated from excised endosperm.

In maize, plant *regeneration* from excised immature endosperm derived callus and suspension cultures, has not been reported.

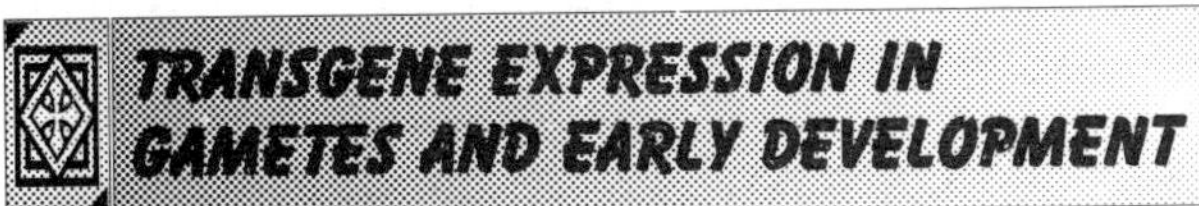

TRANSGENE EXPRESSION IN GAMETES AND EARLY DEVELOPMENT

Transgenic *technology* provides a way to gain insights of gene function by altering the *expression* level of a given gene, for example, by *overexpression* or *expression* of antisense RNA.

A lot of studies have shown that these techniques are well suited to unravel the role of genes important for development, as for example transcription factors.

Moreover, the novel marker, green fluorescent protein (GFP), isolated from *Aequorea victoria* extends the *possibilities* of *transgenic technology*. Due to its *non-toxic* nature and the non-invasive visualisation by fluorescence microscopy, GFP permits real-time *observations* of dynamic changes in living cells. GFP fusion proteins can be used to study *subcellular* localisation, movements of proteins and organelles *in vivo*.

Fusions of GFP with entire proteins of known or unknown function have shown where these proteins are located and whether they move from one *compartment* to another. The GFP based cameleon calcium indicator, developed by Miyawaki et al. may be used to *characterise* the spatial and temporal distribution of calcium ions during fertilisation and early embryonic development *in vivo*.

Recently the function of this indicator was shown in guard cells of *Arabidopsis*. Other GFP based approaches, being of special interest for the application to the *in vitro* fertilisation system, enable *visualisation* of *cytoskeleton* components. A microtubule reporter gene *(gfp-mbd)* was constructed by fusing a GFP gene to the *microtubule* binding domain of the *mammalian* microtubule-associated protein 4 (MAP4) gene.

GFP-MBD labels cortical *microtubules* after transient expression of the reporter gene in living epidermal cells of faba bean. Granger and Cyr showed that *constitutive* expression of the *microtubule* reporter gene in stable *transformed* tobacco BY-2 cells allows spatial and temporal resolution of microtubule arrays as they reorganise throughout the cell cycle.

Labelling of *microtubular* structures in intact *Arabidopsis* plants was recently shown by Camilleri et al.. By using GFP fusion proteins, which bind to actin the *visualisation* of dynamic changes of this component of the cytoskeleton might be achieved. In addition to the cytoskeleton, GFP that *possesses* specific *intracellular* sorting signals for defined cell *compartments* can be used to tag, for example, endoplasmic reticulum, golgi apparatus and vacuoles.

Dynamic changes or *reorganisation* of these cellular *components* during zygote and endosperm development can be observed by using transgenic gametes for *in vitro* fertilisation. These examples show that expression of transgenes in isolated gametes *and in vitro* produced zygotes will become a valuable tool for cytological and functional analyses of these developmental stages.

So far mainly two strategies are followed to study expression of foreign genes in gametes and zygotes: direct delivery of DNA into these untransformed cells via microinjection and the use of *transgenic* gametes and zygotes derived from stable *transformed* plant lines.

Microinjection

Transient expression of transgenes after *microinjection* of plasmid DNA in zygotes was reported by Leduc et al.. In this study the *gus* gene under control of the maize histone H3C4 promoter followed by an actin intron and two *anthocyanin* regulatory genes under control of the 35S promoter were used as reporter genes.

They were injected in zygotes of maize and isolated 24 h after *pollination*. Transient expression, with a frequency of 3.5% on an average was reported in *zygotes* 4 days after injection. Ponya et al. *demonstrated* transient *expression* of reporter genes after *microinjection* of plasmid DNA into egg cells and isolated zygotes of wheat.

A gfp gene under control of the ubiquitin promoter was injected into egg cells, whereas the *gus* gene driven by the 35S promoter was injected into zygotes. Transient expression frequencies of 46 and 52% on an average for egg cells and zygotes, respectively were reported.

High-frequency AC fields, applied to *immobilise* the cells on an electrode were *suggested* by the authors to be a possible reason for such high expression frequencies. However, this remains to be *determined*. In general, immobilisation of cells for *microinjection* is *performed* with a holding capillary or by embedding them in low melting point agarose. After injection of embedded *isolated* maize *zygotes* we obtained transient expression frequencies up to 30% (E. Kranz, *unpublished results*).

In these experiments the GFP gene under control of an enhanced 35S promoter followed by the first intron of the hsp70 gene was used. GFP fluorescence was monitored about 18 h after injection and culture. The described studies focus on the transient *expression* of *transgenes* after *microinjection* of *plasmids* into egg cells or zygotes.

The advantage of this method is that results can be obtained *immediately* after injection of DNA into a cell of interest. It might be a suitable method for evaluation of promoter activities in the target cells. Holm et al. obtained stable transformed plants via *microinjection* of DNA into isolated zygotes. Basis of these *experiments* was an efficient regeneration system for isolated barley zygotes.

This co-culture system with barley microspores *undergoing embryogenesis* allows isolated zygotes to develop into embryo-like structures with a frequency of 75%. Fertile plants were regenerated from *approximately* 50% of these embryo-like structures.

After *microinjection* of the *gus* gene under control of the rice actin promoter into isolated barley zygotes, presence of the construct was confirmed by PCR with a mean frequency of 21% of the derived structures. GUS expression was found in few cases. Two lines of green plants were shown to be transgenic, one of them for an intact copy of the *expression* cassette beside fragments of the construct.

However, the *gus* gene was not expressed. Degradation of the *introduced* DNA was discussed to be a possible reason for the rarely found expression of the transgene after *microinjection*. After *circumvention* of these problems stable transformation via *microinjection* of *zygotes* would be of great advantage for applied purposes, since the use of selectable marker genes is not required.

The regenerants can be screened directly for the presence of the transgene. Efficient *regeneration* systems for isolated zygotes which are the basis for this *transformation* method, were established for wheat and maize.

In vitro produced maize zygotes can also be efficiently regenerated into plants. *In vitro fertilisation* provides the possibility to inject DNA into egg cells before *fertilisation*. This option might have an impact on the integration event.

Transgenic Plant Lines

For investigation of stable integrated transgene *expression* in maize, gametes and zygotes *transgenic* plant lines can be generated by microprojectile *bombardment* of immature embryos.

An advantage of stable transformation over transient expression assays is the fact that transgenic lines can be used for various experiments without the need for new time-consuming *microinjection* experiments.

Nevertheless, due to the long generation time of maize, the time needed to establish and characterise transgenic maize lines has to be considered. There is little *information* on *transcription* and translation activity in maize gametes and zygotes.

The competence of maize gametes and zygotes to express stable integrated *transgenes* was shown in our laboratory with plants transgenic for the *gfp* gene. The same gfp vector (35S: *gfp*), as used for microinjection *experiments,* was introduced. It was optimised for high expression levels of GFP in monocotyledonous plants and codes for a plant codon usage optimised S65T version of the *gfp* gene.

In female gametophytes the 35S: *gfp* construct was expressed. Egg cells, synergids, and central cells showed GFP fluorescence, whereas no fluorescence was detected in transgenic male gametes. After *fertilisation* of non-transgenic egg cells and central cells with *transgenic* sperm cells expression of the *transgene* was induced early after *fertilisation,* and GFP was detected in *zygotes* and early endosperm.

The 35S promoter construct was active in egg cells, central cells, zygotes, embryos and early endosperm. This opens the *possibility* to design new experiments and to express various transgenes under control of this promoter construct during *fertilisation* and early development.

Therefore, we constructed expression vectors adapted to the *requirements* of maize to label *microtubules* and actin filaments in living cells according to the constructs described by Marc et al. and Kost et al.. Double labelling *experiments* with spectral GFP variants or the recently isolated red fluorescent protein might enable analyses of dynamic changes and the *interactions* of actin filaments and microtubules *in vivo.*

We chose GFP to label microtubules and the red *fluorescent* protein to label actin filaments. Transient expression analyses of these two constructs revealed that double labelling of both cytoskeletal components is possible in living cells.

The next step will be the *generation* and *characterisation* of transgenic plant lines expressing both *constructs* in gametes and zygotes. Once established, these lines could be used to study dynamics and interactions of the main cytoskeletal components during early development in vivo.

PROSPECTS

IVF with single *gametes* can now be used for wide *hybridisation* approaches to create new hybrid and cybrid plants. Possibly due to zygotic and postzygotic *incompatibility mechanisms,* resulting hybrid plants might be restricted to hybridisation between more closely related species.

This has been demonstrated in egg activation studies: Cell divisions were triggered in isolated maize eggs by sperm cells of several cereal species. However, zygotic incompatibility was observed after *in vitro* fusion of maize eggs with *Brassica* sperm cells. Also, IVF techniques are valuable *experimental* tools for the elucidation of various processes of double *fertilisation* and early development of embryo and endosperm under defined conditions.

Clearly, important progress towards a better *understanding* of these processes will continue to come from analyses of mutants. However, experimental access to single higher plant gametes and zygotes will facilitate studies on *fertilisation* and early developmental processes which are difficult to investigate in plants.

These studies together with gene cloning, protein isolation and characterisation will *certainly* allow a comparison with *fertilisation-induced* processes *occurring* in lower plants and animals. Fertilisation-induced signal transduction events, changes in the endoplasmic reticulum, cytoskeleton, and nuclear movement are now possible to be studied under defined conditions, e.g., an exact time point after gamete fusion.

Such studies can be performed both in the zygote and in the primary *endosperm* cell allowing *comparative* studies. Thus, they will provide a more precise picture of co-ordinated processes during early developmental stages of the embryo and the endosperm. Molecular analyses are possible with few cells. In maize, cDNA libraries from egg cells and *in vitro* zygotes were constructed by using RT/PCR *techniques* to isolate and to study the function of the cloned egg and fertilisation induced genes.

PCR protocols were adapted for expression studies of known genes by use of single cells, for example, to follow gene expression of cell cycle regulatory genes in a time course during zygote development. Also, fertilised central cells and primary endosperm cells are *promising* target cells for the isolation of unknown genes and *expression* studies by using especially *endosperm* specific genes.

For functional analyses of gene products, existing protocols such as *immunocytochemical techniques* for protein detection and methods for protein isolation are being *currently* adapted to single cells and to small cell *aggregates* in our *laboratory*.

These tools will provide a valuable contribution to the elucidation of common features and differences in zygotic and somatic developmental processes. Many processes involved in early endosperm development might well be studied during development of *in vitro* produced or isolated primary endosperm cells by using defined culture conditions.

These are, for example, the *suppression* of phragmoplast formation between nuclei, the mitotic hiatus, the synchronised re-initiation of mitosis, the periclinal phragmoplast formation, the initiation of *cellularisation* via formation of nucleocytoplasmic domains (NCD) of a radial *microtubular* array, alveolation, the *programming* of nuclear location and division planes during cell wall formation in the *syncytium*. In this respect the expression of GFP based marker genes might be a valuable tool. Stable *transgenic* lines showed that central cells and early endosperm as well as egg cells and early *embryos* are competent to express transgenes.

In vitro fertilisation and culture systems enable direct observation and *monitoring* of the development of individual cells. Combination of this option with the expression of GFP based marker genes for subcellular structures will facilitate new *strategies* to analyse cytological characteristics during fertilisation, early zygotic and *endosperm* development.

The use of fluorescent protein based markers for cytoskeletal components is of high interest, since the plant *cytoskeleton* has crucial functions in cellular processes that are essential for cell morphogenesis and development. Once established through *transgenic* maize plants, *cytological* markers might be of value to correlate expression data with specific developmental stages, e.g., cell cycle phases through *visualisation* of *microtubular structures.*

Also, the GFP based cameleon calcium indicator might be a possibility to characterise the spatial and temporal distribution of calcium ions during fertilisation and early embryonic development *in vivo.* The function of this indicator was demonstrated in guard cells of *Arabidopsis.* Additionally, *transgenic approaches* provide the opportunity for *functional* analyses during fertilisation and very early *zygotic* and endosperm development.

Transcription factors being expressed in egg cells, and cell cycle regulators, both might have a critical role during *fertilisation,* further development or *morphogenesis* and thus are interesting candidates for antisense and *overexpression* studies. A more comprehensive view on the fertilisation processes and early development will certainly be the result of linking *in vitro fertilisation* with *transgenic* technology.

3

Chapter

TRANSFORMATION TECHNIQUES

The production of *transgenic* plants involves the marriage of two critical yet distinct basic technologies. The first directs the introduction of new genetic material into plant cells (*transformation*); whereas the second uses methods based in tissue culture to *regenerate* the resulting transformed cells into transgenic plants.

Of the various methods developed to introduce DNA into plant cells, most include a transformation step that is mediated by *Agro-bacterium tumefaciens*. In nature, *Agrobacterium* tu*mefaciens* is the causative agent of crown gall disease and was discovered at the turn of the last century. However, approx 75 yr passed before it was determined that this ubiquitous soil microorganism is capable of interkingdom DNA transfer.

The crown gall (tumor) represents a *manifestation* of the transfer and expression of bacterial DNA in plant cells. This highly evolved and elegant mechanism of *transforming* plant cells has been harnessed by plant biotech knowledge and profit.

For the purposes of this chapter, we *highlight* some of the salient *features* of *Agrobacterium-mediated* transformation of plant cells and their regeneration into transgenic plants as these features need to be understood from a basic perspective to carry out *effectively* the *procedures* presented.

However, this is not an *extensive* review of the subject and the reader is urged to read recently published reviews on the use of *Agrobacterium* as a vector for gene *transfer* and on *Agrobacterium* as an agent of disease. *Agrobacterium* is attracted to the amino acids, sugars and organic acids that are *released* from wounded plant tissues.

It re *chemoattractants* by seeking out the wounded cells that produced them and then by binding to them by a polar *attachment mechanism*. During *attachment*, *coordinated* expression from a suite of genetic operons critical to the gene transfer process also begins.

These operons–virB, *virC, virD, virE,* and virG–are collectively termed the "vir regulon," and are *coordinately* regulated by *a* virA/virG two-component system. The wound phenolics and *monosaccharides* directly or indirectly cause the *autophosphorylation* of the *virA transmembrane* receptor kinase, which in turn activates the soluble *cytoplasmic transcriptional* factor virG through another *phosphorylation* event.

Activated *virG subsequently* stimulates the transcription of the *individual vir* operons by binding to the upstream "vir box" cis/enhancer elements. Gene products that are generated from *transcription* of the *vir* operons per form *functions* that are critical to the transfer of a DNA fragment called T-DNA from the tumor-inducing (Ti) plasmid *localized* in the bacteria into plant cells.

The gene products virD1 and virD2 are cooperatively responsible for cleavage of the T-strand delimited by the presence of border *sequences* (*right* and *left border*). The virD2 protein binds *covalently* to the 5'-end of the T-strand which is then coated to form a T-complex with the single stran virE2 either in the *bacteria* or *in planta.*

This T-complex is exported via a type 4 bacterial secretion system encoded by the *virB* operon and *virD4.* Both virD2 and virE2 contain nuclear *localization sequences* that interact with the plant *components* that include an importin-a, a type 2C protein phosphatase and three cyclophilins (virD2-interacting factors), and vip1 and vip2 (virE2 interacting factors) which together help target the T-complex into the plant nucleus.

Once inside the nucleus the T-strand is integrated into the plant genome via *nonhomologous recombination* mediated by plant encoded proteins that are likely part of recombination and/or repair process in plants. Instead of the naturally occurring single Ti plasmid, most laboratory strains of *Agrobacterium* used for *transformation* employ a binary system consisting of two plasmids.

One plasmid contains the *vir* regulon se products of which work in *trans* to transfer the T-DNA from a separate plasmid. The oncogenes (*gall-forming sequences*) have been removed from the T-DNA and in their place *engineered* expression cassettes with genes from *virtually* any source may be substituted, usually by *convenient* insertion into multiple cloning sequences that have been *incorporated* into these plasmids.

Different strains of *A. tumefaciens* display different levels of virulence (*transformability*), much of which stems from differences in the *vir* sequences. Once a plant cell has *incorporated* the introduced DNA in a stable manner (i.e., covalently integrated within the host plant's genome), the next step is to regenerate a plant from the *transformed* cells.

Position, *frequency*, and scope of regeneration events are critical to the isolation of *transgenic* plants. Most often, the major limiting step in the isolation of *transgenic* plants is a lack of *regeneration* occurring from within the transformed cell populations.

There is a large amount of *variability* in the frequency and scope of *regeneration* among different angiosperm species as well as among different cultivars of any one species. The two pathways of *regeneration* that have been observed in most angiosperms are *organogenesis* and somatic *embryogenesis.*

Organogenesis involves the regeneration of adventitious shoots or roots through the formation of *organized, meristematic* tissues. The second pathway involves the formation of embryos or embryo-like structures from somatic tissues.

It has been *suggested* that somatic *embryogenesis* and *organogenesis* reflect different developmental events that are most likely mutually exclusive. This chapter presents a method for the organogenic regeneration of tobacco plants from leaf discs following *Agrobacterium* mediated *transformation* that is loosely based on a landmark paper published nearly 20 yr ago.

MATERIALS

Unless stated otherwise, all reagents and chemicals used in this *protocol* were of high purity and were analytical grade and/or tested for molecular biology or plant cell tissue culture applications. The water used was *deionized* and filtered through a *Nanopure* (Barnstead, Dubuque, IA) water *purification* system.

Supplies and Equipment

1. GA7 tissue culture boxes with lids (Magenta or equivalent).
2. Laminar flow hood.
3. Forceps.
4. Scalpels.
5. Sterile, disposable Petri dishes.
6. Sterile filter paper.
7. Cork borers (0.7 mm).
8. Cork borer sharpener.
9. Bunsen burners.
10. Inoculation loops
11. Environmental shaker incubators (25°C).
12. Environmental growth chambers.
13. P20, P200, P1000, and P5000, Pipetman (or equivalent) micropipettors and appropriate tips.
14. 1.5-mL Microfuge tubes.
15. 15- and 50-mL capped centrifuge tubes (Falcon or equivalent).
16. 15% (v/v) Household bleach.
17. 70% Ethanol.
18. Laboratory sealing film (Parafilm or equivalent).
19. Heated water bath at 55°C.
20. Disposable 10-mL sterile syringes.

21. Acrodisc 0.2-μm syringe filter sterilization units (or equivalent).

Reagents, Solutions, and Media

1. 1/2X MSO, pH 5.8: half-strength Murashige and Skoog (MS) medium *(18)* solidified with 0.8% Phytagar (Invitrogen, Carlsbad, CA).
2. *Agrobacterium* strains: any one of several common disarmed (non-gall-forming) laboratory strains (e.g., EHA 101, 105, C58, and LBA4404) containing an engineered binary transformation vector.
3. YEP medium, pH 7.2: 5.0 g/L of Bacto-yeast extract, 10.0 g/L of Bacto-peptone, 10 g/L of NaCl, 15 g/L of Bacto-agar.
4. Filter-sterilized MS20IM *Agrobacterium* induction medium, pH 5.25: MS salts and vitamins supplemented with 2 % (w/v) sucrose, 100 μM acetosyringone, 1 mM betaine phosphate or proline, and 2.5 mM 2-(4-morpholino)ethanesulfonic acid (MES).
5. Cocultivation medium, pH 5.8: MS medium supplemented with 4.5 tM benzylaminopurine (BA), 0.5 μM naphthalene acetic acid (NAA) and solidified with 0.8% (w/v) Phytagar (Gibco).
6. MSBN1.1 shoot regeneration medium, pH 5.8: identical to the cocultivation medium shown above with the exception that selective agents are used as appro*priate*.
7. MSHF rooting medium, pH 5.8: MS medium solidified with 0.8% Phytagar and supplemented with selective agents when appropriate.

METHODS

Growth and Propagation of Tobacco (Nicotiana tabacum)

Most plants offer a number of tissues that will regenerate under the proper *conditions*. However, *efficiencies* may vary greatly. Plants or regenerable plant tissues grown under axenic *conditions* in culture offer the most consistent results with respect to *regeneration*, as some of the *environmental* conditioning that varies with season in plants grown outside of the laboratory has been eliminated.

Material from cultures also leads to fewer downstream *contamination* problems. Shown below is a *procedure* for growing tobacco plants under axenic conditions. It should be noted that the methods have been *optimized* for the cultivar "Xanthi"; however, others, such as "SRI" also have been successfully *transformed* using this procedure.

1. Surface sterilize tobacco seeds by placing them in 15-mL conical centrifuge tubes and filling them with 10 mL of a 15% bleach solution plus one drop of Tween-20.
2. Shake the tubes continuously for 15 min on a gyratory shaker at 110 rpm.
3. Allow the seeds to settle, pipet off the Clorox solution, and rinse three times with sterile distilled water. Rinsing is accomplished by filling the centrifuge tube with 10 mL of sterile distilled water, then allowing the seeds to settle and pipetting off the rinse water. Remove all but 1 mL of water during the final rinse.
4. Dispense the last milliliter of water with seeds using a pipet onto 100 × 20 mm Petri

dishes containing 25 mL of agar solidified 1/2X MSO.

5. Incubate plates at 26°C under soft fluorescent lights with a 16-h photoperiod.
6. After 10–14 d, transfer germinating green seedlings to Magenta boxes containing 50 mL of autoclaved MSHF.
7. Plants may be *multiplied* by removing expanded leaves from rooted plants, cutting the remaining stem between nodes, and inserting the resulting stem pieces into Magenta boxes containing MSHF. Individual plants may be maintained indefinitely without multiplication by simply *propagating* the shoot tip in a similar manner. Repeat subcultures to fresh medium once every 4 wk.

Growth of Agrobacterium and Preparation of Inoculum

Compared to other laboratory strains of bacteria such as *Escherichia* coli, Agrobacterium grows relatively slowly. To grow overnight cultures of sufficient densities consistently and *conveniently*, it is important to inoculate them with cells actively growing on solid medium.

1. Prepare a 50-mL culture tube containing 10 mL of YEP media containing the appropriate selective antibiotics.
2. Inoculate the tube with one loopful of active bacteria (A. tumefaciens containing a binary vector with the gene[s] of interest) taken from a selection plate kept at 4°C.
3. Grow 20–24 h at 25°C with agitation of 100–150 rpm. If an environmental shaker is unavailable, room temperature should be sufficient.
4. Determine the optical density of the cultures spectrophotometrically at 420 nm. Calculate the amount of culture needed to provide an optical density of 0.5 when diluted to 20 mL.
5. Centrifuge the appropriate amount of culture in a 50-mL Falcon tube for 15 min at 2500g.
6. Pour off the supernatant
7. Resuspend the pellet in 20 mL of MS20IM medium
8. Induce the *Agrobacterium* for transformation by shaking on a rotary shaker (100150 rpm) for 5 h at 20–25°C (room temperature).

Preparation and Infection of Leaf Disks

The overall objective in preparing plant material is to maximize the number of wounded, cut surfaces for *Agrobacterium* attachment while *maintaining* enough healthy tissue that will later support efficient regeneration.

1. Remove expanded leaves from rooted plants growing axenically in culture and float them in 100-mm Petri dishes containing sterile MS20IM.
2. Cut disks from the leaves in dishes under MS20IM using a flam cork borer. Prepare leaf disks in batches of approx 50/plate.
3. Set aside approx 16 leaf disks to serve as controls for the traeration procedure by transferring them directly to 100 × 15 mm Petri dishes containing cocultivation medium

overlaid with sterile filter paper gently blotting away excess MS20IM using sterile filter paper.

4. Decant the MS20IM from the plates containing the remaining leaf disks using a sterile pipet and replace it with induced *A. tumefaciens* suspension. Incubate at room temperature (approx 25°C) for 10–20 min with occasional swirling.

Cocultivation

Agrobacterium attachment to plant tissue is completed during the earlier stages of cocultivation. The physical transfer of genetic material occurs later.

1. Remove each disk individually, gently blot off excess culture paper, and transfer to 100 × 15 mm Petri dishes containing cocultivation media overlaid with sterile filter paper. Place about 16 disks/plate.
2. For large scale experiments we routinely cut about 800 disks and inoculate Petri dishes with approx 24 disks/plate.
3. Seal all Petri dishes with laboratory sealing film (Parafilm or equivalent)
4. Incubate cultures at 20°C in the dark for 3 d.

Selection and Regeneration of Transgenic Tobacco Shoots

Several important events occur during selection and *regeneration*. Antibiotic(s) that do not affect plant cells are used to *eliminate* or arrest the growth of *A. tumefaciens*. Conditions are also optimized for the *adventitious, organogenic regeneration* of new plant tissues.

To enrich the population of new growth with transgenic tissues, additional selective agents are incorporated into the *regeneration* medium for the purposes of genetic selection. Genetic selection is the process of *selecting* preferentially for those cells that have been *transformed* by the incoming transgenes.

A selective *advantage* can be conferred on the transformed cells through the introduction of genes encoding antibiotic resistance or resistance to some metabolic inhibitor such as a herbicide. In the presence of the antibiotic or herbicide, the untdie whereas the *transformed* cells grow and multiply.

If no form of genetic selection were used, then one would be faced with the option of screening every shoot that regenerated in a *transformation* experiment. In cases where the *transformation frequency* is high (i.e., the number of transformed cells or shoots arising from an explant), this would be feasible. However, for other species with lower transformation frequencies, this would become a laborious if not impossible task.

Therefore, genetic selection is an essential *component* of any plant transformation protocol and has been accomplished by using various marker genes.

1. Subculture the disks to selective medium. All those infected with *A. tumefaciens* and half of the control disks (no infection with *A. tumefaciens*) should be transferred to MSBN1.1 regeneration medium containing the appropriate selective agents in 100 × 15 mm Petri dishes.

   The control disks under these conditions will provide an indication of nontransgenic regeneration ("escapes") under selection. Transfer the remaining control disks to *regeneration* medium (MSBN1.1) containing only the selective agent used to eliminate Agrobacterium (this is a control to evaluate overall regeneration *frequency*). In all cases, plate at a density of approx 8 disks/plate.

2. Maintain cultures at 20°C in low light (approx 45 µE/m^{2}s). Check regularly for contamination. If contamination is discovered, unaffected disks within the plate may be subcultured to fresh MSBN1.1.
3. All disks should be subcultured to fresh selection plates every 2-3 wk. The disks will expand and develop callus over time. Try to ensure that the expanded disks establish good contact with the media. Shoots will appear in 3-4 wk.

Rooting of Transgenic Shoots to Recover Complete Plantlets

The next step is to recover complete plants from any *regenerated* shoots through root *organogenesis*. In addition, the first meaningful screen to test for *transformation* is often the rooting procedure, as root *organogenesis* is usually more sensitive to the *incorporated* selective agents than shoot *regeneration*.

Shoots recovered from selective regeneration *procedures* that do not root under selection are rarely *transgenic* and should be discarded.

1. Carefully remove regenerated shoots by cutting them at their base using a sterile scalpel and forceps and place them in GA7 boxes (about four shoots per vessel) containing 50 mL of MSHF *supplemented* with selective agents. Roots should become visible within approx 10 d.
2. Subculture only the shoots that have rooted by cutting off the shoot with the top four internodes and introducing these *individually* into a GA7 box containing 50 mL of MSHF supplemented with the appropriate selective agents. These individual shoots may be considered as putative *transformants*.
3. Rooted shoots can be maintained and/or propagated to establish individual lines at monthly intervals as described elsewhere in this chapter. Alternatively, the plants may be *acclimatized* and transferred to the greenhouse to produce seeds. It takes about 3 mo to set seed, depending on conditions.

Analysis of Transgenic Plants

Recovered plants are typically *analyzed* on a number of different levels to determine that they are in fact transgenic. Once plants grow large enough to provide enough tissue for analyses without *compromising* he assayed for transgene *expression* and molecularly for the presence of the appropriate sequences.

The assay for gene *expression* is conducted using methods consistent with the transgene coding sequence and desired results. If such a procedure is impossible or inconvenient, *polymerase* chain reactions (PCRs) may also be performed. Plants that give a positive result must then be analyzed using a DNA blotting procedure (Southern) to confirm the presence of *transgenes* and their abundance.

NOTES

1. Premixed tissue culture reagents are available commercially from a number of different sources. We routinely purchase MS salts and vitamins as a powder or concentrated stock solution from either Gibco or Sigma. Reagents from both sources provide consistent results.

2. When selecting a strain of Agrobacterium for the purpose of *transformation*, the genetic background is a factor that should be considered. Although it is well known that most dicot plants are susceptible to *A. tumefaciens*, resistance of the target plant tissues to this pathogen could be an important factor influencing its virulence and, *ultimately*, affect the efficiency of plant *transformation*. A growing body of evidence indicates, for most of the widely used strains of *A. tumefaciens*, wide variations in virulence that depends on the target plant tissue used. Many of these differences may stem from differences in interactions between the host plant and bacterial vir gene products.

3. This medium has been developed to provide A. tumefaciens for *virulence* induction. Environmental factors such as pH, temperature, and osmotic *conditions strongly* influence the expression and induction of virulence genes. The most direct effects on *virulence* induction are mediated by the presence of phenolic compounds such as *acetosyringone* (3',5'-dimethoxy-4'-*hydroxyacetophenone*), sinapinic acid, coniferyl alcohol, caffeic acid, ethyl ferrulate, and methylsyringic acid, which are known inducers in *Agrobacterium*. The virulence induction is also influenced by the presence of other compounds such as monosaccharides and opines. Betaine, proline, and other *osmoprotective* compounds have been shown to enhance *synergistically* the effect of phenolic compounds. Betaine has been shown to increase the expression of several virulence genes in *Agrobacterium*. Proline or betaine may help the bacteria to adapt to rapid changes in pH and osmotic pressure caused by the proximity of wounded plant cells, thus *increasing* the *transformation* efficiency.

4. Selective agents used for this purpose are usually prepared as stock solutions that are typically 500- to 1000-fold more *concentrated* than their working strength in cultures. They may be stored as filter-sterilized solutions in a freezer (–20°C) for up to 2 mo. Shown are the working concentrations (milligram/liter) of several *antibiotics routinely* used for selection during plant *transformation* procedures: kanamycin—100; tetracycline—5; gentamicin—20; cefotaxime 250–500; and carbenicillin—500. Kanamycin is commonly used to select for transgenic plant cells and tissues whereas the others are used to select for engineered strains of *A. tumefaciens* (tetracycline and gentamicin) or eliminate it (cefotaxime and carbenicillin) from cultures.

5. Growth of tobacco can vary widely depending on the cultivar and growth *conditions*. It may be advisable to use a larger culture conta reasonable amount of time to pass before it becomes *necessary* to subculture, or to *maximize* the leaf material available as source tissue for a transformation procedure. We routinely use glass household canning jars *containing* 100 mL of medium. The plants perform best if the vessels are capped with a sterile plastic cap. Avoid a glass cap and instead use, for example, the bottom of a disposable Petri dish and seal to the container with Parafilm (or equivalent).

6. To ensure that overnight cultures obtain an adequate cell density, it is important to use active inoculum. We routinely maintain the cultures as streaked bacteria on selective plates containing solidified YEP medium. The plates are incubated for approx 48 h at 28°C and then kept in a refrigerator (4°C). The bacteria should be *subcultured* to fresh plates every 4 wk. As an alternative to using a sterile loop to streak plates and inoculate liquid cultures, we routinely use sterile pipet tips. The barrel and ejector of the pipettor are sprayed with 70% ethanol and allowed to dry in a laminar flow hood. The pipettor is then used to place bacteria on a pipet tip that can then be used to streak a plate or ejected into a culture tube *containing* growth medium.
7. As an alternative to using a cork borer to prepare discs, the leaf tissue also may be cut into small squares with a scalpel and forceps. In either case, it is important to be as gentle as possibie, because *unnecessary* wounding may lower *regeneration* frequencies. In addition, excessive drying may also result in adverse effects. Therefore, it is important to work quickly and minimize exposure of the leaf tissue to open air as much as possible.
8. We have observed that *transformation* frequencies trend upwards with increasing cocultivation time, up to 5 d. However, overgrowth of *A. tumefaciens* and subsequent losses of plant material owing to *contamination* result in cocultivation times exceeding 3 d. Overgrowth problems are the result of an interaction between inoculum *concentration,* cocultivation time, and plant species or cultivar. Therefore, concentration and time should be considered variables for *optimization* when establishing a *transformation* system.
9. If one of the transgenes contained within the binary vector is a scoreable marker, it may be possible to conduct a convenient preliminary screen prior to placing the shoots into rooting medium. After excising the *regenerated* shoots from the original explant, a very small piece of stem tissue may be taken from the basal region before it is placed in rooting medium. The cutaway stem tissue may then be used to assay for the expression of the scoreable marker. Decisions about moving forward with the *corresponding* shoots may then be conducted in a more informed manner.
10. It is important to confirm stable *incorporation* of the introduced gene(s) and its *expression* in the putatively transformed plants and their siblings. This is possible only if the incorporated DNA has been integrated into the genome of the transformed plant. In annual plants such as tobacco describe determined easily by backcrossing or selfing the plant to determine if the *introduced* gene is heritable. In the case of perennial species, often time makes this type of analysis impractical. Alternatively, *transformation* can be confirmed through a rigorous and *comprehensive* Southern analysis of the transformed tissue. Typically this analysis should be performed to reveal and identify different segments of the inserted T-DNA, that is, the presence of both internal and border fragments.

PRODUCTION OF HAIRY ROOT CULTURES AND TRANSGENIC PLANTS

Agrobacterium rhizogenes is a soil bacterium responsible for the development of hairy root disease on a range of dicotyledonous plants. This pheno type is caused by genetic *transformation* in a manne development of crown gall disease by *A. tumefaciens.*

Infection of wound sites by A. *rhizogenes* is followed by the transfer, integration, and expression of T-DNA from the root-inducing (Ri) plasmid and subsequent development of the hairy root phenotype. Hairy roots can be induced on a wide range of plants and many can be regenerated into plants, often spontaneously.

Transgenic plants have been obtained after *A. rhizogenes-mediated transformation* in 89 different taxa, representing 79 species from 55 genera and 27 families. Cocultivation of explants with A. *rhizogenes* results in the production of hairy roots that are easily *distinguished* by their rapid, highly branching growth on hormone-free medium and plagiotropic root development.

Plants regenerated from hairy roots often exhibit an altered phenotype characterized by several morphological changes including wrinkled leaves, shortened internodes, reduced apical dominance, reduced fertility, altered flowering, and plagiotropic roots.

These characteristic phenotypic changes result from the transfer and expression of four loci *(rolA, B, C, D)* located on the T-DNA. *A. rhizogenes-derived* hairy roots and plants have application for many areas of research.

For example, hairy root cultures have been used extensively in root nodule research, for artificial seed production, for production of plant secondary metabolites, as an experimental system to study biochemical pathways and responses to chemicals, and to study interactions with other organisms such as nematodes, mycorrhizal fungi, and root pathogens.

Root cultures established by *A. rhizogenes-mediated* transformation are widely used as a source of useful compounds owing to their rapid growth in hormone-free medium and the relatively high production of secondary metabolites compared with the starting plant material.

Hairy roots have been shown to produce a range of secondary metabolites including tropane *alkaloids*, indole alkaloids, terpenoids, aconites, and flavonoids. In addition, hairy roots have been used to express antibodies.

Transgenic plants have been shown to express a wide variety of foreign genes *including* very *complex* proteins such as antibodies. Once established, use of hairy roots as a culture system to express these proteins offers many *advantages* for large scale production.

They are easy to grow, usually requiring no *phytohormones* for growth. These roots can be removed from the original explant/plant and *established* as long-term root clones capable of large increase maintaining their biosynthetic capacity.

The hairy root phenotype is stable and *characterized* by profuse branching and high-density growth.

Over recent years there has been increased interest in the us owing to the effect of *rol* genes on plant morphology and de of these morphological changes such as increased flowering, altered architecture, and increased secondary product production are of *horticultural* use.

In addition, *A. rhizogenes-mediated transformation* has been used to introduce a range of foreign genes

of agronomic use. This chapter describes how to produce and grow hairy root cultures successfully, how to regenerate shoots from these cultures, and how to conduct molecular analysis of these cultures and plants.

MATERIALS

1. *A. rhizogenes* culture or glycerol stock containing 850 μL of bacterial culture and 150 μL of sterile glycerol.
2. Luria Bertani (LB) medium: 1% tryptone, 0.5% yeast extract, 0.5% NaCl, pH 7.0. 3. In vitro seedlings or shoots.
4. Hormone-free plant tissue culture medium, with and without antibiotics. 5. Shoot regeneration medium.
6. Tris-ethylenediaminetetraacetic acid (TE): 10 mM Tris-HCl, pH 7.5, 1 mM ethylene diamine tetraacetic acid (EDTA), pH 8.0.
7. Extraction buffer: 200 mM Tris-HCl, pH 7.5, 250 mM NaCl, 25 mM EDTA, 0.5% sodium dodecyl sulfate (SDS).
8. 2 mM dNTPs: Add 2 μL each of 100 mM dATP, 100 mM dCTP, 100 mM dTTP, and 100 mM dGTP (Roche) to 92 μL of sterile deionized water.
9. Oligonucleotide primers.
10. Electrophoresis equipment.
11. Thermal cycler machine.

METHODS

The methods described in the following subheadings outline (a) *A. rhizogenes* culture, (b) cocultivation of explants to produce hairy root cultures, (c) regeneration of transgenic shoots, (d) molecular characterization of transgenic hairy roots and plants, and (e) transfer of plants to the greenhouse.

A. rhizogenes Culture

A culture of *A. rhizogenes* suitable for explant cocultivation is prepared as follows:

1. Use a single bacterial colony or glycerol stock to inoculate a flask of liquid LB medium containing the appropriate antibiotics for selection of the binary plasmid or 100 mg/L of streptomycin for wild-type A. *rhizogenes* strains.
2. Grow overnight at 28°C .
3. Dilute the culture 1:49 with antibiotic-free liquid LB.
4. Grow for a further 3–4 h before use. At this stage glycerol stocks can be established. Mix tubes thoroughly by vortexing and store immediately at -80°C.

In addition to wild-type *Agrobacterium* strains, foreign genes can be introduced into hairy roots by the use of binary vectors. The options available for binary vector components are covered and the actua binary vector is outlined elsewhere in this chapter.

Binary vectors are introduced into wild-type strains via the freeze–thaw method of transformation.

Transformation by Agrobacteriumn

To prepare *A. rhizogenes* cells competent for transformation:

1. Inoculate 50 mL of LB broth with 5 mL of an overnight culture.
2. Grow for 4–5 h at 28°C.
3. Centrifuge the logarithmically growing cells at 1100g for 20 min at 4°C.
4. Gently wash the cells in 30 mL of sterile TE and pellet as before.
5. Resuspend gently in 5 mL of LB.
6. Aliquot into 500-µL lots and freeze in liquid nitrogen.
7. Store at –80°C. Note the efficiency for transformation will decline after 3 mo.

To transform competent cells:

1. Thaw cells slowly on ice.
2. Mix with 0.5–10 µg of plasmid.
3. Incubate on ice for 5 min.
4. Freeze in liquid nitrogen for 5 min.
5. Thaw in a water bath at 37°C for 5 min.
6. Immediately add 1 mL of LB and incubate with shaking for 3 h at 28°C.
7. Plate 200–500 µL of the mixtures onto LB plates with appropriate selection and incubate at 28°C for 48 h.
8. Select single colonies for PCR to confirm presence of the construct.

Production of Hairy Roots

In Vitro

For the production of hairy roots in vitro, most protocols follow the *conventional* in vitro explant cocultivation method as used for A. tated *transformation*. The major difference is that explain hormone-free medium to enable the selection of hairy root cultures.

The choice of medium is dependent on plant species but is likely to be based on Murashige and Skoog medium. For studies where the aim is rapid production of hairy roots, highly susceptible materials such as Chinese cabbage or potato are excellent starting materials. Various explant sources can be used.

The important feature is that a cut surface is needed. *For Brassica spp.,* in vitro seedling explants such as hypocotyls, leaves, and the cut end of the cotyledonary petiole are routinely used with *A. rhizogenes* strain A4T based on the protocol outlined below developed by Christey et al..

1. Cut hypocotyls into approx 0.5-cm explants and leaves in halves or thirds.
2. Immerse explants briefly (10 s) in a diluted overnight A. *rhizogenes* culture. For cotyledonary petioles, only the cut end of the petiole of each cotyledon is dipped *individually* into the bacterial solution.

3. Blot explants on sterile filter paper.
4. Place explants horizontally onto hormone-free culture medium and coculture for approx 3 d.
5. Transfer explants to antibiotic-containing medium (e.g., 300 mg/L of Timentin or 200 mg/L of cefotaxime) to suppress A. rhizogenes growth. If binary vectors are being used, explants can be transferred at this stage to selection medium or selection can be delayed for 7–10 d.
6. Transfer explants to fresh *antibiotic-containing* medium every 3-4 wk.
7. Once good root growth is noted from the explants, excise explants and transfer to individual containers. It is important to ensure that explants are kept well apart to enable *distinguishing* independent root cultures. Hairy root cultures can be very fast growing and can quickly grow over each other.
8. Once *established*, subculture roots by cutting a 1.5 cm square of culture and transfer to fresh medium every 6–8 wk or as required. Tall Petri dishes (9 cm diameter, 2 cm tall) or pots are preferred as the extra height provides more space for the *plagiotropic* roots to growth into. All culture *manipulations* are conducted at 25°C with a 16-h/d photoperiod, provided by Cool White fluorescent lights, 20 μE/m^2/s. However, hairy roots also grow well in the dark.

Hairy roots can also be initiated from the stem of in vitro cultures by using a needle or other sharp tool to wound the stem of in vitro shoots. The site is then infected with the bacterial culture. Another method used *successfully* involves upturned seedlings.

Explants are excised from in vitro seedlings by cutting the hypocotyl approx 0.5 cm below the cotyledons. Explants are placed inverted on culture medium so that the upper-leaf surfaces are in contact with the medium. A 1- to 3-μL drop of diluted *A. rhizogenes* culture is placed onto the cut surface of the hypocotyl. In both cases, hairy roots are excised as they appear and cultured as described above.

In Vivo

In vivo methods involve wounding of the stem or petiole of *greenhouse* plants with a needle or toothpick dipped in bacterial solution or injection with a needle. High humidity is essential for the production of hairy roots so wound sites are often covered with gauze to *maintain* the high humidity needed to enable hairy root development.

In the absence of appropriate humidity, tumor structures may develop instead, as noted in wasabi. In this case, hairy roots were visible lower down the stem at the soil level where humidity was higher.

A.* rhizogenes *Strain Selection

Opines are carbon compounds produced by the crown galls and hairy roots induced by *A. tumefaciens* and *A. rhizogenes*, respectively. These novel condensation products of plant metabolic intermediates are used as by the *Agrobacterium* strains that induced the growths.

A. rhizogenes strains are characterized by the type of opine they engineer plant cells to produce and that they degrade to use as a growth substance. Agropine (e.g. strains A4T, 15834, TR105), mannopine (e.g., strains TR7, 8196), mikimopine (e.g., A5, A6), and cucumopine (e.g., strains 2588, 2657) type *A. rhizogenes* strains are available.

It is advisable to test a range of *A. rhizogenes* strain types with different genotypes and explant sources to determine the most infective combination for the plant species or cultivar of interest.

Identification of Hairy Roots by Morphology

In the first few weeks after cocultivation, it may be difficult to distinguish hairy roots from normal roots owing to the regeneration of normal roots also. However, after several weeks the difference in morphology between normal and hairy roots should be readily apparent.

If binary vectors are being used, the inclusion of selection agents or reporter genes such as green fluorescent protein (GFP) aids the identification and selection of hairy root cultures from normal roots compared with wild-type strains.

Hairy root cultures are characterized by rapid branching growth on hormone-free medium. With brassicas, these roots are thicker than normal roots, have more root hairs, and the extra branching is easily noted. Hairy root morphology can vary between species.

Inclusion of seedling roots or noninoculated controls should enable the clear differences to be seen. Molecular techniques such as PCR can also be used to confirm the root cultures are of *A. rhizogenes* origin.

Improvement of Hairy Root Production

As noted with *A. tumefaciens-mediated* transformation, the of *transformation frequencies* obtained when using *A. rhizogenes,* which varies between species and between cultivars. The methods available to increase *production* of hairy roots are similar to those used for increasing rates of *A. tumefaciens-mediated* transformation as reviewed in Christey and Braun for vegetable brassicas.

To improve *transformation* rates many factors can be studied. These cover two main areas *concentrating* on manipulation of cultural conditions, that is, both bacterium and explant, and on genetic factors.

1. Bacterial factors include, for example, testing a range of *Agrobacterium* strains or using *acetosyringone* to increase *vir* gene expression. Plant factors include selection of a suitable genotype. In vegetable brassicas, there are clear effects of species and cultivar on *A. rhizogenes-mediated* transformation rates. Three *quantitative* trait loci (QTL) for transgen have been identified in broccoli.
2. Susceptibility of the chosen genotype to *A. rhizogenes* is an important prerequisite for the production of hairy roots. In addition, the actual explant used must be susceptible to A. rhizogenes to enable efficient transformation. The use of the *gfp* reporter gene aids optimizing transformation conditions as gene expression can be monitored rapidly and nondestructively as shown with broccoli. This approach enables the rapid evaluation of a range of variables.
3. In *A. tumefaciens-mediated* transformation of brassicas, several factors are important in

the successful production of transgenic plants including explant source and age, *cocultivation* time, delayed *introduction* of selection, explant preculture, and so on. Manipulation of cocultivation conditions can also increase *transformation* rates. The rate of hairy root production in broccoli was improved by the use of *acetosyringone* in the bacterial culture medium, addition of a *B. campestris* feeder layer, and use of *acetosyringone* and mannopine in the cocultivation medium. Increased rates of hairy root production have also been obtained by inclusion of 2,4-dichlorophenoxyacetic acid in the medium used to resuspend the *A. rhizogenes* prior to inoculation.

Establishment of Liquid Cultures

Although growth on solid medium is sufficient for most studies, for secondary product production and studies on biochemical pathways or the effect of additives to root cultures, liquid cultures or scaleup to larger bioreactors may be required.

1. Inoculation of flasks containing liquid culture medium involves *transferring* a small amount of root culture into the flask, which is then shaken. It is important to ensure an antibiotic to suppress *A. rhizogenes* growth is still *A. rhizogenes* remains associated with the hairy root cultures for a long time. Cultures can be grown in the light or dark. The issues and problems associated with the scaleup culture of hairy root cultures are covered in detail by Doran.
2. To study changes in root growth attributable to the presence of different additives or to study the effect of cultural changes on root growth, fresh weight, dry weight, or image analysis can be used to quantify growth changes.

Regeneration of Shoots From Hairy Root Cultures

A. rhizogenes-mediated transformation is widely used for the production of transgenic shoots after regeneration from hairy root cultures. This method of transformation is used for species where A. rhizogenes-medi*ated* transformation is more efficient than *A. tumefaciens* transformation.

In ad phenotypes obtained from A. *rhizogenes-mediated* transformation such as increased flowering, shortened stature, and increased secondary products are of interest for horticultural purposes. Although the presence of the *rol* genes usually results in an altered phenotype, several studies have shown segregation of Ri and tumor-inducing (Ti)-T-DNA and thus the recovery normal transgenic plants.

In addition, regeneration of plants with normal phenotype does occur from hairy roots and is probably caused by *rol* gene silencing.

1. Regeneration of shoots from hairy root cultures can occur spontaneously on hormone-free medium but often requires the transfer of roots to callus induction and shoot regeneration medium. The actual hormone combination required is dependent on the plant of interest and literature searches will indicate the combination that is most suitable.
2. Healthy root sections of 1–2 cm are excised from an actively growing root culture and placed on the appropriate callus induction medium. In contrast to growth on hormone-free medium, on callus induction medium roots will stop growing and start to thicken and produce callus.

3. This callus can be subbed every 2–3 wk onto the same medium or transferred to shoot regeneration medium. As shoot regeneration may be inhibited by the presence of kanamycin in some plants, it may be advisable to eliminate this from the culture medium. However, an antibiotic such as Timentin should be included to suppress A. *rhizogenes* growth.
4. Once shoot buds are initiated they can be transferred to horm for further development.

Identification of Hairy Roots by PCR

PCR analysis provides confirmation that the selected root cultures are actually of *A.rhizogenes origin.* The production of the hairy root phenotype involves the integration of *rol* genes from the Ri plasmid. A PCR analysis for *rolB* or *rolC is* routinely used to confirm the presence of these genes.

In addition, PCR analysis should be conducted for the gene(s) of interest if binary vectors are being used as DNA is inserted independently from the T-DNA regions of the Ri and Ti plasmids. PCR for A. *rhizogenes virG* gene can be used to confirm lack of bacterial infection.

PCR Analysi

DNA is isolated from in vitro hairy root cultures or shoots using a method modified elsewhere in this chapter

1. Macerate plant material using disposable pestles for 15 s at room temperature.
2. Add 400 μL of extraction buffer and grind for a further 15 s.
3. Centrifuge for 2 min at 16,000g.
4. Add 300 μL of the supernatant to 300 μL of room temperature isopropanol.
5. Invert samples gently, incubate for 20 min at –20°C, and centrifuge for 5 min at 16,000g.
6. Air-dry DNA pellets for 30 min and resuspend in 100 μL of sterile water.
7. Use 1 μL of this template in a 25 μL PCR reaction containing 2.5 μL of 2 MM dNTPs, 1 μM of each primer, 1X PCR buffer (Roche), 1 U of *Taq* polymerase (Roche), and 16.4 μL of water. Cover samples with paraffin oil if required.
8. PCR conditions for *rolB* and *rolC* are: 94°C for 30 s, 68°C for 30 s, and 72°C for 30 s for 40 cycles in an Eppendorf Mastercycler personal thermal cycler.
9. Run 5 μL of the PCR reaction on a 1% agarose (Invitrogen) gel and visualize by ethidium bromide staining.

This crude method works well for many tissue types; however, some plant material may not amplify well. A titration of template (e.g., 0.5, 1, or 2 μL per 25-μL PCR reaction) or further purification may be necessary.

Transfer of Plants to Greenhouse Conditions

Once in vitro shoots have adequate root and shoot growth they can be successfully transferred to greenhouse conditions to enable more accurate observation of phenotype and also for determination of fertility and seed collection.

As plants in tissue culture are used to high humidity it is important to ensure a gradual introduction to the lower humidity and higher light intensity of a green house. This can be obtained by use of a mist bed. Alternatively, a plastic bag can be placed over the pot after transfer of the plant to soil as outlined below.

1. Water the soil mix in the pot (7 cm^3) well.
2. Mist the plant with water immediately prior to transfer to soil.
3. Wash excess agar off the roots carefully before transfer to soil.
4. Place plant in the pot and immediately cover the plant and pot with a plastic bag and secure with a rubber band.
5. Place plants under a greenhouse bench. If the plants are not in direct sun they will not dry out for a least one wk.
6. After one wk, cut a small hole in the top corner of each bag.
7. Make the hole gradually larger over the next week until the bag top is completely open. During this hardening off time check the mix daily for dryness.
8. Remove bags totally 2 wk after exflasking. Plants may now be moved onto a greenhouse bench but may be prone to wilting in hot weather. 9. Repot plants into larger containers as required.

NOTES

1. Antibiotics are added to media after autoclaving from filter sterilized stock solutions.
2. *A. rhizogenes* must be grown at 28°C not 37°C.
3. Acetosyringone (200 µM for brassicas, but level varies wide *cocultivation* medium after autoclaving from a 20 mM filter *sterilized* stock dissolved in hot water. In experiments where acetosyringone is added to the bacterial medium, LB medium containing 5 mM 2-(N-morpholino)*ethanesulfonic* acid (MES), pH 5.6, is used.
4. Feeder layers are established from rapidly growing cell suspension cultures. Approximately 1.5 mL of cells is plated onto the *cocultivation* medium either 1 d or immediately prior to use. A piece of sterile filter pape feeder layer immediately prior to use and the cocultivated explants are placed on top of the filter paper to prevent accidental *transformation* of the feeder layer and not the explant source of interest. Various plant sources are suitable for use as a feeder layer including the species being transformed or other species with high transformation ability such as tobacco.
5. It is important to ensure agar is removed from hairy root cultures as it can inhibit the PCR reaction.
6. Disposable plastic pestles can be reused a number of times as long as abrasive agents such as sand are not used. Wash pestles in detergent, rinse thoroughly and soak overnight in 1 M HCl to ensure degradation of nucleic acids. Rinse three times in double distilled water and autoclave before reuse.
7. Primers used for rolB are: 5'AAAGTATGCTACCATTCCCA3' and 5'000A TAAGCCACGACA-

TCATA3' which produce a 393-bp fragment with strain A4T. The primers for rolC are 5'CGACCTGTGTTCTCTCTTTTTCAAGC3' and 5'GCACTCGCCATGCCT CACCCAACTCACC3', which produce a 514-bp internal fragment with strain A4T (26). Controls should include DNA from the binary vector, the Agrobacterium strain used and DNA from a nontransgenic plant.

8. A simple reprecipitation step can often overcome template problems. Add an additional 100 µL of water to the existing sample and vortex-mix for 30 s. Centrifuge down debris at top speed in a microcentrifuge and transfer the supernatant to a fresh tube. Add 2X starting volume of ice-cold 100% ethanol and 10% 0.5 M NaCl. Mix thoroughly and centrifuge at top speed for approx 10 min. Carefully pour off the ethanol and briefly rinse the pellet with 70% ethanol. Air-dry and resuspend the pellet as before.

STABLE TRANSFORMATION OF PLANT CELLS BY PARTICLE BOMBARDMENT/BIOLISTICS

Particle *bombardment* employs high-velocity microprojectiles to deliver substances into cells and tissues. For genetic *transformation,* DNA is coated onto the surface of micron-sized tungsten or gold particles by precipitation with calcium chloride and spermidine.

Once inside the cells, the DNA elutes off the particles. If the foreign DNA reaches the nucleus, then transient expression will likely result and the transgene may be stably incorporated into host *chromosomes.* Sanford and colleagues at Cornell University developed the original bombardment concept and coined the term "*biological ballistics*" for both the process and device.

"Biolistics" is a registered trademark of E. I. du Pont de Nemours and Co. and has been used to market the devices now sold by Bio-Rad Laboratories, Hercules, CA. However, as there are several homemade "gene guns" or "particle guns," the process often is called by other names such as *microprojectiparticle bombardment,*particle acceleration, or ballistics.

The most widely used device for plant transformation is the Biolistic® PDS-1000/He Particle Delivery System marketed by Bio-Rad Laboratories. The system employs high-pressure helium rele disk to propel a macrocarrier sheet loaded with millions of DNA-coated metal particles (*microcarriers*) toward target cells.

A stopping screen halts the macrocarrier, and the microcarriers continue toward the target and penetrate the cells. Because of its physical nature and simple methodology, the biolistic process can be used to deliver substances into a wide range of intact cells and tissues from a diversity of organisms.

In plant research, the major applications have been transient gene expression studies, production of *genetically* transformed The velocity of the macrocarriers is dependent on the helium pressure in the gas acceleration tube, the distance from the rupture disk to the macroca (A), the macrocarrier (gap distance) (A), the macrocarrier travel distance to the stopping screen (B), the distance between the stopping screen and target cells (C), and the amount of vacuum in the *bombardment* chamber.

(Drawing courtesy of Bio-Rad Laboratories, Hercules, CA.) plants, and inoculation of plants with viral pathogens. Many "firsts" were achieved through the application of biolistic *technology* including chloroplast and mitochondria *transformation*, as well as nuclear *transformation* of *important* monocot species such as wheat, corn, and rice.

Although other technologies have since been proven in these arenas, Sanford in the year 2000, stated the following: "I believe it is accurate to say that most of the presently grown transgenic crop acreage in the entire world was created through the use of the biolistic process—having been *originally* transformed with the gene gun."

As with any plant *transformation* method, several parameters need to be *optimized* for the process to be *maximally* effective. With biolistics, the *parameters* can be grouped as physical, biological, and environmental.

Physical parameters include the composition and size of the microcarriers, the attachment of DNA to the microcarriers, and several instrument parameters. During development of the PDS-1000/He, *instrument* settings were varied over a wide range and tested with numerous organisms.

A vacuum of 28.0 in Hg (94.8 kPa), a helium pressure of about 1100 psi (7584.2 kPa), a gap distance of 6.5–10.0 mm, and a *macrocarrier* travel distance of 6.0-10.0 mm are near optimal for most plant transformation applications.

Gold particles in the range of 0.7–1.0 μm mean diameter *generally* result in the highest rates of stable *transformation*, but the less expensive, more heterogeneous tungsten particles are also widely used. Consistent coating of DNA to the particles and spread of the particles onto the

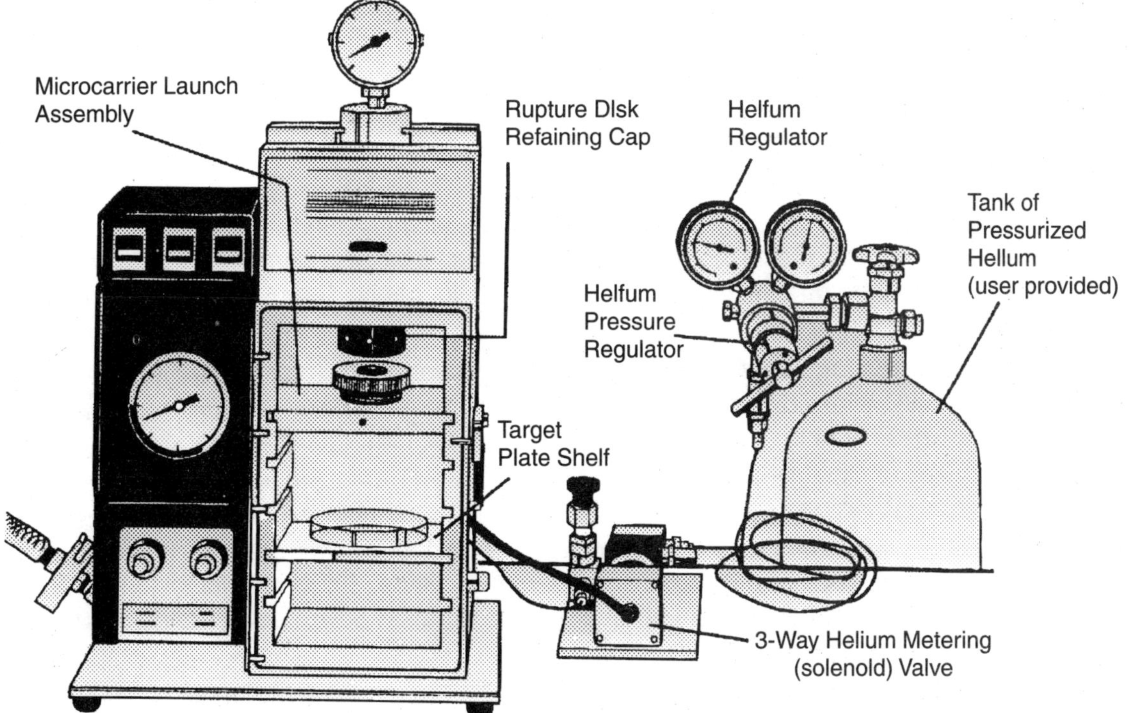

Figure 3.1: Components of the Biolistic® PDS-1000/He particle delivery system.

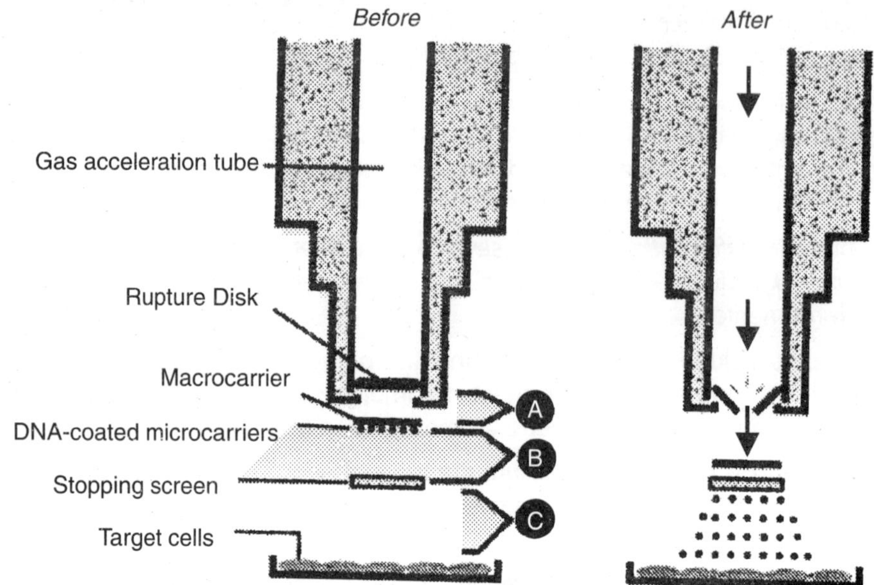

Figure 3.2: The Biolistic® bombardment process. The gas acceleration tube is filled with helium gas until the maximum pressure of the rupture disk is reached. When the disk ruptures, the ensuing helium shock wave launches a plastic macrocarrier onto which the DNA-coated microcarriers have been dried. The macrocarrier flies downward until it impacts a stopping screen. On impact, the macrocarrier is retained by the stopping screen, while the microcarriers are launched and continue downward at high velocity until they impact and penetrate the target cells.

macrocarrier are critical, and proficiency develops with practice. The first biological *parameter* to consider is a gene construct in the form of a circular or linear plasmid or a linear expression cassette (promnator).

It is important to match the promoter and/or other regulatory *sequences* with the plant tissue, so that the gene will be expressed at desired levels. Other *biological* parameters include tissue type, cell size, cell culture age, mitotic stage, general cellular health, target *tolerance* of vacuum, cel turgor pressure.

The *physiological* status of the target influences *receptivity* to foreign DNA delivery and susceptibility to injury that may adversely affect the outcome of the *transformation* process. For recovery of transgenic plants, it is very important to target cells that are competent for both *transformation* and regeneration.

Furthermore, the ability of bombarded cells to regenerate plants depends on the type and *concentration* of the selection agent. In some cases, it is best to start with a low concentration of the selective agent and increase it after 2 or 4 wk of cell culture. *Environmental* factors such as temperature; humidity; and light intensity, quality, and duration have a direct effect on tissue physiology and thus *transformation* success.

In addition, some explants may require a "healing" period after bombardment under special regimens of light, temperature, and humidity. Humidity also is important in *microcarrier* preparation and bombardment. High humidity can cause the microcarriers to clump and/or to bind irreversibly

Table 15.1: Flow Chart of Steps for Particle Bombardment Transformation

Time	Activity (in sequential steps)
	Week prior to bombardment
(–) 6 d	Sterilize supplies
	(Whatman and Sharkskin filter papers, funnels, flasks, water,
etc.). (–)	
5 d	Prepare media needed for transformation procedure.
	GM+NOA suspension culture medium.
	1/2 MS-HF bombardment medium with osmotica.
	1/2 MS-HF medium without osmotica.
	1/2 MS-HF selective medium.
(–) 4 d	Subculture or refresh medium of embryogenic cell
suspensions.	
	Week of bombardmen
(–) 1 d	Set gene gun parameters.
	Weigh gold particles (microcarriers) and place in an oven
overnight.	
	Sterilize macrocarriers, holders and stopping screens.
	Assemble macrocarriers into holders.
Key d	Bombardment day (suggested day, Tuesday).
	Examine embryogenic cell suspension for contamination
	using a microscope.
	Prepare cells on filter paper for bombardment.
	Sterilize microcarriersSterilize microcarriers.
	Coat microcarriers with DNA.
	Bombard cells.
	Incubate cells in the dark at 23 ± 1°C.
(+) 1 d	Transfer cells to medium without osmotica.
	First transfer approx 16 h after bombardment.
	Second transfer approx 24 h after bombardment.
(+) 2 d	Transfer cells to selective medium.

(Table Contd.)

	Analysis of reporter gene (i.e., GUS assay) for transient expression.
(+) 3 d	Examine GUS-positive blue spots per filter paper.
	Postbombardment weeks
(+) 30 d	Transfer cells to fresh selective medium.
	Reporter gene assay for transient expression.
(+) 60 d	Check plates for development of embryos.
	Transfer embryos to germination medium.
	Transfer remaining cells to fresh selective medium.
	Reporter gene assay for long-term expression.
(+) 90 d	Items and procedure as in
(+) 60 d.	Transfer germinated embryos to plant growth medium.

to the macrocarrier, thus reducing transformation rates. High humidity may also affect stocks of alcohol used during the DNA/microcarrier coating steps. Some *researchers* use cold temperatures while coating macrocarriers with DNA, whereas our laboratory uses room *temperature*.

We are not aware of a published study on the effect of temperature on *microcarrier* coating or *bombardment*. There has been much discussion over the advantages and disadvantages of the biolistic process as compared to *Agrobacterium* for the production of transgenic plants.

The physical nature of the biolistic process eliminates concerns about using another biological organism in the *transformation* process. In grapevines, there is often a *hypersensitive* response to *Agrobacterium* that causes plant cell death.

Biolistics obviates both the need to kill Agrobacterium after *transformation* and the occurrence of false positives arising from growth of *Agrobacterium* in the host tissues. Operation of the biolistic device is easy and there are only a few instrument parameters to adjust. Because the Biolistic® PDS-1000/He unit is *commercially* available, the user benefits from convenience, ease of use, technical support, and *standardization* with other labs.

Furthermore, plasmid construction is often simplified and *cotransformation* with multiple transgenes is routine, because plasmid DNA is simply mixed together before coating onto the microcarriers. The use of linear expression cassettes (also called clean gene technology) eliminates the chance that extraneous plasmid backbone DNA will be inserted into the target as can happen with whole plasmids or Agrobacterium.

Biolistics is the method of choice for the study of transient gene expression and for plastid *transformation*. Furthermore, biolistics is the only successful method of transformation currently available for certain genotypes. Some disadvantages of biolistics are that the *transformation efficiency* may be lower than with *Agrobacterium* and the device and *consumables* are costly.

Many researchers have strayed from biolistics because of the tendency for complex integration patterns and multiple copy insertions that could cause gene silencing. Some laboratories have overcome this problem by reducing the quantity of DNA loaded onto the microcarriers and/or by use of linear cassettes.

Random integration is also a concern and is being addressed by several groups, the most promising being the use of the Cre–Lox system for targeted integration geted integration. As many *parameters* need to be optimized for any *transformation* method, often the *experience* of the investigator and nearby colleagues determines which method is chosen.

The user must weigh the advantages and disadvantages of the various methods available. Patents and licensing availability should also be considered. Particle *bombardment* technology is covered by several patents held by E. I. du Pont de Nemours and Co. and PowderJect Vaccines, Inc.

Use of particle *bombardment* for commercial purposes may require a commercial license from the *appropriate* patent holder. There are also patents held by different companies for the use of particle bombardment for certain plant species such as *Zea mays.*

Thus, patents rights must be investigated thoroughly. In comparison, patent rights for *Agrobacterium-mediated* transformation are less clear and are tied up in the legal system. Thus, obtaining a license for Agrobacterium is more difficult for those outside of the patent-holding companies. Our laboratory has successfully employed biolistics to obtain transgenic grapevine plants.

This chapter details a protocol for transformation of *Vitisvinifera L.* 'Chardonnay' embryogenic suspension cultures in which numerous transformation parameters have been optimized. Bombardment with gold particles coated with plasmid pBI426 (double CaMV 35S promoter, *Alfalfa mosaic virus* (AMV) leader sequence, *uidA* gene, nos terminator) resulted in an average of 7883 ± 1928 (-glucuronidase (GUS) positive blue spots per Petri plate at 2 d and 46 ± 32 at 95 d.

A total of 447 embryos were harvested from 84 bombarded plates on selection medium within 5 mo after *cobombardment* with two separate plasmids. This represents more than 5 putative transgenic embryos per bombarded plate. From those, 242 plants were regenerated, which corresponds to a 54% rate of *conversion* of embryos to regenerated plants.

The cotransformation frequency of genes on different plasmids was in the range of 50% in the group of regenerated plants. The basic cell handling and bombardment procedures have been used for numerous other genotypes; however, the media and environmental conditions for cell growth, transformant selection, and plant regeneration must be optimized for each.

MATERIALS

All reagents should be tissue culture or molecular biology grade.

Culture and Preparation of Plant Cells

1. Plant material: embryogenic *Vitis vinifera L.* 'Chardonnay' cell suspension cultures.
2. Medium for cell suspension cultures: (GM + NOA medium): Murashige and Skoog (MS) (15) basal medium (macro- and microelements, vitamins, and inositol) with 18 g/L of maltose hydrate, 4.6 g/L of glycerol, and 5 μM (β-napthoxyacetic acid (NOA). Adjust pH to 5.8 with KOH before autoclaving. To prepare 100 mL of a 1 mM NOA stock solution,

dissolve 20.2 mg of NOA in 2 mL of 1 M KOH. Stir briefly and add 90 mL of Type I water. Continue stirring for 1 h. Bring to final volume and filter sterilize. Store at 4°C; stock is good for 1 yr. Use 5 mL of stock per liter of media.

3. 250-, 500-, and 1000-mL Erlenmeyer flasks, capped with aluminum foil and autoclaved.
4. Double-screen mesh (1.1 mm^2 pore size) in a polypropylene funnel to filter cell suspensions, autoclaved.
5. Disposable 10- and 25-mL plastic pipets, cotton-plugged, sterile.
6. Compound microscope, glass slides, and cover slips.
7. Magnetic stir plate and autoclaved stir bar.
8. Graduated 12- or 15-mL conical centrifuge tube.
9. 100-mL media bottle with screw cap lid, autoclaved.
10. 1-mL sterile polyethylene transfer pipet.
11. Buchner funnel (8 cm in diameter, autoclaved), size arm flask (1 L, autoclaved), and vacuum source.
12. 7-cm diameter Whatman no. 2 filter papers, autoclaved.
13. Bombardment medium (1/2 MS-HF [hormone-free] medium with osmotica: MS medium with half-strength macro- and microelements, full-strength vitamins and inositol, 30 g/L of sucrose, 0.125 *M* mannitol, 0.125 *M* sorbitol, and 2.5 g/L of Phytagel (Sigma, St. Louis, MD). Adjust pH to 5.8 with KOH before autoclaving. Dispense in 10-mL aliquots on top of a sterile, circular filter paper (S&S Sharkskin, 9 cm in diameter, VWR International, South Plainfield, NJ, cat. no. 28314-028) that is contained in a 100 × 15 mm Petri plate. The filter paper should have a small tab of tape attached (homemade) so that once the medium is solidified; forceps can be used to pick up the whole unit by the tab. The sterile medium can be stored in sterile plastic bags at room temperature for 1 mo.

STERILE FORCEPS.

Preparation of DNA-Coated Microcarriers

Sterilization of Macrocarriers and Holders

1. Macrocarriers for biolistic device (Bio-Rad).
2. Macrocarrier holders (Bio-Rad).
3. 70 and 95% ethanol.
4. Glass beaker and glass Petri plate (autoclaved).
5. Sterile Kimwipes or paper towels.
6. Sterile forceps with fine point tips (curved tips work well).
7. Desiccant in glass Petri dishes. A sterile filter paper or inverted plastic Petri plate with holes (homemade) should be placed over the desiccant to provide a stable, dust-free

platform for loading DNA-coated particles onto the macrocarriers. We use Drierite brand desiccant, which changes from blue to pink as it absorbs water. Bake at 180°C for approx 4 h to restore blue color and desiccating ability.

Sterilization of Gold Particles

1. Microcarriers: gold particles, 0.75 *μm* in diameter (Analytical Scientific Instruments, El Sobrado, CA).
2. Small glass vial or tube (1–3 mL).
3. Oven that will reach 180°C.
4. 500-μL micropipettor and tips.
5. Isopropanol, HPLC grade.
6. 1.5-mL microcentrifuge tubes, autoclaved, Treff Lab, Degersheim, Switzerland..
7. Sterile type I water.
8. Glycerol (50% v/v): Mix glycerol 1:1 with type I water and autoclave.

Coating Gold Particles With DNA

1. Micropipettors and tips (5- to 500-μL range).
2. 1.5-mL microcentrifuge tubes, autoclaved, Treff brand.
3. Plasmid DNA at 1 μg/μL in sterile TE buffer (1 mM Tris-HCl, pH 7.8, 0.1 MM disodium ethylenediaminetetraacetic acid [EDTA]).
4. 2.5 M CaCl2, filter-sterilized: To make 50 mL, dissolve 18.38 g of calcium chloride dihydrate in type I water. Filter sterilize and store at 4°C in small aliquots.
5. 0.1 M spermidine free base, filter-sterilized. Solid spermidine is very hygroscopic. Therefore, take a 1-g unopened bottle of spermidine free base, add 1 mL of type I water, adjust the volume to 68.9 mL, vortex to mix thoroughly, filter sterilize and store at –20°C in 1.2 mL microcentrifuge tubes with screw-cap lids. The stock is good for 1 mo. Discard individual tubes after first use.
6. Continuous vortex mixer such as the Vortex Genie-2 Mixer with 15.2-cm platform head.
7. HPLC grade isopropanol.
8. Ultrasonic water bath cleaner (Model B1200R-1; Branson Ultrasonics Corporation, Danbury, CT, or similar unit).

Bombardment

1. Biolistic® PDS-1000/He Instrument (Bio-Rad).
2. Helium gas cylinder; high pressure (2400–2600 psi [16,547.4-17,926.4 kPa]); grade 4.5 or 5.0 (99.995% or higher purity).
3. Vacuum pump; oil-filled rotary vane, with a pumping speed of 90-150 L/min (35 ft^3/min).
4. Rupture disks (1100 psi [7,584.2 kPa], Bio-Rad), sterilize with isopropanol.

5. Stopping screens (Bio-Rad), sterilize by autoclaving.
6. Safety glasses.
7. Hair net and latex gloves.
8. Opaque plastic box sterilized with 70% ethanol to store bombarded plates.

Postbombardment Reduction of Medium Osmoticum

1. Medium (1/2 MS-HF) without osmotica: MS medium with half-strength macroand micro-elements, full-strength vitamins and inositol, 30 g/L of sucrose, and 2.5 g/L of Phytagel. Adjust pH to 5.8 with KOH and autoclave. Dispense in 10 and 20-mL aliquots into 100 × 15 mm Petri plates.
2. Sterile forceps.

Analysis of Transient and Long-Term GUS Expression

1. GUS histochemical staining solution: To prepare 200 mL, combine the following components: 150 mL of type I water, 0.744 g of EDTA, disodium salt, dihydrate, 1.76 g of sodium phosphate monobasic, 0.042 g of potassium ferrocyanide, and 0.2 mL of Triton X-100. Adjust the volume to 198 mL, and the pH to 7.0. Add 100 mg of 5-bromo 3-chloro 3-indolyl (-D-glucuronic acid (X-Gluc) that has been dissolved in 2 mL of dimethyl sulfoxide (DMSO). Filter sterilize and store at –20°C; stock is good indefinitely.
2. Sterile forceps.
3. Petri plates, 100 × 15 mm diameter, sterile.
4. Incubator, 37°C.
5. Stereomicroscope.
6. Plastic sheet with an imprinted grid (homemade).
7. Cell counter.

Embryo Selection, Germination, and Regeneration

1. Kanamycin monosulfate (Km) stock (25 mg/mL, pH 5.8, filter-sterilized). Prepare in type I water. Store at –20°C in small aliquots. Frozen stock is good indefinitely. Warm to add to autoclaved media that has been cooled to 50–55°C.
2. Selective medium: 1/2 MS-HF medium with 30 g/L of sucrose, 3 g/L of activated charcoal, 7 g/L of Bacto-agar (Difco, Detroit, MI), and 10 or 15 mg/L of Km (added after autoclaving). Adjust pH to 5.8 with KOH and autoclave. Dispense in 20-mL aliquots into 100 × 15 mm Petri plates.
3. Embryo germination medium: 1/2 MS-HF (Km-free) with 30 g/L of sucrose, 3 g/L of activated charcoal, and 2.5 g/L of Phytagel. Adjust pH to 5.8 with KOH and autoclave. Dispense 20 mL per 100 × 15 mm Petri plate or 30 mL per baby food jar.
4. Plant growth medium: woody plant medium (WPM) (16), pH 5.8, with 20 g/L of sucrose and 2.5 g/L of Phytagel. Dispense 50 mL per Magenta GA7 vessel (Magenta Corp., Chicago, IL).

5. Parafilm (American National Can, Menasha, WI).
6. Venting Tape (Scotch brand no. 394; 3M Corporation, Minneapolis, MN).

METHODS

Preparation for bombardment should begin 6 d in advance. All steps should be carried out in a laminar flow hood to avoid microbial contamination.

Culture and Preparation of Plant Cells

1. Maintain embryogenic suspension cells in GM+NOA medium in 250- or 500-mL Erlenmeyer flasks at 120 rpm, in the dark at 23 ± 1°C. Each week, the medium should be refreshed by removing and replacing one half of the spent medium with fresh medium using a sterile plastic 10- or 25-mL pipet (s should be poured through a funnel with sterile screen mesh to remove large clumps as needed.
2. Use cells for bombardment 4 d after subculture. The cell suspension culture should be checked immediately before use for microbial contamination by placing a sample on a glass slide with cover slip and observing it under a compound microscope. Fungal strands or bacteria can be easily recognized.
3. Pour all cells needed for bombardment through a sterile screen mesh in a funnel positioned over the mouth of a 1-L sterile Erlenmeyer flask. Add a sterile stir bar and place the flask on a magnetic stir plate (in a laminar flow hood). Turn the stir plate on a low setting to mix the cells.
4. To standardize cell density for bombardment, place a 10-mL sample of the cell suspension in a graduated 12- or 15-mL conical centrifuge tube and allow cells to settle for 15 min (30 min if cell suspension is very fine). Record the settled cell volume and discard the sample in the centrifuge tube. Adjust the density of the cell suspension in the flask to be used for bombardment to 0.2 mL of settled cell volume per 10-mL sample by adding or removing GM+NOA medium.
5. For each plate to be bombarded, place a sterile Whatman no. 2 filter paper in a Bichner funnel positioned on a 1-L side-arm flask. Using a sterile transfer pipet, remove 1 mL of GM+NOA medium from the small media bottle and place on the Whatman no. 2 filter paper to moisten it. While continuing to stir the cell culture, use a sterile 10-mL pipet to collect 5-mL of cells from the culture flask and then spread as a single layer onto the filter. Apply a slight vacuum to draw off excess liquid and to help spread the cells.
6. Transfer the filter paper with attached cells to bombardment medium using sterile forceps.

Preparation of DNA Coated Microcarriers

Sterilization of Macrocarriers and Holders

1. Place macrocarrier holders in a glass beaker and macrocarriers in a glass Petri dish. Fill containers with 70% ethanol and let stand for 15 min.
2. Remove the macrocarrier holders from the 70% ethanol with sterile forceps and place on sterile Kimwipes or paper towels in a laminar flow hood to dry.

3. Using sterile forceps, remove the macrocarriers from the 70% ethanol and dip them briefly in 95% ethanol. Place on sterile Kimwipes or paper towels in a laminar flow hood to dry.
4. Assemble macrocarriers into the holders using sterile forceps and place the units in glass Petri plates with desiccant.

Sterilization of Gold Particles

This protocol prepares enough particles for 60 shots.

1. Weigh 30 mg of gold particles and place into a glass vial.
2. Heat particles in an oven at 180°C for 12 h.
3. After cooling, add 0.5 mL of isopropanol and vortex-mix vigorously for 2 min.
4. Soak for 15 min, vortex-mix (1 min), and transfer into a 1.5-mL microcentrifuge tube.
5. Pellet by centrifugation at 13,000g for 1 min.
6. Carefully remove the supernatant with a pipet and discard.
7. Add 0.5 mL of sterile type I water and resuspend particles by vortex-mixing vigorously for 30 s.
8. Centrifuge for 1 min and discard the supernatant as before.
9. Repeat the water wash for a total of three times.
10. Resuspend particles in 0.5 mL of 50% (v/v) glycerol/type I water. Vortex-mix vigorously for 1 min. Particles are ready for use, or may be stored in 50-μL aliquots at 4°C for 1 mo.

Coating Gold Particles With DNA

This protocol is for six shots.

1. Vortex-mix gold particles vigorously for 2 min and dispense 50 μL of particles into a 1.5-mL microcentrifuge tube. Vortex-mix for 5 s before each subsequent particle dispensement and just prior to adding the DNA.
2. Add the following components sequentially and quickly to the tube:

a. 5 μL of 1 tg/μL plasmid DNA (for cotransformation with two plasmids, use 2.5 μL of each); gently finger vortex.

b. 50 μL of 2.5 *M* CaCl2; gently finger vortex.

c. 20 μL of 0.1 *M* spermidine; gently finger vortex.

3. Incubate on a continuous vortex mixer for 10 min.
4. Pellet by centrifugation at 13,000g for 5 s. Remove and discard the supernatant.
5. Add 140 μL of isopropanol, finger vortex, and centrifuge as previously; then remove and discard the supernatant.
6. Resuspend in 48 μL of isopropanol by gentle pipetting up and down or finger vortexing.
7. Dip the microcentrifuge tubes into an ultrasonic cleaner three times for 1 s each.
8. Finger vortex to homogenate the DNA-coated microcarriers in the suspension and spread

6 µL in a circle approx 1 cm in diameter onto the center of a macrocarrier/holder assembly, which is contained in a Petri plate with desiccant.

Bombardment

1. Read the instrument manual and follow the manufacturer's directions and safety precautions. All users should wear safety glasses. A hair net and latex gloves are recommended to reduce the risk of microbial contamination to the plant samples.
2. Set the PDS-1000/He to the following parameters: 1300 psi (8963.2 kPa) helium (200 psi [1378.9 kPa] above the desired rupture disk value), 1 cm distance between the rupture disk and macrocarrier, 1 cm macrocarrier flight distance, 12 cm of target cell distance, 28-in. Hg (94.8 kPa) vacuum. Sterilize the chamber and all components with 70% ethanol (some components may be autoclaved per the manufacturer's instructions).
3. Place a rupture disk that has been dipped in isopropanol into the retaining cap. Place cap on the end of the gas acceleration tube and tighten.
4. Insert a sterile stopping screen into the support. Load a macrocarrier/holder unit with the microcarriers facing down, on top of the fixed nest. Tighten the macrocarrier cover lid and reposition the microcarrier launch assembly in the bombardment chambebombardment chamber.
5. Place uncovered Petri plate containing target cells into the chamber and close the door.
6. Activate the PDS-1000/He unit by first pressing the vacuum switch. When the pressure reaches 28 in. Hg (94.8 kPa) move the vacuum switch to "hold". Press the "fire" button until the rupture disk bursts. After bombardment, release the vacuum by moving the switch to "vent." Remove the Petri dish with bombarded cells from the chamber; replace the lid and place in anopaque plastic box. Discard the used rupture disk, macrocarrier, and stopping screen.

Postbombardment Reduction of Medium Osmotic Potential

1. Incubate all Petri plates (bombarded cells and nonbombarded controls) in the dark at 23 ± 1°C for 2 d to allow cell repair and DNA integration.
2. Approximately 16 h after bombardment, begin to reduce the osmotic potential of the culture medium by transferring the cells and bombardment medium below as a unit (using Sharkskin filter paper with attached tabs) to Petri plates containing 10 mL of 1/2 MS-HF medium without osmotica.
3. At approx 24 h postbombardment, transfer the cells and bom (using Sharkskin filter paper with attached tabs) to Petri plates containing 20 mL of 1/2 MS-HF medium without osmotica, leaving the 10 mL of medium from the previous transfer behind (discard).

Analysis of Transient and Long-Term GUS Expression

Transient GUS expression is assayed in a portion of the plates 48 h after bombardment. A plate of negative control cells (nonbombard without the *uidA* gene) should be assayed as well. This assay is destructive. The analysis should be repeated in other plates on a monthly basis for 3–6 mo to evaluate rates of long-term GUS expression as an indication of stable transformation.

1. Using sterile forceps, transfer filter papers with cells to empty Petri plates and place 600 μL of X-gluc solution on top of the cells.
2. Incubate at 37°C overnight. Transformed cells will turn blue.
3. Count the number of blue spots per plate using a stereomicroscope. A black grid on transparent plastic (homemade) placed either above or below the cells aids counting. When transformation rates are high, only a portion of the cells on the plates needs to be counted.

Embryo Selection, Germination, and Regeneration

1. Two days after bombardment, cells should be transferred to selective medium with 10 mg/L of Km. Using sterile forceps, lift the original Whatman no. 2 filter paper supports with cells from the bombardment medium and place on top of selection medium. Wrap the Petri plates with Parafilm and incubate at 27 ± 0.1 °C in the dark for embryo induction. After 4 wk (and every 4 wk thereafter) transfer the cells with supporting filter paper to fresh selective medium with 15 mg/L of Km. Putative Km-resistant embryos should be visible beginning approx 6-8 wk after bombardment.
2. Harvest individual embryos with a 1–2 cm long radicle from Km-selective medium and place directly on embryo germination medium in Petri plates. Wrap the plates with Parafilm and incubate embryos for 4 wk at 23 ± I 'C with low light intensity (10 $\mu E/m^2/s$), 14:10-h light/dark (L/D) photoperiod.
3. Transfer embryos every 4 wk to fresh embryo germination medium in baby food jars. Wrap jars with Venting tape and incubate at 23 ± 1°C with increased light intensity (50 $\mu E/m^2/s$), 14:10–h L/D photoperiod.
4. Transfer germinated embryos with elongated roots and open green cotyledons to Magenta boxes containing plant growth medium. Incubate embryos at 23 ± 1°C for root elongation and shoot formation. Transfer to fresh medium every 4 wk.
5. Maintain regenerated plants on plant growth medium in Magenta boxes at 23 ± 1°C for *multiplication*. Transfer shoots to fresh medium every 6 to 8 wk.

NOTES

1. Embryogenic cell cultures are often the best tissue to use for biolistic *transformation* because they can be spread to provide a uniform target of cells, and because they have a high capacity to regenerate into plants. We use *proembryogenic* cells that are finely divided because they spread easily on the filter papers. Small cell clusters also are effective for selection of *transformants* as fewer *nontransformed* escapes result.
2. Supplementing the bombardment medium with osmotica (mannitol/sorbitol) resulted in higher rates of stable transformants for all suspension cultured cells we have tested. However, the benefits of osmotica are less clear when intact tissues such as leaves or whole embryos are used. It is believed that plasmolysis of the cells reduces damage by *preventing* leakage of protoplasm from bombarded cells. Partial drying of cells has also been used.

3. Bio-Rad also sells gold particles in different sizes, with 0.6 tm and 1 tm being most applicable for plant cell transformation. Tungsten particles work well for many plant species and are much less expensive. However, the size is *heterogeneous* and tungsten may degrade DNA or be toxic to plant cells. See Bio Rad bulletin US/EG Bulletin 2015 for a discussion of particle types/sizes.
4. DNA and tungsten particles may stick to the sides of *microcentrifuge* tubes, resulting in loss of particles. We have not tested all brands, but know that Treff tubes work well.
5. DNA should be very pure (free of RNA or protein) or *microprojectiles* may clump. We purify DNA by CsCl gradient centrifugation or a plasmid purification kit (Qiagen, Valencia, CA).
6. Spermidine stocks can degrade even when frozen, causing dramatic reductions in *transformation* efficiency. Fresh stocks should be made monthly.
7. Rupture disks come in a range of bursting pressures from 450 to 2200 psi. The most commonly used for plant tissues are 1100 psi. Rupture disks of higher psi impart higher velocity to the macro- and microcarriers, but also cause more tissue damage. These may be appropriate for more sturdy tissue such as leaves.
8. To dispense 10 mL onto the plates, the medium must be spre plates, or by pipetting extra medium and then removing medium until only 10 mL remains.
9. It is important to design bombardment experiments to be performed comfortably by the operator so that the experiment is not rushed or critical details overlooked. In our laboratory, with two people working together it is possible to bombard a maximum of 50–60 plates of suspension cultured cells in 1 d. One person prepares the target cells and adds them to Petri plates with *bombardment* medium, and the second person prepares the DNA-coated microcarriers and the biolistic device. They then work together to perform the bombardment.
10. The cells in the flasks should be divided into multiple flasks as the population increases. There is no specific formula for dividing the cell culture; rather, the transfer *technician* should develop an eye as to how dense the population should be to maintain a creamy white or light yellow color and a small cell cluster size.
11. Contamination of the original cell culture can be a source of frustration because whole experiments can be lost after the work of bombardment. At each weekly *subculture* of the cell suspension, samples of media and cells should be streaked onto Petri plates with bacterial growth medium and/or plant growth medium and incubated both at 25°C and 37°C. Just prior to preparing the cells for *bombardment*, a sample of the cells and growth medium should be placed on a glass slide with a cover slip and examined with a compound microscope. Use phase-contrast optics if available or move the condenser out of focus to observe cells and possible microbes better. To gain experience in observing microorganisms in culture, researchers should practice looking at plant cell cultures contaminated with various organims as well as those known to be clean.
12. The bore of a 5-mL pipet is too small and cell clumps cause blockage. Attempt to minimize cells lost off of the edge of the filter paper while also achieving a uniform spread across

the whole filter paper. It takes some practice to achieve a uniform layer of cells on the filter paper.

13. Macrocarriers and holders may be assembled and autoclaved as a unit. However, we have occasionally *experienced* shrinkage of *macrocarriers* after auto claving, resulting in premature slipping of the macrocarriers from the holders. Thus, we prefer alcohol sterilization. Macrocarriers should be kept free of dirt and oil (from fingers)and oil (from fingers).
14. We follow the protocol suggested by Sawant et al., in which heating gold particles was shown to reduce particle agglomeration and significantly enhance transformation.
15. Particles settle out of suspension quickly. When removing aliquots, work quickly and vortex-mix often. As stated by Birch and Franks: "The importance of consistent technique in *precipitating* the DNA onto the *microprojectiles* and loading the accelerating apparatus should not be underestimated. Two operators of a single apparatus may obtain a 100-fold difference in transformation frequencies because of slight variations in technique at this stage."
16. Finger vortex-mix each time before *aliquoting microcarriers.* It is important to place macrocarriers in a desiccator to dry immediately after they are loaded. Exposure to high humidity during and after drying may result in clumping of the particles and tight (sometimes irreversible) binding to the *macrocarrier.* Use DNA-coated macrocarriers within 2 h after preparation.
17. The gene gun settings are critical for success and should be *chbombardment.* We use a prototype of the Bio-Rad instrument in which the settings are adjustable over a larger range. However, the settings we describe here can be achieved with the Bio-Rad unit. We use a small plastic ruler to measure the distances. Higher particle velocities are obtained with higher helium pressures, and shorter rupture membrane to *macrocarrier* and macrocarrier to target cell distance. One must be cautious in interpreting transient expression assays because the factors that increase particle velocity also increase the shockwave to the tissue and may actually decrease stable transformation. The settings we use are standard in our laboratory for cell suspension cultures. With intact tissues it may be desirable to increase helium pressure, decrease target cell distance, or bombard each sample multiple times to improve *penetration* of the particles into the tissues. The reader is referred to several reviews for further discussion on the optimization of biolistic parameters.
18. Leaving the Petri plate at or near 28 in. Hg (94.8 kPa) can allow medium to boil and flip out of the plate. This problem can be avoided by using slightly lower vacuum, by increasing the concentration of gelling agent in the medium, or by letting medium set for 2 wk before use.
19. The green fluorescent protein *(gfp)* gene is another commonly employed reporter gene whose assay by UV light is nondestructive to the cells.
20. The procedures and growth media we describe here have been used for *V. vinifera* cultivars 'Chardonnay,' 'Merlot,' and 'Pinot Noir' in our laboratory. Other grapevine species

and cultivars have not been tested with this protocol. Researchers should use the optimal embryo and plant growth medium for the *genotypes* they are working with. Similarly, the type and concentration of selective agent needs to be *optimized* for each genotype and tissue (even for each cell culture line).

21. Embryos could be incubated either at 4°C in the dark for 2 wk for chilling treatment and then incubated at 23 ± 1°C with low light intensity (10 μE/m^2/s), 14:10-h light/dark (L/D) photoperiod, for an additional 2 wk, or incubated at 23 ± 1°C with low light intensity for 4 wk. In our laboratory, we did not find statistical differences between the two treatments.

Chapter 4

IMPROVING TRANSGENIC CROPS

Abiotic stresses represent the most limiting *environmental* factors affecting *agricultural* productivity. To overcome these *limitations* and to improve production, to feed the *ever-increasing* population, it is imperative to develop crop *cultivars* that are stress *tolerant.*

When crop plants are subjected to *environmental* stress *conditions,* they fail to express their full genetic potential for production. The effect of stress depends on the developmental stage, *genotype* of plant species as well as *duration* and intensity of the stress.

Generally, plants respond to these stresses under low or moderate levels, but when the stress levels *exceed* a certain *critical* level (which varies from crop to crop), the *physiological mechanisms* imparting tolerance to plants start breaking down causing *ultimately* plant death. Consequently, the abiotic stress factors cause a massive loss to the *productivity* of crop plants.

According to the ICRISAT Report, biotic and abiotic stress factors lead to a loss of US$ 15.74 billion in five most important crops of semi arid tropics— sorghum, pear millet, pigeonpea, chick pea and groundnut. These crops are the main food source for poor people of the developing countries.

Amongst the various stresses *affecting* crop plants, loss due to abiotic *stresses* is much more *significant* as compared to the losses that occur due to insect/pests, weeds and diseases. Classical plant breeding *methods* involving inter-specific or *inter-generic hybridization* and *in vitro* induced *variation* have been applied to improve the abiotic stress *tolerance* of various crop plants but without much success.

The *conventional* breeding *strategies* are limited by the *complexity*

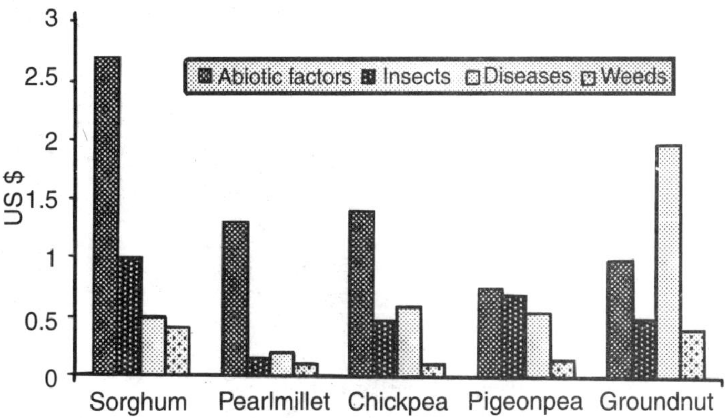

Figure 4.1: Loss due to abiotic factors, insects, diseases and weeds.

of stress *tolerance* traits, low genetic variance of yield components under stress condition and lack of *efficient* selection criteria. It is important, therefore, to look for alternative *strategies* to develop stress *tolerant* crops.

Recently, marker assisted selection of *specific* traits that are linked to yield, e.g. osmotic adjustment, membrane stability or *physiological tolerance* indices, has been *recommended.* However, QTL that are linked to tolerance at one stage in plant development can differ from those linked to *tolerance* at other stages.

Furthermore, desirable QTLs can require *extensive* breeding to restore suitable traits along with the *introgressed* tolerance trait. The best alternative, therefore, is the direct introduction of genes by genetic *engineering* to incorporate tolerance traits in target crops.

Research over the past two decades has provided a better *understanding* of the molecular biology of stress responses in plants. Many genes and gene products have been *identified* which get induced upon exposure of plants to various abiotic stresses—drought, salinity, low and high *temperature* stress, etc.

Consequently, *biotechnological* tools have been applied to *transfer* some of these useful genes implicated in stress tolerance to plants. In addition to these stress-induced proteins, genes *encoding enzymes* of the biosynthetic *pathways* of different osmolytes such as proline, glycine betaine, trehalosc, sorbitol, pinitol, etc. have been *cloned* and *exploited* in improving abiotic stress-tolerance in plants *through* genetic engineering.

In this chapter we have made an attempt to *summarize* the progress made *towards understanding* the role of different genes implicated in stress tolerance and the genetic *engineering* efforts towards developing *stress* tolerant transgenics in crop plants of *economic importance.*

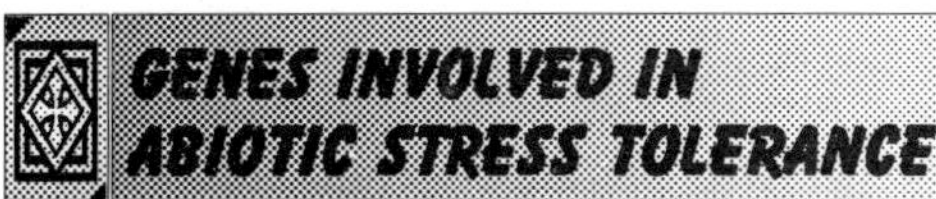

GENES INVOLVED IN ABIOTIC STRESS TOLERANCE

Under different abiotic stress *conditions,* a large number of genes show elevated *transcript* levels in plants. Up-regulation of these genes does not always confirm their role in stress tolerance.

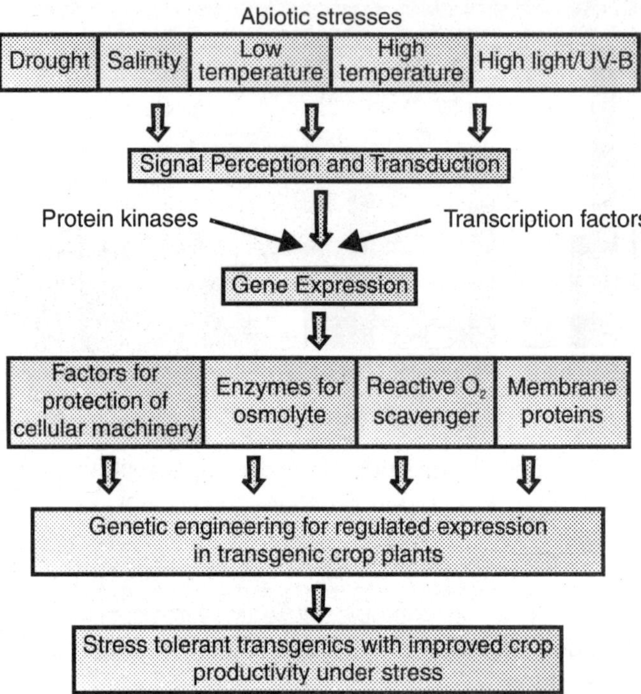

Figure 4.2: Schematic representation of stress perception and transduction, stress-induced gene expression, and genetic engineering utilizing the candidate genes for developing stress tolerant transgenic crop plants.

Changes in gene *expression* may be due to disruption of *physiological* and metabolic processes of the cell.

However, precise *physiological* function of any such gene can be *studied* by its altered expression (overexpression or suppression) in transgenic plants. Indeed, *transgenic approach* has emerged as a valuable tool in determining or *confirming* the precise function of the stress-induced genes and to develop stress-tolerant *transgenic* crop plants.

Normally, genes isolated under stress conditions are first tested in model species such as tobacco and *Arabidopsis* for their role in stress tolerance before *transferring* them to *economically* important crop species. Stress-induced genes and gene products that *accumulate* under abiotic stresses have been reviewed by *Shinozaki* et al., Grover et al. and Abdin et al..

There are four categories of stress induced genes/proteins with known function which have been *exploited* for *generating* stress tolerant *transgenic* plants. These genes and their role in model plant species have been *described* below.

Genes Involved in Osmolyte Biosynthesis

Osmolytes are highly soluble *compatible* solutes that are neutral at *physiological* pH. Being neutral at *physiological* pH, increased concentration of compatible osmolytes does not interfere with *macromolecular* conformation.

Enhanced *accumulation* of *osmolytes* under stress conditions lead to the lowering of osmotic

Table 4.1: Some examples of osmotic stress induced genes and gene products

Category	*Proteins*	*Genes*
Genes involved in osmolyte biosynthesis	*Enzymes for synthesis of:*	
	Proline	*P5CS*
	Polyols-mannitol, ononitol	*MtlD, IMT*
	Fructans, Trehalose	*SacB, TPSI*
	Polyamine-putrescine	*ADC, ODC*
	Quarternaryamine-glycine betaine	*codA, CDH, CMO*
	Osmotin-induced proline	*Osmotin*
Genes encoding factors for protection of cellular machinery	*Antifreeze proteins*	*AFP1, AFP2*
	LEA proteins	*LEAI, Dehydrins, HVA1, LEAIV*
	LEA-like proteins	*COR14, COR15*
	Osmotin	*Osmotin*
Genes encoding membrane proteins	*Water channel proteins*	
	Aquaporins	*y-TIP, PM28A, $AthH_2$*
	Transport proteins	
	H^+ ATPase	*AHA3, PMA2*
	Ca^{2+} ATPase	*LCA1*
	K^+ transporters	*HKt1, Hak1*
	K^+ channels	*AKt1, AKt2*
	Na^+/H^+ antiporter	*AtNHX1*
Genes for reactive oxygen scavenger proteins	Superoxidase dismutase	*Cu/Zn SOD, MnSOD, FeSOD*
	Ascorbate peroxidase	*Apx*
	Glutathione synthetase	*GS*
	Glutathione reductase	*GR*
	Catalase	*Catalase*
	Glyoxalase	*GlyI, GlyII*
Genes encoding transcription factors	Ethylene responsive element binding factors (ERF)	*CBF1, Tsi, DREBF1*
	Basic domain Leucine Zipper (BZIP)	*ABF3, ABF4*
	Myb and Myc like protein	*Atmyb2, rd22BPI*

(Table Contd.)

Genes encoding protein kinases	*Mitogen activated protein kinases*	
	MAPK	*At MPK 3/6, At MPK4*
	MAPKK	*At MPKK 4/5, At MKK 1/2*
	MAPKKK	*At MEKK1, At ANP1*
	Ca^{2+} dependent protein kinases	*AtCDPK1, AtCDPK2*

potential of cells which inturn results in uptake of water and *maintenance* of cell turgor. Various kinds of osmolytes are known to *accumulate* in plants under stress such as proline, *mannitol, glycine betaine, trehalose,* etc.. Proline, an important *osmolyte* is *synthesized* from glutamate by the catalytic action of enzyme A^1-pyrroline 5 *carboxylate* synthetase (P5CS).

Overexpression of this *enzyme* in *transgenic* tobacco showed *enhanced biomass* production, better plant growth and flower development under drought and salinity stress conditions.

We recently reported accumulation of free proline in *transgenic* tobacco plants *over-expressing* osmotin gene. The transgenic plant showed tolerance to osmotic stress caused by drought and salinity; however, the precise role of osmotin in imparting tolerance could not be *ascertained.*

Among polyols, mannitol *overproduction* through *E. coli* mannitol 1-phosphate dehydrogenase *(MtlD)* gene expression in transgenic tobacco provided enhanced tolerance against salinity stress. Overaccumulation of D-mannitol upto a remarkable limit of 600 mM in cytosol provided osmotic tolerance to *transgenic* tobacco.

Similarly, fructan synthase *(Sac B)* gene responsible for fructan *biosynthesis,* showed tolerance to freezing and PEG-mediated water stress in *transgenic* tobacco. Engineering of trehalose *metabolism* by *transferring* trehalose 6-phosphate synthase (TPS1) gene in tobacco plants showed improved drought tolerance.

However, the transgenic plants exhibited stunted growth, reduced sucrose content and lancet-shaped leaves. Experiments are in progress to *circumvent* these growth related problems. Polyamines are also known to have positive effects on plants exposed to abiotic stresses.

Spermine and spermidine are two major polyamines synthesized from putrescine. Ornithine decarboxylase (ODC) and arginine decarboxylase (ADC) are the key enzymes involved in putrescine biosynthesis. Although the role of putrescine in stress tolerance remains to be elucidated, the biosythesis is *stimulated* in the presence of osmotic stress.

A *quaternary* amine, glycine betaine is another important osmolyte whose *enhanced* accumulation was observed in halophytes and *bacterium* under drought and salinity stress.

Choline oxidase (COD) from *Arthrobacter globiformis,* or choline dehydrogenase (CDH) and choline *monoxygenase* (CMO) in plants are the key *enzymes* involved in glycine betaine biosynthesis. Transgenic tobacco and *Arabidopsis* plants producing COD, CDH and CMO have shown enhanced *tolerance* against salinity stress.

However, it has been reported that availability of choline is a limiting factor in glycine betaine producing *transgenic* plants. This problem can be overcome to some extent by *exogenous* choline supply.

Engineering osmolyte biosynthesis is *emerging* as a viable approach in producing *transgenics* for enhanced *tolerance* to osmotic *stresses* in plants. However, the major focus is on enhanced *biosynthesis* of trehalose and glycine betaine through genetic *engineering*.

Genes Encoding Factors for Protection of Cellular Machinery

Protection factors such as antifreeze proteins (AFPs) bring about *lowering* of freezing point by *inhibiting* binding of *additional* water molecules to ice crystals. Larger ice crystals have more harmful effects on *tissues* as compared to small crystals.

When a synthetic fusion protein (based on type I AFP) was *expressed* in yeast, inhibition of *recrystallization* was observed as a result of AFP *expression*. Transformed yeast cells also showed a two-fold increase in survival after rapid freezing.

In another study, no effect on freezing tolerance in transgenic tobacco plants *expressing* the type II *antifreeze* protein was observed. Further studies are required for defining the exact role of AFPs in abiotic stress tolerance. Another kind of protection factors are late *embryogenesis* (LEA) proteins that are highly *hydrophilic*. They accumulate in seeds during desiccation.

Group II LEA proteins, also known as dehydrins help in *maintaining* folded form of proteins and thereby function as chaperons. These proteins are *generally* induced during cold *acclimatization* and dehydration. *Overexpression* of group I LEA proteins from wheat in yeast cells showed attenuation of growth *inhibition* in high osmolarity media.

However, their role in freezing *tolerance* remains unknown. Group III Lea *proteins* have been *suggested* to function against *desiccation tolerance* by sequestration of ions. But there is no report available on transfer of HVA1 gene encoding LEA III proteins in model species.

Overexpression of group IV LEA protein in yeast has shown tolerance against low *temperature* and salinity stress. Another group of LEA-like proteins are *hydrophilic* COR proteins having repeated amino acid sequence motifs forming *amphipathic* α-helix.

Based on this property, these proteins have been suggested to increase freezing and *dehydration* tolerance by stabilizing proteins and membranes. Constitutive *expression* of cold regulated *COR15a* gene in transgenic *Arabidopsis* plants showed an increase in both *chloroplast* and *protoplast* freezing tolerance. However, effect of low *temperature* was not measured in transgenic *Arabidopsis* plants *over-expressing* the barley gene Cor14b.

Genes Encoding Membrane Proteins

The membrane proteins involved in osmotic stress tolerance include water channel and transport proteins. Water channel proteins control cellular water transport in response to drought and salt stress. The recently identified *aquaporins* are complex family of water channel proteins having control over water flux in and out of the cell.

Aquaporins also maintain proton *gradient* for osmotic balance by *preventing* the ion flow through water channel. Phosphorylation of aquaporins through membrane bound protein kinase has been suggested as an essential factor for regulation of activity of water channel proteins.

Transgenic *Arabidopsis* plants with antisense construct of plasma membrane aquaporin have revealed the role of aquaporins in maintaining cytosolic osmoregulation. In high saline environments, plants take up excessive amounts of Na^+ and Cl^- at the cost of K^+ and Ca^{2+}. K^+ is required as a cofactor for many enzymes and Ca^{2+} is essential in signal transduction. A number of transport proteins play an important role in *maintaining* ion homeostasis under stress condition.

In salt tolerant plants, H^+ ATPase maintains H^+ ion flux across the plasma membrane. Ca^+ homeostasis for reducing toxic effects of NaCl is *maintained* by Ca^+ ATPase. K^+ transporters and K^+ channels maintain K^+ and Na^+ uptake for mediating ion homeostasis. Na^+/H^+ antiporters use electrochemical proton gradient for transporting Na^+ into vacuole.

This gradient is provided by vacuolar H^+ *translocating* enzymes. *Compartmentation* of Na^+ into vacuole helps in *accumulating* water into the cell and thus in maintaining osmotic balance. Consequently, *overexpression* of the gene encoding vacuolar Na^+/H^+ antiporter showed tolerance to 200 mM NaCl in *Arabidopsis thaliana.*

Genes for Reactive Oxygen Species Scavenger Proteins

Under stress conditions, plants produce various active oxygen species (AOS) such as superoxide O_2, hydrogen peroxide H_2O_2, and hydroxyradical OH^-. Plants generally respond to these active oxygen species by inducing antioxidant system involving superoxide dismutase (SOD), ascorbate peroxidase (APx), *glutathione synthetase* (GS), glutathione reductase (GR) and catalase enzymes.

For detailed analysis of contribution of these antioxidant enzymes to stress tolerance, a large number of *experiments* have been conducted with transgenic model plants overproducing the *antioxidant* enzymes. Most of these transgenics provided tolerance against oxidative stress, and *photooxidative* and ozone damage.

Glyoxalate system is known for being involved in protection against *cytotoxicity.* The first evidence investigating the role of *glyoxalase* I enzyme in imparting tolerance to plants under salinity stress came through the studies of Veena et al..

The same group has now *overexpressed* glyoxalase II in tobacco either *independently* or in concert with *gly I* . Transgenic plants inheriting both the genes showed many fold increase in salinity tolerance over the single gene transgenics depicting a synergistic effect of the *gly I* and *gly* II genes.

Genes Encoding Transcription Factors

Transcription factors play an important role in controlling the expression of stress-responsive genes. Few important families of *transcription* factors are:

Ethylene Responsive Element Binding Factors (ERF)

All ERFs are suggested to have a conserved 58-59 amino acid domain that can bind to C-repeat/ dehydration responsive element (DRE). DRE motifs are involved in regulation of ABA independent gene expression under drought, salinity and cold stress.

Therefore, overexpression of single *ERF* gene may help in *improving* tolerance to a range of abiotic stresses. The role of *ERF* gene in freezing tolerance was confirmed, through *overexpression* of CRT/DRE binding factor CBF1 in *Arabidopsis thaliana.* The *ERF* gene imparted tolerance to multiple stress factors such as drought, salinity and cold stresses imposed together.

Overexpression of tobacco stress induced gene (Tsi) in transgenic tobacco further confirmed the role of *ERF* gene in conferring tolerance to osmotic stress.

bZIP Transcription Factor

bZIPs belong to a large family of *transcription* factor genes and possess a basic domain adjacent to leucine-zipper motif. A number of bZIP proteins are found to be involved in stress signaling. The first genetic evidence of importance of bZIP proteins in stress tolerance was provided by *overexpressed* ABRE binding factor/ABA responsive element binding protein of *bZIP* family in transgenic *Arabidopsis thaliana.*

Myb and Myc Binding Proteins

Myb-like proteins contain helix turn helix related motif and Myc-like proteins have basic helix loop helix domain for DNA binding. Expression of this class of *transcription* factors is induced by ABA. In *Arabidopsis,* application of *exogenous* ABA induces a dehydration *responsive* gene *rd22.*

Expression of this gene requires protein *synthesis* as revealed by the use of cycloheximide, an inhibitor of protein synthesis. The promoter of *rd22* contains a 67bp DNA sequence, which is *sufficient* for the expression of the gene.

Abe et al., identified the presence of MYB and MYC recognition sites in the 67bp region by *transforming* tobacco plants with this region. cDNA encoding MYB related DNA binding protein was termed *as At MYB2* and gene encoding MYC related protein was given the name *rd22* BP1.

Protein Kinases

Mitogen Activated Protein Kinases (MAPKs)

MAPKs are serine/threonine protein kinases which *phosphorylate* a number of *substrates* involved in various cellular responses including gene expression. They play essential role in plant signal *transduction* pathways.

MAPK cascade is regulated by MAPK kinases (MAPKK) and MAPKK kinases (MAPKKK). In this cascade, signal is sensed by MAPKKK first that phosphorylates the MAPKK, which in turn phosphorylates the MAPK. A number of abiotic stress factors such as wounding, low temperature, high *osmolarity,* high salinity and reactive oxygen species act as a signal in activating MAPK cascade.

To our knowledge there seems to be no report as yet on *transgenic* with *overexpression* of MAPK cascade genes. Studies are underway on cloning these genes on the basis of sequence homology and specific antibody *recognition.* A detailed analysis of mitogen *activated* protein kinase *signaling* cascade has been presented by Guillaume et al..

Calcium Dependent Protein Kinases

A number of abiotic stress factors such as cold, salt and drought elevate Ca^{2+} levels in cells for achieving control over various cellular *mechanisms.* Ca^{2+} influx mediates this control by *phosphorylation/dephosphorylation* of various proteins through Ca^{2+} dependent protein kinases (CDPKs).

These kinases contain a calmodulin like regulatory domain and a Ca^{+} binding site at C terminal. Around 40 different CDPKs have been investigated in *Arabidopsis thaliana.* Sheen introduced eight CDPK isoforms of *Arabidopsis* into maize *protoplasts,* and found that only two isoforms, AtCDPK1 and AtCDPK2 induced the expression of specific stress genes thereby *suggesting* the presence of specific CDPK isoforms for different stress signaling pathways.

Table 4.2: Some examples of transgenic crop plants tolerant to abiotic stresses.

Transgenic	Gene introduced	Source of	Performance of transgenics under stress crop the gene
Wheat	*HVAI*	Barley	Improved biomass under water deficit conditions
	HKTI	Wheat	Enhanced growth under salinity
	MtlD	*E. coli*	Improved growth under water stress and salinity
Rice	*CodA*	*A. globitbrmis*	Early recovery from salt induced damage
	CodA	*A. globitbrmis*	Tolerance against salt stress
	GS2	Rice	Enhanced tolerance to salt stress and cold stress
	P5CS	Mothbean	Increased biomass under salt and water stress
	OSCDPK7	Rice	Improved tolerance against cold and salt/ drought
	HVAI	Barley	Significantly increased tolerance to water deficit and salt stress
	HVAI	Barley	Improvement in drought and salt tolerance
	PMA80 & PMA1959	Wheat	Enhanced dehydration and salt stress tolerance
	ADC	Oat	Enhanced tolerance to drought and salinity
	SAMDC	*Tritordeum*	Enhanced NaCl stress tolerance
	Catalase	Wheat	Improved tolerance against low temperature stress
	OtsA +OtsB	*E.coli*	High tolerance against drought, salinity and low temperature stress
	TPS + TPP	*E.coli*	Enhanced tolerance to drought, salinity and cold stress
Mustard	*Glutathione synthetase*	*E. coli*	Enhanced cadmium accumulation and tolerance
	Glutathione reductase	*E.coli*	Targeted expression in chloroplast showed cadmium tolerance
	CodA	*A. globitbrmis*	Tolerance against salt and water stress
	AtNHX1	*A. thaliana*	Enhanced salt tolerance
	Osmotin	Tobacco	Enhanced drought and salt tolerance
Soybean	*Antisense P5CR*	*A. thaliana*	Tolerance to drought stress as compared to control ones
Alfalfa	*MnSOD*	Tobacco	Enhanced freezing stress tolerance
	MnSOD	Tobacco	Enhanced water deficit tolerance
	MnSOD	Tobacco	Enhanced winter survival
	FeSOD	*A. thaliana*	Increased winter survival, no change in oxidative stress tolerance

Table Contune

MitMnSOD + ChlMnSOD		Tobacco	Improved biomass, stress tolerance not detected
	Alfin	Alfalfa	Improvement against salinity tolerance
Cotton	*MnSOD*	-	Enhanced tolerance to photooxidative and low temperature effect
	MnSOD	-	No tolerance conferred to low temperature and high light
	Apx	Pea	Protection to photosynthesis against moderate chilling and high
	GR	*A. thaliana*	photon flux density
Potato	Cu, ZnSOD	Tomato	Enhanced tolerance to oxidative stress
	Osmotin like protein	Potato	No appreciable role in freezing tolerance but showed increased tolerance to late-blight
	Osmotin	Tobacco	Enhanced tolerance to drought and salt stress
	AFP (synthetic antifreeze protein)	Synthesized based on Winter flounder	Enhanced tolerance to freezing stress
	OtsA	*E.coli*	No trehalose accumulation,abiotic stress tolerance not determined
	OtsB		
	TPSI	*S. cerevisiae*	Improved drought tolerance
	Glyceraldehyde -3 phosphate dehydrogenase	*Oyster*	Improved salt tolerance *mushroom*
	CDSP32	Potato	Enhanced tolerance to oxidative damage
Tomato	*HALL*	Yeast	Improved salt tolerance
	ATNHXI	*A. thaliana*	Improved fruit yield and K^+/Na^+ selectivity
	CBFI	*A. thaliana*	Tolerance against 200mM NaCl stress, enhanced tolerance to water deficit stress, catalase activity increased and H_2O_2 decreased
	CBF3	Tobacco	Elevated tolerance to chilling and oxidative stresses, catalase activity induced
Oat	HVA1	Barley	Higher osmotic tolerance
Carrot	*ODC*	Mouse	Response against abiotic stress not studied

DEVELOPMENT OF STRESS-TOLERANT TRANSGENIC CROPS

Wheat

Wheat is an important cereal crop.There are only few reports on *transgenics* for abiotic stress tolerance in this *economically* important crop. For instance, improved biomass *productivity* and water use efficiency was observed when wheat cultivar Hi-Line was transformed with HVA1 gene encoding LEAIII protein.

These transgenic lines were shown to have higher dry mass, root fresh and dry weight and shoot dry weight as compared to control plants. For elucidating the role of *HKT1, transformed* wheat with sense and antisense construct of *HKT1* were raised.

The transgenic plants exhibited better growth and reduced Na^+/K^+ ratios as compared to control plants under saline conditions. The role of mannitol *accumulation* in imparting stress *tolerance* is known in model transgenic plants.

Based on this fact, transgenic plants were generated with *mtlD* gene of *E.coli* in sense and antisense orientation. Wheat plants do not *synthesize* mannitol by their own metabolism. The transgenic wheat plants with *mtlD* gene accumulated very low level of mannitol which was not sufficient for osmotic adjustment.

However, the *transgenic* plants showed improved growth under water stress and salinity conditions probably due to protein *stabilizing* effect of osmolytes under stress.

Rice

Rice is a highly drought and salt sensitive crop. A number of studies have been performed for its *improvement* through genetic *engineering*. In 1998, Sakamoto et al. developed transgenic rice by introducing *codA* gene from *Arthrobacter globiformis* for glycinebetaine synthesis.

These transgenic plants could not show tolerance against salinity stress but their stress *recovery* rate was high. They showed that transgenic plants with CodA enzyme targeted to *chloroplasts* were more efficient in protecting photosynthetic machinery against stress than transgenic plants with *codA expression* in cytosol.

Further, the role of *codA* gene in improving salt stress tolerance was *confirmed* by Mohanty et al., in transgenic lines of Indica rice. In a recovery period after exposure to 0.15 M NaCl for one week, the *transgenic* plants survived well whereas control plants failed to recover and died.

For *elucidating* the role of photorespiration in protection against salt stress, transgenic rice plants over expressing chloroplast glutamine *synthetase* (GS2) were generated. One of the *transgenic* lines retained more than 90% PSII activity whereas control plants lost it *completely* after two weeks of stress.

The same transgenic line also exhibited resistance to cold stress as observed in a *preliminary experiment*. Zhu et al. overexpressed full length cDNA of A^1-pyrroline 5 carboxylate synthetase (P5CS) in rice under ABA-inducible promoter complex (AIPC).

The *transgenic* plants showed better fresh root weight as compared to controls under salt stress (100 mM NaCl). The transgenics showed higher growth rate as compared to the control plants under water stress as well. A full-length cDNA encoding CDPK was cloned from rice and *overexpressed* in rice under the control of CaMV 35S promoter for detecting its physiological function.

The *transgenic* plants showed tolerance against cold and salt/drought stresses. Overexpression of the *OsCDPK* in rice induced the *expression* of many other genes such as rab16A, *SalT and Wsi18* under salt/ drought but not under cold stress.

This suggested the presence of two distinct ABA-induced *pathways* using a single CDPK, one that is induced by salt/drought stress, whereas, the other induced by cold stress. For *engineering* Lea group of genes in rice, *suspension* culture of rice, *Oryza sativa L. (cv.* Nipponbare) were transformed with *HVA1* gene encoding the LEA III group of proteins.

Later, the *HVA1* gene was *overexpressed* for the *improvement* of abiotic stress tolerance in Basmati rice. The transgenic plants maintained growth rates higher than control plants under water deficit and salt stress conditions. However, the use of stress-inducible promoter gave better results in term of stress tolerance than the *constitutive* promoter under stress conditions.

Further, transgenic plants *harborlng PMA80* gene (encoding LEA II group protein) *and PMA 1959* gene (encoding LEA group I protein) were *developed* separately and the role of these proteins against *dehydration* and salt tolerance was studied.

The tolerance level of transgenic plants with *PMA80* gene was higher than the plants with *PMA 1959* gene. In an attempt to decipher the role of polyamines in stress tolerance, Malabika Roy and Ray Wu *generated* transgenic plants with *adc* gene *and samdc* gene, *respectively.*

Both the types of *transgenic* plants which accumulated *polyamines* to a significant level exhibited increased tolerance to *environmental* stress to almost an equal extent. The evidence *confirming* tolerance against low temperature stress in rice came through *overexpression* of catalase gene.

The transgenic rice plants *overexpressing* the catalase gene displayed less damage as compared to control plants against a treatment of 5°C for 8 days. This *enhanced* tolerance to cold stress in *transgenics* was attributed to higher detoxification of H_2O_2 by enhanced catalase activity.

Tolerance to multiple abiotic stresses was introduced by the *overexpression* of *trehalose* biosynthetic genes *(OtsA and OtsB)* as fusion gene in rice plants. The transgenic plants showed better growth, less photo-oxidative damage and more *favourable* mineral balance than that of the non-transgenic controls under drought, salinity and low *temperature* stresses.

More recently, Jhang et al. reported tolerance against drought, salinity and low *temperature* by *introducing* gene encoding a bifunctional fusion protein trehalose 6-phosphate synthase and trehalose 6-phosphate *phoshatase,* in transgenic rice plants.

High level of trehalose *accumulation* resulted in multiple stress tolerance that was attributed to enzymatic activities of both the enzymes.

Mustard

Mustard is one of the important oilseed crops grown all over the world. *Brassica juncea,* the Indian mustard is the second most important oilseed crop in India. A number of transgenics have been developed in *Brassica* species with improved abiotic stress *tolerance*. Among them, *overexpression* of glutathione synthetase showed enhanced *accumulation* and tolerance to cadmium. In another study, *overexpression* of *glulathione* reducatase (GR) targeted to *cytoplasm* did not show any cadmium *tolerance*, whereas targeted expression in chloroplasts did show higher cadmium tolerance. Transgenic mustard showing tolerance to salinity stress have been developed.

Glycine betaine *biosynthesis* pathway gene *codA* encoding choline oxidase was *introduced* into *B. juncea*. The transgenic plants showed significantly improved performance as compared to control plants in terms of *chlorophyll* loss, photosystem II activity and shoot growth under stress conditions.

A very interesting example of salt tolerance came through overexpression of *AtNHX1* in transgenic *B. napus*. These plants grew well in the presence of 200 mM NaCl, flowered and set seeds. An increase in proline content was observed attributing to osmotic adjustment.

Our recent studies have shown that *overexpression* of osmotin gene in transgenic Indian mustard enabled plants to tolerate drought and salinity stresses. The *transgenic* plants exhibited increased level of water retention by excised leaves at the laboratory bench as *compared* to the wild type plants of cultivar Pusa Jaikisan. In addition, loss of *chlorophyll* in the presence of salt stress (100-200 mM NaCl) was retarded in transgenic leaf discs.

Soybean

Soybean is an important source of nutrition to human beings. Antisense soybean transgenic plants with L-A^1-pyrroline 5 *carboxylate* reductase *(P5CR)* gene under the control of an inducible heat shock promoter (IHSP) confirmed the *potential* role of proline in stress tolerance.

Investigation of antisense plants under stress conditions provides a means to understand plant metabolic pathways. The IHSP was fully activated at 32 and 42°C along with mannitol stress. The antisense expression of *P5CR* gene resulted in significant decrease in proline *accumulation* in transgenic plants.

In contrast, control plants showed higher proline content, thus exhibiting better growth under similar stress conditions. This clearly suggests that *overexpression* of genes encoding *enzymes* required for proline *biosynthesis* will lead to increased stress tolerance in transgenic crops *including* soybean.

Alfalfa

Medicago sativa is an important perennial forage legume all over the world. First *transgenic* alfalfa plant with improved tolerance to abiotic stress was *developed* by McKersie et al. by overexpressing MnSOD cDNA under CaMV35S promoter. The transgenic plants showed more rapid growth recovery after exposure to *freezing* stress than that of control plants.

After 3 years of field trials in 1996, data suggested that these plants also showed improved survival to water deficit stress, as *determined* by chlorophyll *fluorescence* and *electrolyte* leakage. During these *experiments* only few transgenic alfalfa plants were obtained.

Moreover, variety RA3 used for transgenic development was popular at the time of experiment but showed poor *agronomic* performances. Consequently, two different clones of alfalfa, N4 and

S4 were transformed with *MitSOD and ChlSOD* genes. Results confirmed the *hypothesis* that MnSOD overexpression improves survival of *transgenic* alfalfa against abiotic stresses. Further McKersie et al. *overexpressed FeSOD* in transgenic alfalfa for *investigating* its role in stress tolerance as compared to the *MnSOD.*

The transgenics showed increased *FeSOD* activity along with increased winter survival. However, this *improvement* in winter survival was not due to improvement in oxidative stress tolerance associated with photosynthesis. For testing the *synergy* between SOD *transgenes* and stress tolerance, gene-pyramiding studies were conducted.

Samisk et al., crossed a hemizygous Mit-MnSOD plant and hemizygous *Chl-MnSOD* transgenic plants. F1 progeny containing joint expression of the two genes *(MitMnSOD + Chl-MnSOD)* had lower shoot and storage organ biomass compared to either of the parent, whereas, the progeny containing either of the transgene had significantly higher shoot and storage organ biomass.

In another experiment, *overexpression* of *transcription* factor Alfin1 in transgenic alfalfa improved growth properties of plants exposed to 128 mM NaCl stress for 17 days. *Alfin1,* cDNA encodes zinc finger family of transcription factor which binds to promoter fragment of root-specific *MsPRP2* gene.

The *MsPRP2* gene is also induced by NaCl stress. The transgenic plants with *Alfin1* overexpression showed MsPRP2 *accumulation,* thereby *confirming* the role of *Alfin1* in imparting enhanced NaCl stress tolerance to alfalfa plants.

Cotton

As photosynthesis in cotton is highly sensitive to low temperature and high light stress, focus has, therefore, been on developing transgenic to protect the *photosynthetic* machinery under abiotic stresses. Overproduction of MnSOD in chloroplasts of cotton conferred a *substantially* enhanced tolerance to photo-oxidative stress (high light) and low *temperature.*

However, Payton et al. failed to achieve photosynthetic stability against low temperature stress in transgenic cotton *overexpressing* chloroplast *MnSOD.* Attempts were also made to improve cotton for tolerance against abiotic stresses by overproducing chloroplast targeted glutathione reducatase (GR) and ascorbate peroxidase (APx).

Elevated levels of GR or Apx activity improved *photosynthetic* capacity after chilling treatment at 10°C and high photon flux exposure.

Potato

Potato is highly sensitive to abiotic stresses. Perl et al. developed transgenic plants by *transforming* potato tubers with Cu/Zn superoxide dismutase. These *transgenic* lines showed elevated tolerance to superoxide *generating* herbicide *paraquat* (methyl viologen).

Induction of osmotin-like protein by low temperature stress in potato was shown by Zhu et al.. However, transgenic potato expressing sense and antisense genes for osmotin-like proteins showed no statistical difference among sense/antisense *transgenics* and control plants against low temperature stress measured as *electrolyte* leakage.

This ruled out the possibility of role of osmotin-like proteins as a major freezing tolerance determinant. Our *unpublished* results with osmotin overexpressed transgenic potato have confirmed the role of osmotin protein in imparting tolerance to osmotic stresses caused by drought and salinity.

The first evidence of potato transgenics *tolerating* freezing stress came through the expression of a synthetic *AFP-PHA* (*antifreeze protein gene fused* to *phytohemagglutinin*) gene construct. *Phytohemagglutinin* acted as signal peptide directing the antifreeze protein molecule to extra cytoplasmic space where ice crystallization occurs.

Transgenic plants showing *maximum* level of *AFP* expression showed the highest degree of tolerance against freezing stress as evidenced by significantly reduced electrolyte leakage in transgenics as compared to the wild type plants.

Goddijin tried to develop stress tolerant transgenic potato by *engineering* trehalose biosynthesis. However, surprisingly no trehalose *accumulation* was observed in transgenics, which was attributed to *trehalase* activity.

Later, the role of trehalose as an osmoprotectant was confirmed by expressing TPS1 (Trehalose 6-phosphate synthase) gene in potato plants. Although, the transgenic potato plants showed abnormal morphological characteristics, such as dwarfism, *yellowish* lancet shaped leaves and aberrant root development, drought resistance capacity of these plants was significantly increased.

Overexpression of glyceraldehyde 3-phosphate dehydrogenase in transgenic potato showed increased tolerance to salt stress. Overexpression of chloroplastic drought-induced stress protein (CDSP32) conferred protection to transgenic potato against photooxidative stress induced by *incubation* with either methyl viologen or t-butyl *hydroperoxide* or by exposure to low temperature. On the contrary, plants without CDSP32 expression showed enhanced damage to photosynthetic membrane.

Tomato

Tomato is a widely grown vegetable crop. Higher ability to withstand salt tolerance was observed in transgenic lines of tomato expressing *HAL* gene. Further elucidation of these transgenics for long term salinity effects showed many improved characteristics as compared to control.

On exposure to 35 mM NaCl concentration, 58% reduction in fruit yield was observed in control plants whereas in transgenic plants expressing *AtNHX1* the loss was 30%. Similarly, loss of leaf water content was higher in controls than the transgenics under 100 mM NaCl. These plants also maintained higher K^+/Na^+ selectivity values.

A remarkable example of tolerance to 200mM NaCl and preserving fruit quality at such a higher concentration was shown in transgenic tomato plants overexpressing Na^+/H^+ antiporter gene. Accumulation of salts was observed in leaves without affecting the fruit quality.

Overexpression of a transcription factor gene encoding *CBF1* in transgenic tomato conferred enhanced tolerance to water deficit stress. Lack of water for 4 weeks showed 80% survival in transgenic plants as compared to less than 6% survival of control plants.

Water content of transgenics was relatively high during stress *treatment*. However, these plants showed retardation in growth resulting into reduction in number and fresh weight of fruits.

Oat

Oat, a cereal crop serves as an important component of human and animal diets. This crop requires sufficient water for growth and grain production. *Overexpression* of HVA1 in *transgenic* plants showed higher osmotic tolerance than non-transgenics.

Under NaCl and mannitol mediated stresses, there were *significant differences* in wilting, death of old leaves and necrosis of young leaves between the transgenic and *non-transgenic* plants.

Carrot

To our knowledge, there seems be no report on transgenic carrot development tolerant to drought, salinity or low temperature stress. Efforts have been made in this direction to increase polyamine levels by *expressing* ornithine *decarboxylase* (ODC) in transgenic cell lines of carrot.

Detailed metabolic studies of transgenic lines revealed higher rate of putrescine anabolism as well as *catabolism* producing spermine and *spermidine* as compared to non-transgenic cell lines. However, the effect of abiotic stress was not tested on these transgenic cell lines.

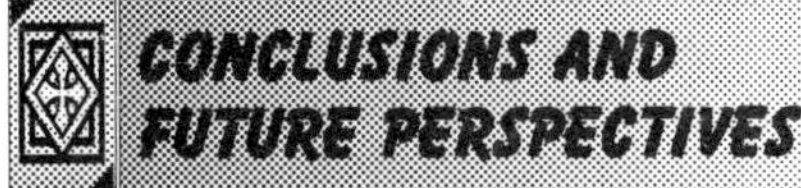

CONCLUSIONS AND FUTURE PERSPECTIVES

Development of crop cultivars tolerant to abiotic stresses is an important goal of national and *international institutions* engaged in plant research. Both traditional plant breeding methods and *transgenic technology* are being employed to achieve the above objective.

Since *conventional* breeding *approaches* were not found *sufficient*, scientists are now trying to explore the *advantages* of the transgenic *technology* to develop *transgenic* crops tolerant to abiotic stresses viz. drought, salinity, cold and high temperature, etc.

Although numerous studies have demonstrated the feasibility of developing such *transgenics* in an array of crop species, substantial data are lacking on the response of these transgenics subjected to field stress conditions. Abiotic stress *tolerance* is a complex trait that is controlled by multiple genes.

Studies in early 1990s *demonstrated* that a battery of genes get up-regulated in plants that are exposed to drought or salinity stress. However, function of *majority* of these stress-induced genes/gene products remained largely unknown. With the advent of high *throughput sequencing* of genes (genomics) and *proteomics*, more and more ESTs/cDNA/genes or proteins are being added to the list by the global effort with little *information* on *elucidation* of their function or the *mechanism* of stress tolerance in plants.

Genome wide approaches coupled with reverse genetics approach will surely allow deciphering the role of specific gene / gene combinations in stress tolerance. Undoubtedly, studies on stress signal perception and transduction have identified genes that play a significant role in controlling the expression of stress-induced genes.

As a result, *transgenic* development with genes encoding *transcription* factors and/or protein kinases have provided tolerance to multiple stresses to *significantly* high levels, and has increased the hope of *generating* transgenic crops cultivars with improved stress tolerance.

Although there are numerous examples of *transgenics over-expressing* genes encoding *enzymes* for increased osmolyte biosynthesis, stress-induced proteins, ROS *scavengers* and *membrane* proteins, their field *performance* is awaited.

To make the transgenic route more effective with respect to tolerance against abiotic stresses at the field level, it will be important that crop species-specific research *programmes* are undertaken for developing transgenics considering the crop phenology, water *requirement*, type of stress *experienced* by the crop, growth stages sensitive to stress, and the existing response of the crop to a given stress.

For each crop, it is necessary to understand the basis of effective *engineering* strategies leading to greater stress tolerance. Information on genetic regulation and complex interaction of genes with *environment* is scanty and further studies in this direction will help understanding the molecular mechanism of stress tolerance in plants. Difference in *molecular* response of plants subjected to drought and salinity stress also need to be addressed, as salt-specific effects are different than drought.

For making the transgenic technology more effective, it is required that *transgenes* are *expressed* in a specific tissue in a *developmental* or stress-inducible manner. Moreover, integration of cellular and whole plant response is required for *combining* increased stress tolerance with high yields.

5 Chapter

IMPROVING MULBERRY CROP

Application of *biotechnological* methods for crop improvement has *significantly contributed* to the success of modern day agriculture. Enhancement of yield potential, *improvement* of qualily, resistance to pests and diseases, tolerance to abiotic stresses and resistance to *herbicides* are the main focus of crop *improvement* in many *agricultural* crops through *biotechnological* approach. Mulberry (*Morus spp.*) is a crop of economic *importance* in the *sericulture* industry.

Its foliage forms the sole source of food for the *domesticated* silkworm, *Bombyx mori L.* Mulberry is a dioecious, *heterozygous* and perennial tree. In spite of the problems associated with tree crop *improvement*, considerable progress has been achieved in mulberry breeding through conventional approaches. However, *biotechnology* application holds a great promise in further improvement of mulberry crop especially in those areas where *conventional research* has not achieved the desired success.

Already considerable progress has been made in this direction. The article attempts to *consolidate* the *important* outcome of the biotechnological applications in mulberry and also *discusses* the need for future research priorities in mulberry *improvement, utilization* and conservation.

GENOME CHARACTERIZATION

Understanding of genetic structure of the plant is very important for crop improvement, *utilization* and conservation. Mulberry being a perennial, *heterozygous* tree, *traditional* methods of analysis have not provided sufficient insight into the genetic *architecture*.

Compared to the phenotypic characters, molecular markers are highly

heritable, *consistent*, fast and easy to measure and evaluate. Among the molecular markers, isozyme and DNA markers are widely employed for genome characterization and analysis of plants and animals.

Isozyme Markers

Hunter and Markert were first to introduce isozymes as genetic markers in plants. Hirano used peroxidase isozyme *technique* to evaluate the affinities in mulberry and its relatives and showed that the results supported the *conventional* view.

The study of inheritance of peroxidase isozyme of mulberry was initiated in Japan and established that particular isozyme banding type was *significantly* correlated with leaf stalk length. Hirano also used isozyme *technique* to analyze 284 mulberry varieties.

He used seven enzyme systems and a sap protein to characterize these varieties. Based on the *electrophoretic* pattern he *categorized* 131 varieties into seven groups and *established* the gentic *relationship* among them. The study also *demonstrated* the correlation between amino acid content and *peroxidase enzyme* in the leaf.

Katagiri and coworkers successfully utilized peroxidase isozyme technique to *differentiate* hexaploid mulberry strains collected from Mexico. In India, *peroxidase* isozyme studies were reported on introduced species from *Indonesia*, triploids and *aneuploids* of mulberry.

Even though isozyme analysis is *comparatively* easy, less costly and the *markers* are *codominant* in expression, they are less *attractive* compared to the DNA markers because of lack of *sufficient polymorphism*.

DNA Markers

Studies on mulberry genome was first initiated in Japan. Katagiri and coworkers successfully isolated chloroplast DNA from mulberry. Later Machii reported the *isolation* of total DNA by *ultracentrifugation* method.

Chengfu and coworkers detected DNA marker variation using RAPD *technique* in 12 mulberry varieties with 24 primers. Relationships among the operational *taxonomical* units (12 species and 2 varieties) of *Morus* were *examined* with 20 random decamer primers, generating 238 polymorphic markers.

Phylogenetic analysis of RAPD data indicated that grouping so obtained is in conformity with morphological classification. *Polymorphism* in genomic DNA of five parents and their four *resulting* hybrids were analyzed by RAPD technique. Of the F1 patterns, most of the markers appeared were same as their respective parents, however, few were unique not found in their parents.

Sharma and coworkers assessed the genetic diversity in *Morus germplasm* collections using *fluorescence-based* AFLP markers. The wide range in the genetic *similarity* (0.58–0.99) indicated that the mulberry *germplasm* collection *represents* a genetically diverse population.

However, the study also concluded that the genetic base of cultivated mulberry is narrow. A recent study showed that as many as five RAPD and one DAMD primers generated profiles can together *differentiate* all the nine mulberry varieties in terms of unique bands. Central *Sericultural Germplasm Resources* Centre, Hosur in *collaboration* with *Seribiotech* Research Laboratory, Bangalore has characterized number of mulberry germplasm using DNA *fingerprinting techniques*.

RAPD analysis of 15 mulberry species revealed few species diagnostic markers indicating the *usefulness* of the *technique* in *identification*. Phylogenetic analysis of RAPD and ISSR markers showed the separation of wild and cultivated mulberry species into a different cluster.

Study of 44 cultivated mulberry varieties and 27 *M. laevigata* collections with RAPD marker data has resulted in generation of useful information on genetic diversity and identity. A research project on "Genome analysis of mulberry" is currently *underway* at *Central Sericultural Research* and *Training Institute* at Mysore.

The results indicate that RAPD can be effectively used to DNA fingerprint mulberry *cultivars* and also can be *successfully* employed to study the inheritance pattern and for the development of molecular linkage map.

MICROPROPAGATION BY TISSUE AND ORGAN CULTURE

Most of the initial studies on mulberry tissue culture concentrated on the *regeneration* of complete plantlets from various explants like shoot tip, axillary bud, winter bud, leaf, cotyledon, hypocotyls etc. Ohayama for the first time *successfully* obtained complete plant from axillary bud of *M. alba* on MS medium supplemented with growth regulators.

Since then, shoot proliferation was observed in many mulberry *genotypes* using different explants and *supplementing* the media with cytokinins like BAP. However, BAP had a negative response at a higher concentration on shoot proliferation of mulberry genotypes.

Modification of basal media with macroand micro-salt were tested on different genotypes for shoot *proliferation*. Micropropagation of shoots of *M. indica was* tested with MS salts and B5 vitamins. The pH level of various media tested ranged from 4 to 5.6 for shoot *multiplication* in different mulberry genotypes. However, the optimum pH level appears to be in the range of 5.6–5.8 for many *genotypes*.

Best shooting response was obtained at 0.8% of agar *concentration*. Auxin rich media induced rooting within 10–14 days of culture in *M. laevigata*. In several mulberry species, rooting was enhanced by treatment with NAA and IAA.

Combination of IBA, IAA and IPA helped root *proliferation* in *M. australis, M. lhou, M. cathayana and M. serrata*. In *M. alba* shoots produced roots in auxin-free media. Hardening of *regenerated* plantlets is an essential perquisite for successful establishment in the field.

Various kinds of potting mixtures like steam *sterilized* peat and *agroperlite* (2:1), *autoclaved* soil, soilrite mixture and vermi-compost have been used for establishment of *regenerated* plants. Half-strength Hogland's nutrient solution and water was used to irrigate the plantlets.

CALLUS FORMATION AND DIFFERENTIATION

Induction of callus of mulberry genotypes from different explants sources like stem segments, young leaf and *hypocotyls* segments were *successfully* attempted on MS media *supplemented* with 2-4 D. Addition of Kn, IAA and NAA in the media resulted in the better proliferation of calli.

Calli can be prolonged in the culture medium up to eight weeks in good conditions by adding ABA and PABA.

Calli of *M. bombycis, M. alba and M. multicaulis* were regenerated in medium *supplemented* with auxins and cytokinins. Shoot *regeneration* from callus of *M. alba was* obtained on MS medium *supplemented* with BAP.

In *M. bombycis* shoot bud induction was reported in the callus on LS medium *supplemented* with BAP. Addition of GA3 and DTT to the culture medium enabled to break the pseudo-dormancy and obtained *regeneration* in stored calli. Rhizhogenesis of calli was *frequently* reported from the cultures on media *containing* auxins.

Rooting was also obtained from the cell suspension of the callus from hypocotyl tissue. From the callus of *internodal* segment and leaf explants of *M. laevigata, rhizogenesis* was observed on MS medium *supplemented* with NAA. Recently, few workers have reported the complete *regeneration* of mulberry plants from callus culture using TDZ.

DEVELOPMENT OF HAPLOIDS

As already discussed, *mulberry* is a dioecious, *outbreeding* and *heterozygous* tree species. Development of *homozygous* lines through *conventional* method has not been successful. Homozygous lines are *extremely* important in genetical studies and *exploitation* of hybrid vigor in crop improvement programme.

In this *background,* constant efforts have been made in mulberry to develop *homozygous* lines through the production of *haploids.* Lin and coworkers *successfully* reported the *regeneration* of haploid plants from uninucleate anthers in a Chinese mulberry variety.

Venkateshwaralu and Katagiri *reported* globular and heart-shaped *embryoids* on B5 medium in a Japanese variety. Similar results were also obtained by Sethi and coworkers in an Indian *mulberry* variety on MS medium.

Katagiri reported the colony formation and induction of callus from pollen culture studies. *Katagiri* and *Venkateswaralu* observed embryo like *structures* on culturing the pollen in B5 medium. Addition of fructose to B5 medium resulted in profuse division and obtained a compact calli.

On MS media supplemented with glutamine, coconut water and 2–4 D, Tewary and coworkers obtained globular embryoids from pollens isolated from anthers starved at 10–12°C for 72 h in S-1 variety. Lakshmi Sita and Ravindran for the first time reported the gynogenic haploids plants from the ovary culture of mulberry.

Dennis Thomas and coworkers [75] developed a reproducible protocol for the production of gynogenic haploids of a female clone of mulberry (*M. alba L.* Cv. K-2) from unpollinated ovary culture.

PROTOPLAST ISOLATION, CULTURE AND SOMATIC HYBRIDIZATION

Genetic barrier in hybridization due to sexual incompatibility and other associated problems can be *successfully* overcome by somatic *hybridization* of protoplast cells. Methodology for isolation of protoplast, its culture and fusion of cells play a critical role in successful *regeneration* of plants. Protoplast isolation in mulberry was attempted from callus and mesophyll cells. Ohnishi and Kiyama showed that primary callus culture gave a better *protoplast* yield than secondary callus cultures of mulberry. Tewary and Lakshmi Sita reported the optimized *concentration* of cellulase (2%), *macerozyme* (1%) and *macerase* (0.5%) for better protoplast yield in mulberry.

Katagiri observed the colony *formation* in cultures of mulberry *mesophyll protoplasts*. Differences in division of mesophyll protoplasts cultured on different media and *underdifferent* light *intensities* were studied in few mulberry species.

Ming and coworkers *demonstrated* the regeneration of complete plant from the callus derived from mesophyll protoplast of mulberry through organ ogenesis and somatic embryo genesis on MS medium. Protoplast fusion in mulberry was *successful* using *chemical* fusogen and *electro-fusion*.

IN VITRO METHODS FOR CONSERVATION OF GENETIC RESOURCES

Conventional approach to germplasm conservation of *reclalcitrant* seed species as well as vegetatively propagated crops did not overcome the inherent limitation in storage *technique*. In contrast, *in vitro* conservation methods offered suitable alternative to seed and field gene bank.

In vitro conservation refers to maintenance of germplasm in a relatively stable form under more or less defined nutrient conditions in artificial environment. Potential advantages of conserving mulberry genetic resources by *in vitro* methods are:

(i) can be utilized for germplasm collection in the field

(ii) rapid multiplication of germaplsm genotypes

(iii) pathogen-free germplasm can be maintained

(iv) require very small storage space

(v) loss due to diseases, pests and natural calamities avoided

(vi) germplasm exchange is easier as quarantine requirement is effectively met

Some of the methods which are attempted/employed for conservation of mulberry genetic resources are discussed below:

Synthetic Seeds

Synthetic seeds, also called artificial seeds, are prepared by *encapsulating* the apical/axillary buds with 3–5% sodium alginate and 100 mM calcium chloride solution as a *complexing* agent. Sodium alginate solution is mixed to liquid medium *supplemented* with all macro- and micronutrients and growth *regulators* necessary for the development of mulberry plant.

About 50 ml of sodium alginate and 120 ml of calcium chloride *solution* making a total of 170 ml is sufficient to make 200–220 encapsulated beads (artificial seeds). The artificial seeds can be germinated either *in vitro* or *in vivo*. However, success of *germination in vivo* is *comparatively* less.

For *in vitro* germination of artificial seeds of mulberry, MS medium was found suitable. A cytokinin *supplement* in MS medium enhances the *germination* but inhibits root formation. Even though, *encapsulation* of apical buds are of limited value in germplasm *conservation*, these artificial seeds retain viability upto 45 days at +4°C and for a long period under cryopreservation. These artificial seeds are also useful in *germplasm exchange*.

Slow-Growth Storage

Slow-growth condition in *in vitro* provide a secondary storage method for field gene bank, a storage mode for *experimental*, or a rescue of germplasm for plant *distribution*. Slowgrowth storage may provide short- or medium-term conservation strategy for *germplasm* materials depending on the period of storage achieved.

This is done by *maintaining* the cultures under growth limiting *condition*, which reduces the *requirements* of sub-culturing and associated risks. Even though, *in vitro* slow-growth storage appears to be good choice for *conservation* of *vegetatively* propagated species, the *information* on germplasm *conservation* is limited to few genera.

In vitro technique has been *utilized* to conserve wide range of species *including temperate* woody plants, fruit trees, *horticultural* species, and *numerous* tropical species. A recent FAO survey indicates that only 37,600 accessions are conserved *in vitro* worldwide.

Slow-growth storage is *routinely* used in the conservation of only few species like banana, potato and cassava. In mulberry, single shoots of *M. nigra L.* stored on *multiplication* medium at 4°C for 16-hour *photoperiod* survived for only six months.

Survival was enhanced to 42% at nine months by storing them at 25°C with activated charcoal as supplement. High viability (80%) for six months was observed in 15 genotypes of *M. alba* stored at 4°C and in dark on shoot proliferation medium.

Rooting was observed in all the shoots and shoots retained their multiplication potential. *In vitro* techniques are becoming increasingly popular in storing and distributing germplasm throughout the world.

Certification *programme* insist on *in vitro* cultures for providing virus-free plants from stock collections. However, additional research is needed to be carried out in the field of genetic stability of *in vitro* grown plants. Field *experimentation* and molecular analysis are needed to *confirm* the genetic stability.

Additional research to develop standard method along with regular *evaluation* of culture *materials* will provide safe storage for *in vitro* cultures.

CRYOPRESERVATION

Cryopreservation (*storage* in *liquid nitrogen* at –196°C) is *considered* an ideal method for long-term germplasm storage. At cryogenic *temperature* cell divisions and all metabolic *activities* are stopped, *minimizing* the possibility of any genetic change.

Cryopreservation can be applied to different plant parts/structures *including* seed, apical or *axillary* buds, embryos, pollen *and in vitro* cultures. Sakai was first to report the survival of plant tissue exposed to ultra-low *temperature*, when he demonstrated that very hardy mulberry twigs could *withstand* freezing in liquid nitrogen (LN) after *dehydration* mediated by extra-organ freezing.

Generally, the *technique* of preserving at low *temperature improvised* with chemical cryoprotectant, slow *dehydration*, cooling followed by rapid immersion in LN, storage in LN, rapid thawing, washing and recovery. As mentioned earlier; *cryopreservation* technique possibility was first demonstrated using mulberry.

Since then, considerable work on cryopreservation of mulberry has been *undertaken especially* in Japan. Shoot tips of pre-frozen winter buds of *M. bombycis* Koidz. cv Kenmochi were able to withstand storage in LN, however, grafts and cuttings could not on *immersing* in LN.

With modification of this method Wang and coworkers were able to *regenerate* plants of *M. multicaulis* Loud cv. Lusang through tip culture of frozen winter buds. Shoot segments were prefrozen at –3°C for 10 days, –5°C for 3 days, –10°C for 1 day and –20°C for 1 day before *immersion* in LN. Buds were cultured on MS medium after thawing in air at 0 to 20°C.

Observed survival rate was 55 to 90%. Excised shoot tips from winter buds of *M. bombycis* cv. Kenmochi prefrozen to –20°C at 5°C/day were able to produce more shoots compared to the buds prefrozen at 10°C/day. Prior to *prefreezing* at –20°C, partial dehydration to 38.5% improved the *recovery* rates.

The survival rates of the winter buds stored in LN from one month to 3.5 years did not change. Direct dehydration with silica gel at 25°C of excised shoot tips (2 mm long) from winter bud could be done before *immersion* in LN.

With decreasing water content shoot formation *increased* and at about 19% water content, a *maximum* of 80% survival rate was observed. Encapsulation by *alginate* coating of winter hardened shoot tips of many *Morus* species had 81% of shoot formation with 22–25% water content. *In vitro* grown shoot tips of thirteen cultivars of mulberry were tested for cryopreservation.

Slow freezing (0.5°C/min to – 42°C), vitrification (PVS2, 90 min) and air drying (24% water content) or *encapsulationdehydration* (33% water content) was tested for survival, which ranged from 40 to 81.3%. Niino and coworkers also reported long-term storage of mulberry winter buds by *cryopreservation*.

Winter buds from *M. bombycis* with about 10 mm vascular tissue were kept at 0°C for 1 day before freezing. Buds were cooled to –10°C steps at daily intervals from 0 to –30°C. They were kept for one day at –30°C prior to immersion in LN or before *transfering* to –135°C.

After storage, buds were rapidly thawed at 37°C in a water bath and then cultured on MS medium supplemented with 2% fructose and 1 mg/l 6-BAP. Rate of shoot formation did not vary much in buds stored in LN or deep freezer at –135°C after a storage period of 3.5 years.

GENETIC TRANSFORMATION

Genetic transformation has been successfully attempted in many agricultural crops. According to an estimate about 50 million ha of transgenic crops were cultivated worldwide in 2001. These estimates do not include those cultivated in China.

In spite of the resistance to the genetically modified plants (GMPs) from some quarter, the popularity is gaining among the cultivators. "*Golden rice*" is a remarkable achievement and a major leap. This genetically modified rice is *nutritionally* enriched with Vitamin A and iron content, which can effectively prevent *malnutrition* among the population, especially in Asian countries, where rice is a staple food.

Even though, genetically *transformed* mulberry is yet to be released for *cultivation, preliminary* work in this direction has been initiated. Machii used *Agrobacterium tumefaciens* LBA 4404 as vector to incorporate a foreign gene into mulberry.

He transferred kanamycin *resistance* gene and 8-glucouronidase (GUS) gene through Ti plasmid PB1121 to mulberry leaf discs and showed their expression in *transformed* plantlets. Oka and Tewary induced hairy roots in *in vitro* grown mulberry *(M. indica L.) hypocotyls* using Japanese wild *Agrobacterium rhizogenes* strains.

Specific *amplification* of DNA fragment by PCR showed that portions of the *rol* genes in the T-DNA core region of the Ri plasmid were integrated into the hairy roots. A genomic clone, *Mahmg 1,* was isolated from *M. alba* and its expression *characterized* in mulberry and transgenic tobacco.

FUTURE PRIORITIES

Biotechnological tools are of immense value in generating genetical *information* in crops *especially* in problematic plants like trees. It holds a great promise in mulberry *improvement, utilization* and *conservation.* India has large resources of mulberry, which needs to be characterized unambiguously with DNA marker technology and the total diversity required to be assessed as a supportive research work for breeding.

Developing DNA *fingerprints* of indigenous mulberry cultivars and important genotypes for their *individualization* will be of immense value to the breeders as well as for the curators of gene banks. DNA fingerprints of mulberry can be successfully used as '*molecular* I.D. cards' in context of IPR/patent protection and also protection of Plant Breeders' Rights.

Based on the *molecular* data, a core collection is required to be developed for *efficient* utilization of mulberry *germplasm* for crop *improvement.* There is an urgent need to identify DNA markers for important agronomic traits, resistances to biotic stresses and tolerance to adverse edaphic and climatic *conditions,* which can be utilized to hasten the *mulberry* breeding programme and thereby saving *considerable physical* and financial *resources.*

The major values of molecular markers lie in the long-term strategic research. An important aspect in this direction is the study of *quantitative* trait loci (QTLs) of mulberry. Absence of any linkage map based on morphological/ agronomic traits, necessitates the *immediate* development of molecular framework linkage of mulberry.

The map can be used to tag genes of agronomic importance and to perform map based cloning of target genes. Genetic *transformation techniques* needs to be further fine tuned for stable *expression* of cloned genes.

The silkworm is completely dependent on mulberry leaves for their entire nutritional requirement. Hence, the development of transgenic mulberry with qualitatively superior protein and *carbohydrate* content of the other known system, which may have *significant* impact on silk production, is also an important area.

In the *in vitro* culture front, further *refinement* is required to obtain a consistent regeneration of plants from callus culture. This will help in a long way in successful *regeneration* of *transformed* cells. Further, *in vitro* protocols already *developed* needs to be *practically utilized* for medium and long-term conservation of mulberry genetic resources.

6

Chapter

TRANSGENIC CROPS IN SOIL COMMUNITIES

Along with the increasing potential for widespread commercial use and the *potential* benefits of *transgenic* crops, considerable concerns on their safety have been raised *including* safety aspects relating to their potential impact on the environment.

Besides ecological effects on *organisms* in the *aboveground compartment*, effects on the below-ground compartment, in particular on soil and rhizosphere, have gained increasing attention. Soil has been *recognized* as a valuable resource for agriculture and therefore it has to be managed in a sustainable manner in order to maintain its quality.

Soil quality can be described based on physical, *chemical*, and biological soil characteristics, of which soil biological, and in particular soil microbiological, characteristics are least defined.

Soil *microorganisms*, however, play a central role in soil processes, such as nutrient cycling, formation of soil structures, and *transformation* of pollutants, but they can also act as plant growth promoters or plant pathogens.

Soils have been reported to contain up to 10^{10} microbial cells per cm^3, but this number may largely depend on the ecosystem and soil type. Arable soils appear to contain fewer microbial cells and a lower diversity than pasture or forest soils, but still hundreds or thousands of genotypes have been described in agriculturally managed soils.

In an agricultural field experiment near Basel in Switzerland, for example, a bacterial species richness of about 1300 has been estimated in soils after 25 years of defined organic or conventional management. However, only about 1% of these bacteria can be cultivated with current *cultivation* techniques, *representing* a strong bias for cultivation-based approaches. This has resulted in a large knowledge gap on functions and physiologies of soil *microorganisms*. Therefore, it is currently difficult or impossible to define which of these *organisms* are essential for a specific ecosystem, and which changes in *abundance* and diversity represent damage of a given soil ecosystem.

These *difficulties* represent the main reason for the lack of soil quality *definitions* that are based on specific *microbiological* indicators. Recent efforts to define microbial indicator groups of known importance for soil quality resulted in the definition of a set of functional groups.

Potential microbial soil *indicators* perform key soil functions and include *mycorrhizal* fungi, nitrogen-fixing bacteria, ammonia-oxidizing bacteria, decomposers of recalcitrant organic *compounds*, and antagonists of plant pathogens as well as plant pathogens. The indicator quality of these groups still remains to be confirmed and possibly other groups like plant growth-promoting bacteria, entomopathogenic fungi, or endophytic microorganisms may also represent indicators for soil quality.

A large body of *information* has been *accumulated* over the years, which indicates that *agricultural management* has various effects on microbial soil characteristics. It has been clearly *demonstrated* that soil tillage, fertilization, and crops have strong Influences on *microbial* soil characteristics. In addition, soil type has been shown to be a major determinant of the *microbiota* present in soils.

These many factors that inthence soil microbial *communities*, their possible *interactions*, and the large proportion of unknown members of these communities represent the main current obstacles to the definition of "*healthy*" soil microbial communities and to defining soil quality based on soil microbiological characteristics.

Nevertheless, if a specific factor causes a *significant* change in soil *microbial communities*, this may be taken as an indication that microbiological soil *characteristics* are affected; however, further analyses may be required to assess the importance of such an effect. This approach also represents the basis for assessing the effects of transgenic plants on soil ecosystems.

METHODS USED FOR ASSESSING SOIL MICROBIAL CHARACTERISTICS

A number of techniques have been developed for the analysis of *microbiological* soil characteristics and to assess the impact environmental or anthropogenic factors may have on soil *ecosystems*.

Commonly applied bulk soil microbial *parameters* include *determination* of *activities* of enzymes, such as phosphatases, proteases, cellulases, and dehydrogenases, total microbial biomass, and basal soil respiration.

Many cultivation-dependent approaches are available to retrieve *microorganisms* from soils, but they are all affected by the cultivation bias *precluding* analysis of the entire microbial *diversity* in soils.

More detailed analyses based on *simultaneous* cultivation of soil microbial *communities* on an array of specific substrates have improved the capacity of cultivationdependent analyses.

However, these substrate utilization-based approaches, referred to as community-level physiological profiles (CLPP) or community-level substrate *utilization* (CLSU), are restricted to culturable *microorganisms.*

During the last two decades, the development of *cultivation-independent* approaches, which are based on analyses of molecular markers, has allowed for less biased analyses of soil microbial communities.

The main targets for this type of analysis are DNA and fatty acids, which can both be directly extracted from soil and which contain *information* on the organisms present. With the DNA-based approach, specific marker genes can be analyzed in soil DNA extracts by means of *polymerase* chain reaction (PCR) amplification.

Commonly used marker genes are those encoding ribosomal RNA, as these represent *phylogenetic* markers that allow identification of the *microorganisms* present in soil. In addition, functional markers are available, which allow the analysis of specific functional *microbial* groups in soils, such as nitrogen-fixing bacteria and ammonium-oxidizing bacteria.

Commonly applied analytical procedures to resolve *community* structures of detected soil microbial communities are based on genetic profiling, which allows the display of the various microbial *genotypes* present in a soil.

Different genetic profiling *approaches* for soil microorganisms have been developed, all targeting *differences* in marker gene DNA sequences.

Restriction *fragment* length polymorphisms (RFLP), *amplified ribosomal* DNA restriction analysis (ARDRA), or terminal RFLP (T-RFLP) distinguish sequences based on different locations of restriction enzyme recognition sites.

Denaturant gradient gel *electrophoresis* (DGGE) relies on differences in DNA duplex stability, while single-strand *conformation* polymorphism (SSCP) analysis detects differences in secondary *structures* of single-stranded DNA.

Length heterogeneity (LH) and *ribosomal* intergenic spacer analysis (RISA) resolve length *differences* of the amplified marker gene fragment. Such marker gene profiles allow analysis of the presence and abundance of specific genotypes in a PCR amplification product; however, they do not provide *quantitative* analyses of microbial groups in soil.

For this purpose quantitative PCR approaches have been developed. In addition, PCR-based genome-typing protocols have been developed, which allow for the distinction of microbial isolates according to profiles of amplified genomic sequences.

Examples of these analyses are ERIC- and BOX-PCR. For the fatty acid-based approach, cell wall lipids of the soil microbiota are extracted from soil. Specific marker fatty acids have been identified for specific groups of *microorganisms,* which can analytically be *distinguished* and thereby allow monitoring of their presence or *abundance* in soil.

Similar to genetic *profiling,* fatty acid profiles can be used to detect *differences* or changes in microbiological soil characteristics. Often used fatty acid *profiling* approaches are based on separation and *identification* of fatty acids, and are referred to as phospholipid fatty acid (PLFA) analysis or fatty acid methyl ester (FAME) analysis.

Both the classical *cultivation-dependent* and the more recent molecular approaches are *currently* applied to assessing the effects of environmental and anthropogenic factors on *microbiological* soil *characteristics*.

ASSESSING EFFECTS OF TRANSGENIC CROPS ON SOIL MICROBIOTA

Potential negative effects of transgenic plants on soil *microorganisms* may arise in different ways and may differ from those of conventional *agricultural* practices. Some soil *microorganisms* live in close contact with plants or plant debris in the field and may thereby be exposed to specific active compounds of transgenic plants.

Genetically *engineered* plants may also release their *engineered* gene products via their root exudates into the soil, which then may persist in soil and retain their activities. In turn, these *substances* may affect *microorganisms* in soils even after plants have been removed, and may possibly alter populations of plant-beneficial or plant-pathogenic microorganisms.

These different routes of exposure may have different effects on soil *microorganisms* and can be grouped into four categories.

Effects on soil *microorganisms* may arise from:

1. Close contact with the living plant (e.g., *rhizosphere* or *plant interior*)
2. Close contact with plant litter, also after crops have been harvested
3. Exposure to released transgene products that may persist in soil
4. Horizontal gene transfer from transgenic plants, their debris, or released

DNA to soil indigenous *microorganisms*

In addition to direct effects of the transgene product, altered plant *physiologies* due to indirect (pleiotropic) effects of genetic *transformation* may occur and affect plant-associated microorganisms. Therefore, it is not sufficient to test for effects of the *engineered* trait, but rather to assess the performance of engineered plants in the environment and to compare them with different genotypes of *conventionally* bred cultivars.

The following sections will focus on studies assessing effects of transgenic plants and transgene products on soil microbial community structures and performances. Persistences of *transgenes* and transgene products as well as horizontal gene transfer have been summarized by others and are not within the scope of this review of the scientific *literature* on the effects of *transgenic* plants on soil microbial communities, although some of the studies presented have also addressed one or more of these aspects.

Altogether, these *considerations* reveal that a variety of potentially negative impacts of transgenic plants on soil microbial communities have been suggested. As a result, an increasing number of studies have been published in the recent past, and much *information* has been collected by applying an array of different analytical methods and approaches. In the following, an overview of results published in the scientific literature will be provided.

This review does not claim to be complete, but it may be representative of the type of research questions addressed to assess potential effects of *different* transgenic traits in *various* plant types on soil microbial communities and the type of results one may expect from these analyses.

STUDIES ASSESSING EFFECTS OF TRANSGENIC PLANTS ON SOIL MICROBIAL COMMUNITY STRUCTURES

Crops Engineered for Herbicide Tolerance

In 2005, the worldwide area planted with herbicide tolerant transgenic crops was 73.8 million hectares. *Commercialized* genetically engineered herbicide tolerant traits confer resistance to active substances, such as *glufosinate* (e.g., Basta®) and glyphosate (e.g., Roundup®).

Effects of genetically engineered herbicide tolerant plants on soil microbial ecology have been addressed in numerous studies and the data have been reviewed by others. Nine studies addressing the effects of *genetically engineered* herbicide tolerant plants on soil microbiota have been identified in the scientific literature.

Five of them were performed with canola *(Brassica spp.)*, three with corn *(Zea mays)*, and one with soybean *(Glycine max)*, all of them *addressing* potential effects of the engineered trait on soil *microbial* communities.

Herbicide Tolerant Canola

In a field study, endophytic and rhizosphere microbial communities of different canola cultivars were analyzed, including Quest, a transgenic variety tolerant to the herbicide *glyphosate*. CLSU and FAME profiling were used to characterize the microbial *communities* associated with the root interior and the rhizosphere.

Both techniques revealed differences between both the *endophytic* and the rhizosphere microbial communities of the transgenic cultivar Quest and nontransgenic cultivars. In a follow-up study, the *differences* between endophytic bacteria were confirmed with FAME analysis of root endophytic bacterial isolates.

These results were supported by a 2-year field study with four *genetically* modified and four *conventional* canola varieties, where CLSU and FAME analyses of microbial community structures in the roots and the *rhizospheres* were applied.

These analyses revealed that the root interior and *rhizosphere* bacterial community associated with the genetically modified varieties differed from those of conventional varieties. Finally, in a contained *experiment* with genetically modified glufosinate tolerant canola and *associated* herbicide applications, shifts in *rhizosphere* bacterial communities and *Pseudomonas* population structures were assessed.

Rhizosphere soil was sampled at different stages of plant *development* and DGGE analyses of PCR-amplified 16S rRNA gene fragments were applied. Bacterial community and *Pseudomonas profiling* revealed slightly altered microbial *communities* in the rhizosphere of transgenic plants; however, effects were minor when compared to the plant *developmental* stage-dependent shifts.

In addition, invertase, urease, and alkaline *phosphatase* activities were *significantly* enhanced in the *rhizospheres* of senescent transgenic plants when compared to wild-type plants. The authors attributed the observed differences between transgenic and wild-type lines to altered root *exudation* of the herbicide tolerant canola.

Herbicide Tolerant Corn

Bacterial communities in *rhizospheres* of field-grown glufosinate tolerant *transgenic* corn have been assessed with SSCP analyses of PCR-amplified bacterial 16S rRNA gene fragments. Neither the genetic *modification* nor the use of glufosinate affected the rhizosphere bacterial SSCP profiles.

On the other hand, clear *differences* have been detected between the *rhizospheres* of corn and sugar beet controls, clearly *demonstrating* the sensitivity of the approach chosen. A less pronounced but *significant* difference has been detected at certain growth stages in rhizosphere samples obtained from the fine root fraction.

The same authors *confirmed* this lack of strong effects of herbicide tolerant corn on rhizosphere bacterial communities, again based on bacterial SSCP profiles. In this second study no *differences* between cultivars or treatments have been detected that were greater than the variability between replicates.

These data have been *confirmed* with results obtained in *glasshouse* and field studies using CLSU and DGGE analyses. These analyses have revealed stronger differences in bacterial *community* structures among soil textures than among corn genotypes, leading the authors to the *conclusion* that bacterial communities in corn *rhizospheres* may be more strongly affected by soil texture than by the engineered herbicide tolerant trait.

Herbicide Tolerant Soybean

Bradyrhizobium japonicum contains a glyphosate-sensitive 5-enolpyruvylshikimic acid-3-phosphate synthase and it has been demonstrated that at high concentrations, *glyphosate* may result in growth inhibition or death of *B. japonicum.*

In an overview, the effects of glyphosate application and *glyphosate* resistant soybean on its *nitrogen-fixing* symbiont were assessed. In glasshouse studies it has been shown that nitrogenase activity in *glyphosate* tolerant soybean could be transiently inhibited after glyphosate application, indicating the potential for reduced nitrogen fixation in the herbicide tolerant soybean system.

Crops Expressing Insecticidal Bt Toxins

In 2005, the worldwide area planted with insect resistant *transgenic* crops was 26.3 million hectares. Commercialized *genetically* engineered insect resistant crops expressed variations of *insecticidal* proteins from subspecies of *Bacillus thuringiensis, i.e.,* Bt toxins.

There are numerous studies on potential effects of Bt crops on soil microbial communities and several reviews have *summarized* their results.

In the present review, 21 studies addressing effects of Bt-based genetically engineered insect resistant plants on soil microbiota were identified in the scientific literature.

Four of them assessed the effects of purified Bt toxins, while 13 *investigated* insect resistant corn *(Z. mays)* and two each investigated insect resistant cotton *(Gossypium spp.)* or rice *(Oryza spp.).*

Purified Bt Toxin

In a study on effects of transgenic cotton lines on microbiological soil characteristics, control treatments included *application* of purified toxin from *B. thuringiensis* subsp. *kurstaki* (Btk toxin). In this study, the purified Btk toxin did not reveal any *significant* effects on plate counts of bacteria and fungi.

These data were confirmed in a study where purified Bt toxin was added to soil, revealing no *significant* changes in the numbers of culturable bacteria in *rhizosphere* soil, except for nitrogen-fixing bacteria at a Bt toxin concentration of 500 ng/g soil.

This *represents* a rather high Bt toxin concentration when compared to the *concentrations* detected in the rhizospheres of Bt corn, which have been reported to reach 10 ng/g soil as detected with an enzyme-linked *immunosorbent* assay (ELISA).

Furthermore, the effects of purified Bt toxins have been assessed by in vitro studies on a selection of *microorganisms*. A variety of bacteria, fungi, and algae were tested in pure and mixed cultures, as well as in disk-diffusion and sporulation assays with *purified* free and clay-bound Bt toxins.

In these analyses no antibiotic effects were detected. Recently, however, *preliminary* results on the *significantly* higher half-life of the herbicides glyphosate and glufosinate in soils amended with purified Btk toxin have been reported.

These authors concluded that the absence of Btk toxin effects on soil microbial biomass and the rapid decrease of insecticidal activity as determined with a bioassay may indicate indirect effects of the Btk toxin on soil properties and/or *mechanisms* that inthence herbicide degradation.

Insect Resistant Bt Corn

Extractable lipids in Bt and *conventional* corn shoots and soil were *analyzed* at harvest. Concentrations of total alkenes, n-alkanes, and n-fatty acids were increased in soils planted with Bt corn, while *unsaturated* fatty acid contents were higher in soil planted with non-Bt corn.

Cumulative CO_2 released from soils was lower under Bt corn, indicating that cultivation of Bt corn may reduce microbial activity. In a growth chamber experiment, two lines of Bt corn *expressing* either Cry1Ab or Cry1F were compared with *nontransgenic* isolines in three soil types.

PLFA profiles of bulk soil and CLPP profiles of rhizosphere soils revealed only for one soil significant Bt corn effects in the rhizosphere. Expression of Bt toxin also *significantly* reduced the presence of eukaryotic PLFA biomarkers in bulk soils; however, it remained unclear which *eukaryotes* they represented.

From this data, the authors concluded that potential effects of Bt corn on soil and *rhizosphere* microbial *communities* may be small. In a *glasshouse* study, the effects of Bt-176 corn on the *rhizosphere* bacterial community have been analyzed.

Bacterial plate counts and CLSU revealed no significant differences between plant *genotypes*. On the other hand, *differences* between the rhizosphere and bulk soil bacterial communities could be detected. Bacterial RISA revealed *differences* in the rhizosphere communities at different plant growth stages, as well as between Bt-176 and control corn.

The authors attributed the different bacterial communities in the rhizospheres to altered root exudates of the transgenic corn. In soil samples from field trials with Bt corn *expressing* Cry1Ab, microbial communities were *analyzed* based on CLSU and PLFA profiling, as well as based on protozoa analyses.

Two occasions were reported when soil *protozoa* populations under Bt corn were reduced as compared to non-Bt corn. CLSU profiling revealed one occurrence of differences between Bt and control corn cultivars.

The effects of Bt corn were classified by the authors as small and *comparable* to the variation expected in these agricultural systems. Finally, PLFA profiling was used to analyze the microbial *communities* in soil samples collected from fields with Bt corn.

Analyses revealed a reduction in fungal abundance and ratios of Gram-positive to Gram-negative bacteria in soils from Bt corn; however, the authors have stated that the causes of these observed effects remained unknown and require more detailed investigations. Several studies focused on mycorrhizal fungi for the assessment of effects of Bt corn.

An *experimental* model system was used to study the effects of root exudates of Bt corn on different stages of the life cycle of the arbuscular mycorrhizal fungal species *Glomus mosseae*. Root exudates of Bt176 corn significantly affected *presymbiotic* hyphal growth and development of appressoria, as compared to Bt-11 and control corn.

Differential hyphal morphogenesis occurred irrespective of Bt or control corn, suggesting that Bt toxin did not interfere with fungal host *recognition* mechanisms. In microcosm experiments, the impact of genetically modified Bt-11 and Bt-176 corn on soil respiration, rhizosphere, and bulk soil bacterial communities, and the mycorrhizal symbiont *G. mosseae,* were further assessed. DGGE profiling of bacterial 16S rRNA gene fragments showed *differences* in rhizosphere bacterial communities associated with all corn lines, while *mycorrhizal colonization* was significantly reduced for Bt-176 corn only.

Additional glasshouse experiments confirmed the differences between Bt and non-Bt corn, and addition of Bt corn residues to soil affected soil respiration, bacterial communities, and mycorrhizal establishment. In another study, *colonization* with arbuscular *mycorrhizal* fungi and activity of rhizosphere soil microbiota were determined during growth of Cry1Ab-expressing Bt corn in the field.

The results suggested that Bt corn and conventional corn may differ in their C/N ratios. In addition, reduced colonization with *arbuscular mycorrhizal* fungi and increased *microbial* activity were found during early Bt corn development.

The authors conclude that genetic *transformation* might have led to changes in plant physiology and root-exudate composition, which in turn may have affected symbiotic and rhizosphere *microorganisms*. There are also a number of studies which revealed no effects of Bt corn on microbiological soil *characteristics*. For instance, soils were planted with Cry1Ab-expressing Bt corn or amended with Bt corn biomass and compared to controls.

Analysis was based on a cultivation-dependent approach and revealed no significant differences in the plate counts for bacteria and fungi, as well as in the numbers of protozoa between *rhizosphere* soil of Bt and control corn. Also, amendment with plant biomass of these plants revealed no different effects. The authors concluded that the Bt protein in corn-root exudates and plant biomass appeared not to be toxic to protozoa, bacteria, and fungi. In a field study, effects of corn rootworm *(Diabrotica spp.)* resistant Bt corn expressing Cry3Bb and *application* of the insecticide *tefluthrinwere* assessed.

Analyses included soil microbial biomass, N-mineralization potential, short-term nitrification rate, basal respiration, and bacterial community structures based on T-RFLP analysis. The data showed no effects of Bt corn on microbial measures or bacterial community structures when compared to the near isoline.

T-RFLP analysis revealed substantial temporal differences and tefhthrin application reduced soil respiration. The authors concluded that *Diabrotica* resistant Bt corn may pose little or no threat to soil microbiology.

In other field studies with Cry1Ab-expressing Bt corn, the persistence of Bt toxin in soil and the effects on rhizosphere bacterial communities were assessed. An improved ELISA method for Bt toxin *quantification* and SSCP analysis of PCR-amplified bacterial 16S rRNA gene *fragments* were used.

Despite the presence of Cry1Ab protein in the rhizosphere of Bt corn, effects on bacterial community structures were small when compared to other factors, such as plant age or field heterogeneities. In *glasshouse* and field studies, bacterial diversity in Bt and conventional corn rhizospheres was determined.

CLSU profiling and DGGE of PCR-amplified 16S rRNA gene fragments allowed differentiation of bacterial communities among different soil textures but not among corn varieties. From these results the authors concluded that cultivation of transgenic varieties may not affect *rhizosphere* bacterial communities.

These results have been supported by a recent glasshouse *experiment* on the effects of Bt corn (Cry1Ab) and the insecticide deltamethrin on soil microbiota. The Bt trait induced an increase of protozoa, but *significant* effects on soil microbial community structure, as determined with CLSU and PLFA analyses, were caused only by soil type and plant growth stages.

Results from this glasshouse *experiment* were in broad agreement with those of a field experiment using the same plant material grown in the same soils.

Insect Resistant Bt Cotton

Leaves of Bt cotton and purified Bt toxin were placed in soil and analyses included plate counts of *indigenous* soil bacteria and fungi. Two transgenic Btk cotton lines caused at some sampling dates a transient increase in total bacterial and fungal plate counts.

Transient changes in bacterial species *composition*, measured by *biochemical* tests, CLSU, and ARDRA, were also observed for the two transgenic Bt cotton lines. In contrast, neither a third Btk cotton line nor the purified Btk toxin had any significant effects.

The plant line *specificity* of the effects observed and the lack of effects of purified Bt toxin suggested that the observed effects may have resulted from *pleiotropism*. In another field study, the effects of Bt cotton on soil microbiota were monitored.

Bt toxin released from cotton roots was determined with ELISA and microbial populations were *analyzed* by selective plate counts. Significant differences were found in the culturable fraction of bacteria in the rhizosphere of Bt cotton, but no significant differences were found after the growing season.

Furthermore, only the addition of 500 ng purified Bt toxin per gram of soil resulted in *significant changes* in the numbers of culturable nitrogen-fixing bacteria. From these results the authors concluded that pleiotropic factors might possibly be involved.

Insect Resistant Bt Rice

In a laboratory study, the impacts of Bt rice straw *amendment* on biological activities in water-(boded soil were investigated. The results revealed some differences in protease, neutral phosphatase, and cellulase activities between soil amended with Bt rice straw or *conventional* rice straw but none of these *differences* was persistent.

However, differences in dehydrogenase activity, methanogenesis, hydrogen production, and anaerobic respiration persisted over the course of the experiment. The results *indicated* shifts in microbial populations or changes in their metabolic abilities.

In a second study, *nonpersisting* occasional differences in plate counts of *actinomycetes*, fungi, anaerobic fermentative bacteria, denitrifying bacteria, hydrogen-producing acetogenic bacteria, and *methanogenic* bacteria were detected between the paddy soils amended with Bt rice straw and *conventional* rice straw. These effects supported the results from the first study.

Crops Engineered for Virus Resistance

Genetically engineered virus resistances still play a minor role in commercialized crops but may have an increasing potential in the future. Commercially cultivated transgenic virus resistant crops were papaya *(Carica papaya)* and squash *(Cucurbita pepo)*.

Three studies investigated the effects of plants engineered for virus resistance on microbiological soil characteristics, i.e., two using the papaya system and one focusing on potato *(Solanum tubero sum)*.

Virus Resistant Papaya

The inthence of papaya ringspot virus resistant transgenic papaya on soil *microorganisms* was assessed in soil samples collected from areas where transgenic and a *nontransgenic* papaya were grown for 9 years, as well as from an area where no papaya was grown.

Moisture content, pH value, total organic carbon contents, and total nitrogen contents were *comparable* among the soils. Plate counts for fungi and *actinomycetes* were highest in *upperlayer* soils around transgenic papaya plants and lowest in lower-layer soils where no papaya was grown. ARDRA, T-RFLP, and DGGE analyses revealed that soil bacterial *communities* shared more than 80% similarity between the areas planted with *transgenic* and *nontransgenic* papaya.

The authors concluded that *cultivation* of virus resistant *transgenic* papaya had only limited effects on soil microorganisms. In another study, soil was amended with replicase-transgenic or *nontransgenic* papaya under field *conditions* and soil properties, microbial *communities*, and enzyme activities were recorded.

Total nitrogen in soils planted with transgenic papaya was *significantly* different. *Significant* increases in plate counts of bacteria, kanamycin resistant bacteria, actinomycetes, and fungi were found in the *transgenic* papaya treatment.

Transgenic papaya and *nontransgenic* papaya induced *significantly* different activities for *arylsulfatase, polyphenol oxidase, invertase,* cellulase, and *phosphodiesterase.* The authors concluded that transgenic papaya could alter soil chemical properties as well as microbial communities.

Virus Resistant Potato

PLFA profiling was used to analyze the effects of potato virus Y (PVY) resistant transgenic potato on microbial communities in field soils. A decrease of fungal abundance in soils from PVY resistant transgenic potato was reported.

Contrasting differences were found in the ratios of Gram-positive to Gram-negative bacteria in different depth layers. The authors state that the causes of these differences are unclear and require further investigation.

Crops Engineered with Proteinase Inhibitors

Proteinase Inhibitor-Expressing Potato

Only one study has been found in the scientific literature that *investigated* effects of crops *expressing* protein inhibitors on soil microbial communities. The system studied was a potato line genetically engineered for nematode resistance with chicken egg white cystatin (two lines) or modified rice cystatin (one line), both being cysteine proteinase inhibitors.

In a field study, the effects of these plants were compared to those of aldicarb, an oxime carbamate *nematicide.* PLFA analyses were used to investigate effects on soil bacteria and fungi. In the first year, chicken egg white cystatin-expressing potato was tested, and one *transgenic* line revealed increases and the other decreases in fungal marker fatty acid abundance later in the growing season.

In the second year, rice cystatin-expressing potato and nematicide treatment were used. The nematicide treatment reduced the bacterial fraction of the microbial community, while the rice cystatin-expressing potato reduced both bacterial and fungal community components.

No *differences* in the rate of leaf litter decomposition were observed. These results indicated that nematicide use and different transgenic lines may *differentially* influence *componentsof* soil microbial communities without affecting soil functions such as litter decomposition.

Crops Engineered with Antimicrobial Activities

Some microorganisms represent a serious threat to agriculture and genetic engineering offers an attractive approach for the production of disease resistant crops. A variety of genes coding for antimicrobial proteins from plant, animal, or microbial origin have been used to transform crops for improved disease resistance.

However, justified concerns have been raised that these *engineered* traits may also affect beneficial *microorganisms,* such as mycorrhizae, rhizobia, plant growth promoting microorganisms, or other *microorganisms* improving plant health, as well as microorganisms involved in plant litter decomposition and nutrient cycling.

Genetically engineered *antimicrobial* activities in crops actually have the potential for direct effects on endophytic, epiphytic, symbiotic, rhizosphere, and soil *microorganisms.* An increasing number of studies that have assessed potential effects of antimicrobial transgenic plants have become available, and for this review 17 were found in the scientific literature.

Ten studies assessed potato *(Solanum tuberosum),* two each aubergine *(Solanum melongena)* and woodland tobacco *(Nicotiana sylvestris),* and one each tomato *(Solanum lycopersicum),* wheat *(Triticum aestivum),* and silver birch *(Betula pendula).*

T4 Lysozyme-Expressing Potato

Potato genetically engineered to produce *bacteriophage-derived* T4 lysozyme for enhanced bacterial resistance has gained considerable attention in the scientific literature, with seven studies on potential effects of this genetically engineered trait in potato. Changes in plant-associated bacterial populations were monitored during a 2-year field release of T4 lysozyme potato.

No significant *differences* in aerobic plate counts were observed between *transgenic* and control plant lines. In addition, no significant differences in counts of auxin-producing and *phytopathogen-antagonistic* isolates were found.

Among 28 different antagonistic species isolated, seven were found only on control plants. However, the observed difference was minor when compared to the *variability* during the monitoring period. In further field evaluations, *T4* lysozyme tolerant mutants of two *antagonistic* plant-associated bacterial isolates, i.e., *Pseudomonas putida* and *Serratia grimesii,* were used for seed tuber inoculation of transgenic *T4* lysozyme-expressing and control potato.

Both introduced isolates colonized the rhizo- and geocaulosphere of transgenic and control potato. At fbwering, significantly higher plate counts of the *T4* lysozyme tolerant P. *putida* were recovered from transgenic *T4* lysozyme-expressing potato.

Effects of the inoculants on the indigenous bacterial community were monitored by DGGE analysis of PCR-amplified fragments of 16S rRNA gene fragments. Neither dominance of the inoculated strains nor differences between inoculated and uninoculated potato were detected.

In order to further assess potential effects of these plants, a total of 68 *representative* bacterial strains of the group enterics and *pseudomonads* were isolated from parental and transgenic *T4* lysozyme-expressing potato.

They were identified with FAME analysis and typed by phenotypic profiling, i.e., *antagonistic* activity, auxin production, and sensitivity to *T4* lysozyme, as well as genotypic profiling with BOX-PCR. The majority of identified bacterial groups included isolates from all potato lines analyzed.

The authors concluded that no correlations between bacterial types and plant genotype have evolved. In a further study, a polyphasic approach was chosen to analyze *rhizosphere* bacterial communities of the *T4* lysozyme-expressing potato lines and control plants at two field sites over *3* years.

The polyphasic approach included heterotrophic plate counts, *identification* of isolates with FAME, CLSU profiling, DGGE profiling of bacteria, *actinomycetes,* and alpha- and betaproteobacteria, as well as DNA sequence analyses.

These analyses revealed that *environmental* factors related to season, field site, or year of *sampling* infhenced the rhizosphere communities but no effects related to the *T4* lysozyme trait were detected. Some transgenic line-specific differences were attributed by the authors to pleiotropic effects of genetic engineering.

In a separate series of glasshouse experiments, the effects of *T4* lysozymeexpressing potato on rhizosphere bacterial communities in different soil types were analyzed. *Soil* enzyme activities involved in C-, P-, and N-nutrient cycles and T-RFLP-based bacterial community structures were assessed.

Trcnsgenic potato induced differences in soil enzyme *activities* and structures of rhizosphere bacterial communities; however, the impact of genetic modification was only transient, minor, or comparable to those caused by soil type, control plant genotype, vegetation stage, and pathogen exposure.

In a second study, the authors assessed the effects of *T4* lysozyme expression on endophytic bacteria of potato by using T-RFLP profiling and 16S rRNA gene *sequencing* approaches. Genetic *transformation* induced small differences in the endophytic community structures; however, the effects were also minor or comparable to the variations induced by environmental factors.

The authors pointed out that effect assessment studies on transgenic crops should include different environmental factors in order to allow for ranking of potential transgene-related effects. Finally, a detailed study has been *performed* in order to assess potentially harmful effects of *T4* lysozyme exudation into the rhizosphere.

The bactericidal effects of *T4* lysozyme-expressing transgenic potato were assessed in a model system with *Bacillus subtilis* associated with hair roots of the plants. *Significantly* decreased survival of *B. subtilis* was observed on hair roots of *T4* lysozyme-expressing potato lines in this model system.

However, the authors conclude that no strong negative effects of *T4* lysozyme-producing potato on soil *bacteria* may be expected in the field.

Attacin/Cecropin-Expressing Potato

Attacin and cecropin are insect-derived proteins with *antimicrobial* activity. In glasshouse *experiments* the effects of attacin/cecropin-expressing potato on rhizosphere bacterial communities were analyzed. *Soil* enzyme activities of C-, P-, and N-nutrient cycles, as well as bacterial *community structures* based on T-RFLP profiling of bacterial *16S* rRNA genes, were determined.

In general, the *T4* lysozyme trait used in the same experiment (described in the previous section) had stronger effects than the attacin/cecropin trait.

Therefore, for the attacin/cecropin trait the authors conclude that the effects of genetic modification were not stronger than those of soil type, control plant genotype, vegetation stage, and pathogen exposure.

In the follow-up study, effects of attacin/cecropin-expressing *transgenic* potato on endophytic bacteria were assessed by using T-RFLP profiling. Similar to the *T4 lysozyme-expressing* potato used in parallel, attacin/cecropin *expression* induced *differences* in the community structures of endophytic bacteria; however, also in this case the effects were not larger than those of environmental factors.

Magainin II-Expressing Potato

The gene for the *antimicrobial* peptide magainin II, derived from the African clawed toad *(Xenopus laevis),* showed in vitro activity against a range of *microorganisms* including rhizosphere isolates. Transgenic potato *expressing* magainin II revealed increased resistance to the bacterial potato pathogen *Erwinia carotovora.*

Bacterial and fungal plate counts on different media were used to assess effects on *communities* associated with magainin II-producing potato plants. Analyses revealed no *significant differences* in the bacterial counts from leaf and root samples. Higher numbers of *culturable* fungi were detected in root samples and *significantly* lower numbers of total bacteria in tubers of magainin II-expressing transgenic potato.

Defensin-Expressing Aubergine

Dm-AMP1 is an *antifungal* plant defensin from *Dahlia merckii.* Aubergine *transformed* for constitutive expression of defensin showed increased resistance to the pathogenic fungus *Botrytis cinerea.* The protein was released in root exudates of the transformed plants and was active in reducing the growth of the pathogenic fungus Verticillium *alboatrum,* whereas it did not interfere with recognition responses and symbiosis establishment by the arbuscular *mycorrhizal* fungus *Glomus mosseae.*

In an experimental model system, effects of Dm-AMP1 defensin-containing root exudates of aubergine on different stages of the life cycle of *G. mosseae* were assessed. In contrast to root exudates of Bt-176 corn (described above), no differences were found in mycelial growth and fungal host recognition mechanisms.

gox *Gene-Expressing Tomato*

It has been shown that plants engineered with the *gox* gene, encoding for the enzyme d-glucose oxygen 1-oxidoreductase, have elevated H_2O_2 concentrations and exhibit *increased* resistance to plant pathogens.

Also, *transgenic* tomato plants engineered with the *gox* gene revealed increased resistance to some pathogens and contained more nitrogen and insoluble lignin as well as less soluble protein than control plants.

Soil amended with leaves from the transgenic tomato line revealed reduced soil *respiration* during the first 2 days of incubation. This was explained by the authors as due to the different *composition* of the plant material, and may in part be related to the pleiotropic effects of genetic engineering.

KP4-Expressing Wheat

The viral *kp4* gene is derived from a double-stranded RNA virus infecting corn smut (Ustilago *maydis).* The gene codes for a "killer protein" (KP) that is *expressed* in infected *U. maydis* and inhibits growth of competing *U. maydis* strains lacking viral infection.

Further studies revealed that KP4 may reversibly block ion channels and therefore *represents* a growth inhibitor rather than a killing protein. Various bacteria and fungi have been tested for their *sensitivity* toward KP4 and it has been shown that only specific genera of the order

Ustilaginales, which cause smut and bunt diseases in cereals, were affected. In order to test whether KP4 may confer resistance to specific fungal diseases if used in genetic plant *engineering,* spring wheat varieties were transformed with the *kp4* gene. Tests in climate chambers using artificial infection with stinking smut *(Tilletia caries)* revealed an increased *resistance* of the kp4-transgenic wheat.

These results have been confirmed in a recent study, where two kp4-transgenic spring wheat varieties were grown in a convertible *glasshouse,* allowing exposure of the plants to the open environment but also more strictly *containing* them if required.

Laboratory bioassays and glasshouse studies with the collembola *Folsomia candida* revealed no effects of the kp4-transgenic wheat, while differences among different wheat varieties were detected. In addition, investigations in the convertible glasshouse system revealed no effects of the *kp4* transgene on wheat infesting insects, i.e., aphids and cereal leaf beetle.

T-RFLP profiling of PCR-amplified ribosomal RNA gene *fragments* from bacteria (PCR primers 27F and 1378R) and from fungi (PCR primers NS1 and FR1) was performed on DNA extracted from bulk soil (Widmer, unpublished results).

Statistical analysis revealed a significant ($p < 0.05$) effect of the factors "sampling time" and "wheat variety" on community structures of bacteria and fungi. For the factors "kp4-transgenic" and "Tillecia *tritici* inoculation", no *significant* effects on bacterial and fungal *community* structures were detected.

Chitinase-Expressing Woodland Tobacco

Transgenic woodland tobacco *(Nicotiana sylvestris) expressing* different tobacco chitinases was used to assess colonization of the root system by the root pathogenic fungus *Rhizoctonia solani* and the vesicular–arbuscular *mycorrhizal* symbiont *Glomus mosseae.*

Transgenic *N. sylvestris* expressing the vacuolar tobacco chitinase A or an N-terminally truncated version of this chitinase revealed increased resistance to R. *solani.* Transgenic *N. sylvestris* expressing a C-terminally truncated *chitinase* A showed no enhanced resistance.

All these transgenic *N. sylvestris* lines were equally well colonized by G. *mosseae,* indicating that expression of the different chitinase A forms did not interfere with the vesicular–arbuscular *mycorrhizal* symbiosis.

In a second study, genetically engineered tobacco lines expressing various pathogenesis-related proteins (PRs) were *examined.* Constitutive expression of various tobacco PRs, e.g., a basic tobacco chitinase, a cucumber acidic chitinase, and some combinations of these genes, did not affect the time course or the final level of colonization by G. *mosseae.*

Glucanase-Expressing Woodland Tobacco

In the same series of experiments as described in the previous section, *N. sylvestris* lines genetically transformed to express glucanases were examined. Constitutive expression of various tobacco PRs, a cucumber acidic chitinase, or a basic beta-1,3-glucanase had no effects on the time course or the final level of *colonization* by vesicular–arbuscular mycorrhizal symbiont *G. mosseae.*

Only *constitutive expression* of the acidic isoform of tobacco PR2, a protein with beta-1,3-glucanase activity, resulted in delayed *colonization* by *G. mosseae.*

Chitinase-Expressing Silver Birch

The decomposition of leaf litter from eight transgenic silver birch lines expressing sugar beet chitinase IV was studied in a field experiment. Leaf litter decomposition was analyzed based on total litter mass, as well as content of total microbial biomass (based on substrate-induced respiration (SIR)), of total fungal biomass (based on ergosterol contents), and microbial activity (basal respiration).

Mass loss of transgenic leaf litter did not differ from controls and no differences in either the fungal or total microbial biomass were recorded. Only one transgenic birch line, which revealed high levels of chitinase IV expression, showed distinct temporal dynamics of nematode populations and might indirectly indicate microbial differences in this litter.

This transgenic line-specific effect may be related to the high level of chitinase expression, but may also be an indication of possible pleiotropic effects of genetic engineering on plant litter quality.

Plants Engineered for Environmental Applications

Genetic *engineering* allows the *introduction* of traits into plants of interest for specific applications in the *environment.* Examples of these applications are phytoremediation or the specific design of plant *rhizospheres.*

Five studies in the scientific literature addressed potential impacts of such plants on soil microbiology. Two studies each used birdsfoot trefoil *(Lotus corniculatus)* and tobacco *(Nicotiana tabacum),* while another was based on black nightshade *(Solanum nigrum).*

Opine-Expressing Birdsfoot Trefoil and Black Nightshade

Opines are small amino acid and sugar *conjugates representing* specific bacterial growth substrates. Therefore, transgenic plants releasing these substances in root *exudates* may support and select specific natural or possibly *recombinant* rhizobacteria.

This principle was verified with opine-producing transgenic birdsfoot trefoil *(L. corniculatus),* by showing that engineered opine-producing plants induced targeted alterations in their root-associated bacterial communities, resulting in a stimulation of opine-utilizing populations.

The fate of the opine-utilizing bacterial *community* was investigated over time and under different experimental conditions. After removal of the transgenic plants the density of opine-utilizing bacteria in the fallow soils remained unchanged.

If soils were replanted with wild-type *L. corniculatus,* only specific bacterial populations able to utilize opines were affected. Numbers of nopaline *utilizers* decreased to the level of control plants, while numbers of mannopine utilizers remained at an intermediate level.

Data indicated that opine-utilizing bacterial *populations* respond to engineered plant exudation and that certain alterations in bacterial communities may be more responsive to crop rotation. In a follow-up study [85], it was *demonstrated* that this targeted alteration of *rhizosphere* bacterial populations was not restricted to the *L. corniculatus* system described above, but was also effective with black nightshade (*S. nigrum)* growing in another soil type.

Ferritin-Expressing Tobacco

Ferritin is a ubiquitous iron storage protein that plays an *important* role in iron metabolism. Its ability to sequester iron *provides* a dual function, i.e., iron *detoxification* and iron storage. Ferritin over-expressing transgenic tobacco with activated iron transport and increased iron phytoextraction may deplete iron from its rhizosphere and thus select for iron *stress-sensitive rhizobacteria.*

Plate counts on media depleted in or supplemented with iron were used to determine the abundance of iron stress-sensitive bacteria. Ferritin over-expressing *tobacco* revealed highest iron *accumulation* at the fbral bud stage, the time point when the d ensity of iron stress-sensitive bacteria *recovered* was *significantly* increased in the *rhizosphere* of these plants.

This effect, however, was soil type and plant stage dependent. Data indicate that the ferritin *over-expressing* transgenic tobacco plants are able to extract and *accumulate* more iron from the rhizosphere, and that they may select in their *rhizosphere* for bacteria that are less *susceptible* to iron stress.

Metallothionein-Expressing Tobacco

Transgenic tobacco plants expressing yeast metallothionein in *combination* with a *polyhistidine* cluster displayed increased accumulation of and tolerance for cadmium. These plants were assessed for their effects on the arbuscular *mycorrhizal* fungus *Glomus intraradices* in a pot experiment.

Mycorrhiza tended to decrease the *phytoextraction* efficiency of the transgenic tobacco, while it increased that of nontransgenic plants at cadmium levels in the soil that are inhibitory to growth of tobacco. These results indicate that plant-mycorrhiza interactions may be important for phytoextraction *efficiencies* and may depend on the plant genotype.

Crops Engineered for the Production of Biomolecules

Plants may be genetically engineered for the production of substances of interest to industry. These substances may include enzymes for industrial processes and also substances for pharmaceutical applications. In addition, plants may also be engineered for improved nutritional quality.

Reports on the assessment of such plants concerning their effects on the soil ecosystem are still scarce in the scientific literature. Four studies were retrieved and three analyzed effects of *transgenic* alfalfa *(Medicago sativa)*, while another study assessed transgenic potato (S. *tuberosum).*

Alpha-Amylase- or Lignin Peroxidase-Expressing Alfalfa

Rhizosphere bacterial communities of two transgenic alfalfa lines, one expressing bacterial alpha-amylase and the other expressing fungal lignin peroxidase, were analyzed based on CLSU profiling. Genetic profiles of bacterial consortia present in individual substrate wells of the Biolog GN plates were determined with ERIC-PCR.

Analyses of the CLSU profiles indicated consistent differentiation of lignin peroxidase-expressing alfalfa plant rhizospheres. ERIC-PCR profiles revealed consistent differences in the substratespecific consortia enriched from each alfalfa genotype rhizosphere.

ERICPCR-based typing of bacterial isolates obtained from substrate wells *suggested* that a limited number of bacteria were responsible for specific substrate *utilization*. Data suggested that transgenic plant genotypes may affect rhizosphere *microorganisms*.

The same transgenic alfalfa plants were then used in a field study in *combination* with recombinant *Sinorhizobium meliloti* in order to assess the effects of *genetically* engineered *organisms* on soil ecosystems. Analyses included plant shoot weight, soil chemistry, enzyme activities, SIR, plate counts of indigenous soil bacteria and fungi, and counts of *protozoa*, as well as CLSU and ARDRA profiling of soil bacterial communities.

The lignin *peroxidase-expressing* plants had significantly lower shoot weight, and higher nitrogen and phosphorus contents. Significantly higher soil pH and lower activity of soil *dehydrogenase* and alkaline *phosphatase* were associated with the lignin peroxidase-expressing alfalfa, while plate counts for culturable aerobic spore-forming and cellulose-utilizing bacteria were increased.

CLSU profiles *distinguished* all three alfalfa genotypes, but *particularly* the lignin peroxidase-expressing plants. Counts for protozoa, ARDRA profiles of indigenous soil bacteria, and SIR rates were not *significantly* affected by any of the transgenic alfalfa *treatments*.

The primary effects observed were *associated* with the transgenic lignin peroxidase-expressing alfalfa and could possibly be explained by the different plant characteristics found for this genotype.

Ovalbumin-Expressing Alfalfa

Fourteen genetically modified lines of alfalfa, expressing a methionine-rich ovalbumin from Japanese quail, were evaluated for nodulation ability and plate counts for different aerobic bacteria in the rhizosphere. Higher counts of ammonifying, spore-forming, *denitrifying*, and nitrifying bacteria were *observed* in the rhizospheres of *transgenic* lines, while counts for cellulolytic bacteria and *Azotobacter spp.* were decreased.

In spite of some differences in colony numbers in samples isolated from the rhizosphere of transgenic and nontransgenic alfalfa plants, no statistically significant difference between individual lines could be detected.

Potato Engineered for Altered Starch Composition

For certain industrial products amylopectin offers advantages as compared to amylose. Therefore a transgenic potato line was developed, which expresses the mRNA for the granule-bound starch synthase gene *(gbss)* also in an antisense direction.

This approach results in reduced levels of this enzyme in the potato plants and in a *modified* starch composition. This transgenic potato line was *evaluated* for its effects on soil *microbiology* by analyzing DGGE profiles of bacterial and fungal ribosomal RNA gene fragments from bulk soil samples.

It was shown that no significant differences between the two cultivars and the transgenic line were found. For rhizosphere samples only bacterial DGGE patterns differentiated the *conventional* cultivar *SOLANA* from those of the parental line *SIBU* and the *transgenic* line *SIBU S1*, and the sequence of the *differentiating* band showed the highest similarity with *Enterobacter amnigenus*.

Pseudomonas-specific DGGE analyses revealed differences between the *rhizospheres* of the transgenic line *SIBU S1* and the parental cultivar *SIBU*. However, this analysis also *indicated* clear differences between the cultivars *SOLANA* and *SIBU*. Therefor, *differentiation* detected for the transgenic line was comparable to the one observed among different cultivars.

CONCLUSIONS

A large number of studies on effects of genetically engineered plants on soil microbiological characteristics have become available in the recent past. Many different types of *engineered* plant species and traits have been studied, and a large array of classical and more recently developed tools have been applied.

Effects have been studied in laboratory systems, micro-cosms, glasshouse systems, and in the field. In many studies *differences* in soil microbiological characteristics between soils planted with transgenic or control plants have been detected, although a large number of studies found no effects.

In some studies effects detected were compared to those caused by *environmental* factors or other crop types, and often it was found that these factors have a greater inthence on soil microbiological characteristics than the *genetically* engineered trait. Effects are often restricted to the *rhizosphere* of the transgenic plants or to the time period when these plants were present.

In addition, many of the effects described were based on analyses of symbiotic microorganisms that live in close association with the plant, such as mycorrhizal fungi or endophytic bacteria. Effects on these *plantassociated* microorganisms may well be *disadvantageous* for the crop itself, and may therefore represent a potential economic *restriction* for applying this crop rather than a concern for the ecosystem.

In addition, many of the effects found appeared spatially and temporally limited, and therefore may also potentially affect the transgenic crop itself. However, these conclusions represent hypotheses based on the available data, and need scientific evaluation in future *experiments* and monitoring of fields planted with *genetically* engineered crops.

The result of the studies presented here indicate that the tools for sensitive detection of changes in soil microbiological characteristics are available; however, they also reveal that at present it is very difficult or impossible to define which alterations in these *characteristics* may represent unacceptable damage to a soil system.

This limitation becomes evident from the scientific *literature* presented here, as no study reported damage of a soil system, but rather potentially adverse effects. The definition and identification of indicators that quantitatively represent soil quality or soil damage will be one of the great *scientific challenges* in soil ecology for the near future.

Analyses of soil microbial *communities* with their diverse *functions* may allow for the identification of such indicators, which may be used in specific diagnostics for assessing damage to soil systems.

Chapter 7

TRANSGENIC PLANTS WITH INCREASED TOLERANCE AGAINST INSECT PESTS

Control of insect pests represents one of the major input costs of world *agricultural* production and consumes billions of dollars annually, *predominantly* in chemical pesticides and lost *production*. Insect control with pesticides is, however, *becoming* more problematic in both developed and third world countries. Farmers and consumers are increasingly aware of the environmental and ecological impacts of excessive pesticide use.

As the target insects are repeatedly exposed to the same pesticide chemistries, they often develop heritable *resistance* to those pesticides and require the use of *higher* and higher doses or more toxic insecticide blends to achieve economic levels of pest control.

Plant breeders, seed companies, and farmers are now turning to biotechnological solutions to these important pest problems in agriculture because of the *environmental* and economic advantages of *deploying* inbuilt insect control strategies as opposed to external *applications*.

Over the past 10 years, transgenic crops protected against insects have been generated in some of the *important* broadacre crops, including cotton and corn, as well as in *horticultural* crops such as potato, and have been released *commercially*.

BACILLUS THURINGIENSIS CRY GENES AS A SOURCE OF INSECTICIDAL GENES FOR CROPS

The bacterium *Bacillus thuringiensis* has had a long history of use as a sprayable microbial biopesticide. It has been used predominantly in horticulture and to a smaller extent in broadacre crops, especially those grown organically.

During *sporulation*, the bacterium produces a series of insecticidal proteins assembled into a parasporal crystal. A mixture of the dried spores and crystals is *reconstituted* with water and sprayed on plants. On ingestion by the target insects, the *crystals* are *solubilized* and activated by *digestive* proteases to form highly potent and specific toxins that bind to *particular* gut receptors.

The toxins are thought to aggregate and form *ionpermeable* pores that lead to gut dysfunction, lysis of gut epithelial cells, and the eventual death of the insect. Individual crystals in the *bacterium* may be a complex mixture of toxins each with its own range of insect specificities.

The individual proteins within the crystals are encoded by both plasmid and *chromosomal* Cry genes that were identified as early targets for *incorporation* into crop plants to protect them from insects. There are now hundreds of identified *Cry* genes, and there is a standard nomenclature to describe them based on sequence similarities. Initial attempts to express Cry genes in *transgenic* plants were not *particularly* successful, and this was attributed to the bacterial origins of these genes and especially their high AT content, which resulted in low levels of insecticidal protein.

Resynthesis of the *Cry* genes removing cryptic plant polyadenylation signals, putative *messenger* RNA (mRNA) *destabilization* signals, improving the codon usage bias, and increasing the GC content were strategies that increased *expression* to a useful level (0.2-0.3% of total soluble protein) in *transgenic* plants.

Modified and unmodified, full-length and truncated Cry genes have so far been *expressed* in an array of plant species (from trees such as poplar, larch, and eucalypt; cereals like wheat, maize, and rice; legumes like chickpeas, soybeans, and peanuts; *vegetables* such as potato, tomato, cabbage, broccoli, and sweet potato; and fruits like apples and strawberries), but *intellectual* property ownership has restricted *commercialization* to a few high-value *agricultural* species, such as cotton and corn and to a lesser extent potato.

COMMERCIALIZED BACILLUS THURINGIENSIS (BT) CROPS

Bt-Corn

The United States is the largest corn-producing country in the world. One of the *significant* pests of U.S. and Canadian corn is the European corn borer (ECB) (*Ostrinia nubilalis*), a lepidopteran insect, whose larvae are difficult to control as they bore into the corn stalk, where they are protected from applied *pesticides*. Only a few percent of the total acreage of corn is sprayed for control of ECB, so economic losses from this insect can be high.

Btcorn varieties targeted at ECB control were first released in the United States in 1996 and were so rapidly adopted by farmers that over a quarter of all the corn sown by 1999 was Bt-corn. Five different types of Bt-corn are *currently* registered by the U.S. *Environmental* Protection Agency (EPA), each with either *different Cry* genes (*CrylAb, CrylAc, or Cry9C*) or different levels or patterns of expression.

The Monsanto and Syngenta Yieldgard corns express truncated codon-modified *CrylAb* genes derived from *B. thuringiensis* subsp. *kurstaki*. The Syngenta corn line has been backcrossed into both field and sweet corn varieties and, as with the Monsanto line, the *CrylAb* gene is expressed *throughout* the plant, *including* the silks and kernels, but is particularly high in leaves.

Bt-corns called KnockOut (Novartis) or NatureGard (Mycogen) also express *CrylAb* but use a novel two-gene strategy to target expression to ECB-susceptible tissues. One *CrylAb* is controlled by the corn *phosphoenolpyruvate* carboxylase (PEPC) gene directing *expression* in green *photosynthetically* active tissues. A pollen-specific promoter from the maize *calcium-dependent* protein kinase (CDPK) gene controls the second.

The combination of PEPC and pollen promoters provides high *CrylAb* gene expression in leaves and pollen, where it is highly effective in controlling European corn borer. Changes in business structures have resulted in the phaseout of KnockOut and NatureGard corns, and their registration will not be renewed. All existing stocks of these events can now be used only until the 2003 corn-growing season. A Dekalb Bt-corn called Bt-Xtra contains three genes, the *CrylAc* gene from *B. thuringiensis* subsp. *kurstaki*, the *bar* gene from *Streptomyces hygroscopicus*, and the potato proteinase inhibitor *pinII.*

While proteinase inhibitor genes expressed at high levels can inhibit insect digestive proteases and confer insecticidal properties to transgenic plants, the *pinII* gene in BtXtra corn was truncated during integration into the corn genome and no protein expression is detectable. CrylAc is very similar to CrylAb but has a slightly different insecticidal activity spectrum.

Since the purchase of Dekalb by Monsanto, the Bt-Xtra corn has been phased out in favour of Yieldgard. Finally, StarLink is a Bt-corn *expressing* a completely different type of *Cry* gene, the *Cry9C* from *B. thuringiensis* subsp. *tolworthi.* The Cry9C protein is active against ECB and some other lepidopteran pests of corn, including black cutworm (*Agrotis ipsilon*), but not the corn earworm (*Helicoverpa zea*). StarLink corn was registered only for animal feed and nonfood industrial use as there were some questions raised at registration *concerning* its potential allergenicity in humans.

Subsequently, *Cry9C* was detected in corn chips and other corn food products, in violation of the original animal feed use registration. StarLink was voluntarily withdrawn from registration in 2000, and there is now an *extensive* program in place to track and remove remnants of StarLink corn from the human food chain.

At the time of its withdrawal, it had been sown on less than 1% of the corn area in the United States. Thus, only two of the five original transgenic Btcorn lines will be available commercially in the next few years. Bt-corn varieties have been shown to be very effectively protected against ECB, but levels of infestation vary from year to year and region to region.

It has been estimated that in 10 of the last 13 years growers would have received an economic benefit had they been growing Bt-corn when ECB pest pressures were high. Since their release, modest reductions (1.5%) in pesticide usage have been realized, but given that *insecticides* are rarely effective for ECB control and hence seldom used, this is still significant.

Indirect benefits are also likely as the reduced ECB damage to Bt-corn is also likely to reduce sites for entry of pathogens, particularly those that produce *mycotoxins* that are health hazards to humans and farm animals eating the corn.

The CryI-expressing Bt-corn varieties have clearly allowed farmers to better control a very difficult agricultural pest (ECB), for which effective and affordable pest control options were unavailable. Yield losses from this insect have reached as much as 300 million bushels of corn in a single year. Such losses could be virtually *eliminated* using Bt-corn. New additions to the current suite of Bt-corn varieties are likely in the next few years; the first, a CrylF-expressing corn (lepidopteran active), received *conditional* registration in 2001.

Of particular interest will be the first Bt-corn targeted at beetle pests, especially the corn rootworm (*Diabrotica sp.*). Corn rootworm is really a complex of three or four different species of *Diabrotica* that are serious pests in the United States, with estimated costs of over U.S. $1 billion in chemical control and lost production.

The larvae of these beetles attack the roots, and so control is *primarily* with soil insecticides, crop rotations, and foliar insecticide applications to kill the adult beetles and prevent further egg laying. Monsanto have developed a new transgenic corn (MaxGard) expressing the beetle-active *Cry3Bb* gene that appears to be very effective in *controlling* the larval *stages* of corn rootworm.

The gene construct is believed to be a codon-modified synthetic *Cry3Bb* with a leader region from the wheat chlorophyll alb binding protein gene, an intron from the rice actin gene, and a terminator from the wheat *hspl7* gene. Monsanto applied for full registration of a number of events of its MaxGard corn in late 1999. The petition for *nonregulated* status was *withdrawn* in 2001, but Monsanto continues to do largescale trials all over the U.S. corn belt.

The transgenic corn will have to compete with other nontransgenic corn rootworm-resistant varieties. These nontransgenic varieties may be more acceptable to *consumers* who are *concerned* about GM corn products.

Bt-Cotton

Cotton is a major world crop grown primarily for its fiber but also for its oil and seed meal. Cotton is a *demanding* crop requiring *significant* inputs of both water and agricultural chemicals (*insecticides, herbicides, fungicides, defoliants,* and *fertilizers*).

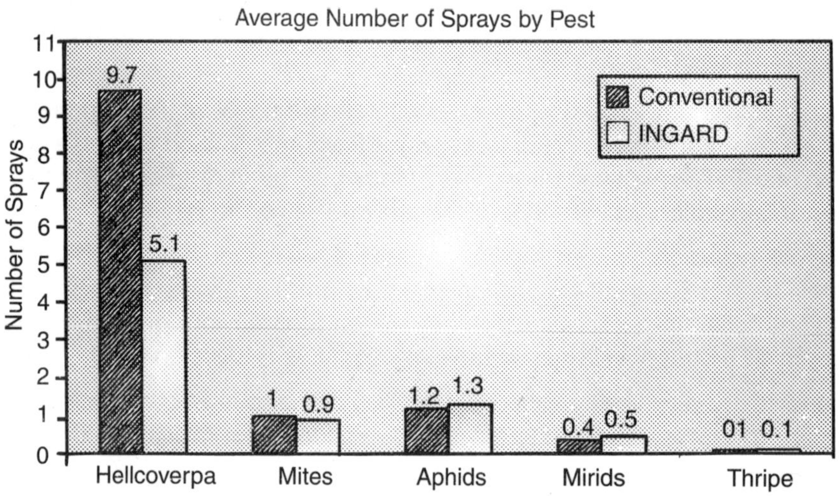

Figure 7.1: INGARD cotton under commercial production required significantly fewer pesticide sprays for caterpillar pests than similar conventional varieties in the 1999-2000 season. An area of 191,000 ha of cotton was surveyed, of which 28% was INGARD cotton. Pesticide applications to INGARD were 47% less than on conventional fields, and there were no major differences in pesticides applied for other pests.

High inputs and high returns have made cotton one of the leading crops for the application of biotechnology, and by 1999-2000 about 12% of the world cotton area was sown with genetically modified varieties. In 2000 over 70% of the U.S. crop was sown with insectand/or herbicide-tolerant GM cotton varieties: about 60% were herbicidetolerant varieties and 40% were Bt varieties (about three *quarters* of the latter were *stacked* with a herbicide tolerance trait).

The Bt varieties (Bollgard) were first released in the United States in 1996 primarily for the control of *Heliothis virescens* (tobacco budworm, TBW) but also for other pests such as *Helicoverpa zea* (cotton bollworm, CBW, or corn earworm) and *Pectinophora gossypiella* (pink bollworm). Bollgard cotton varieties contain a single insertion of a codon-modified hybrid *CrylAb/CrylAc* gene from *B. thuringiensis* subsp. *kurstaki.* Three lines of Bt-cotton, 531, 757, and 1076, were initially deregulated, but only one, 531 (Bollgard), was released commercially in the United States.

Initial sowings of Bollgard cotton in 1996 were about 1 million hectares (about 12% of the U.S. cotton area). This was a difficult year for a commercial launch because there were unusually high levels of CBW rather than the more usual cotton pest, TBW (CBW is less susceptible to *CrylAb/c* than TBW). Many thousands of hectares of Btcotton in the U.S. southeast became infested with CBW and had to be sprayed with pesticides.

This poor performance was blamed on the increased corn area that year (which increased populations of CBW) and the hot dry weather that *appeared* to decrease *expression* of the *CrylAb/c* gene, particularly later in the season. Subsequent years proved less difficult for growers, and the performance of Bt varieties has improved as growers have adjusted their adoption and management of Bt-cotton to suit their particular pest problems and *economics.* The benefits of Bt-cotton varieties in the United States have been difficult to quantify despite extensive surveys since their *introduction.*

Attributing effects on yield, pesticide usage, and profits due to Bt is a statistical challenge as many other factors can influence yield and pesticide usage even on a single farm. However, a number of analyses have indicated that there are at least three benefits to growers of Bt-cotton. First, there have been statistically significant reductions in yield losses due to the target pests in many areas.

Pesticide usage has also declined in many areas, but again statistical analyses suggest that this decrease is small and mainly for the pesticides other than major organophosphates and synthetic pyrethrins. These increases in yields and decreases in pesticide usage translate to higher net returns to growers who adopt Bt-cotton technology. Australia saw the first release of Bt-cotton in 1996, as INGARD varieties (Bollgard was already registered as a proprietary name for a different technology), on a relatively small area (30,000 ha or about 10% of total cotton area).

In Australia, the main insect pests of cotton, as in the United States, are also the larvae of heliothine moths, in this case *Helicoverpa armigera* and *H. punctigera.* Infestations are normally extreme by comparison with that in the United States, and it is not unusual to spray 12-14 times per season to control these pests (compared with 2-3 in the United States).

The total crop in 2000 occupied about 500,000 ha (about 180,000 of it INGARD) and insect control costs on conventional cotton often exceed AUS$100 million annually, for a crop worth about AUS$1.6 billion. Both *H. armigera* and *H. punctigera* are naturally less susceptible (by about 10-fold) to the CrylAb/c protein expressed in INGARD (or Bollgard) cotton and are much more abundant in cotton-producing areas than the similar pests in the United States. Early research trials indicated that although INGARD cotton controlled *H. armigera* well, particularly during the early part of the season, efficacy declined late in the season when fruit was being set. Annual surveys of the usage of *pesticides* and economic returns to growers using Bt-cotton have been carried out in Australia since 1996.

Because INGARD cotton can be only a proportion of the cotton on any one farm, detailed paired *comparisons* between the performance of INGARD and corresponding conventional varieties were possible. Pest control costs represent a significant proportion of the annual variable costs of cotton *production* in Australia, so the impact of INGARD on pesticide use appears to be much more apparent than in the United States. In all 4 years there was a significant reduction in overall use of pesticides (across all pesticide groups) and particularly those used against the *Helicoverpa* caterpillars.

In 1999-2000, for example, there was a 40% decrease in pesticides targeted at all pests (down from 10.3 sprays in conventional cotton to 6.2 in Btcotton) or 47% reduction in pesticides targeted specifically at *Helicoverpa* species (from 9.7 down to 5.1 sprays on Bt-cotton).

There was a 75% reduction in endosulfan use (a pesticide under threat in Australia because of its high toxicity to fish and the very low tolerance set for endosulfan contamination in rivers) and a 43% reduction in pyrethrins. This should reduce the pressure on synthetic pyrethroids that have selected a high incidence of resistance among cotton pests. The main concern to growers has been the high variability of lepidopteran control in Bt-cotton crops.

The number of effective days of *Helicoverpa* control (time from planting to first foliar spray of insecticide) varies from as little as 20 days up to 140 days with considerable differences in the performances of different transgenic varieties. Reduced control has been correlated with a decrease in both Cry IAb/c protein and mRNA and possibly increases in secondary metabolites that decrease the efficacy of Bttoxins.

Most of the benefit of Bt-cotton is realized in the first half of the season, when little insecticide now has to be used to control both major *lepidopteran* pest species. Careful crop *monitoring* and spraying when pests reach their economic thresholds (new thresholds were established specifically for INGARD varieties) has *stabilized* the performance of INGARD cotton.

There is a strong tendency to sow INGARD cotton in *environmentally* sensitive areas (fields close to waterways and towns as Australia has very strong pollution control laws in relation to pesticide *contamination* of rivers *etc.*) *to* capture the *significant environmental* benefits of reduced pesticide applications.

The economic benefit to the grower has been variable, in line with the variability in successful insect control. Of the paired comparisons carried out, 54% recorded some economic benefit and the rest were about break-even. The Bt technology clearly has benefits, but some *limitations* have emerged in Australia (and *presumably* in Asia, where *H. armigera* is a major pest of cotton).

In response to the poorer efficacy of Bt-cotton in Australia (and to enhanced *H. zea* control and better resistance *management* in the United States), a double gene product is being developed that contains two different Bt-toxin genes, the *CrylAb/c* gene (in INGARD and Bollgard) and *a Cry2Ab* gene also from *Bacillus thuringiensis.*

These two gene cottons (Bollgard II) are still in the breeding stage, but initial field studies have indicated much better *H. armigera* control. Bt-cotton is now approved for food use in Argentina, Australia, Canada, China, Japan, Mexico, and South Africa, as well as the United States.

Bt-cotton was grown on about 0.5 million hectares in *mainland* China in 2000-much of it Bollgard, but also some Bt-cotton developed in China, e.g., with outcomes very similar to that observed in Australia, where the lepidopteran pests are similar.

A number of Asian, European, and Latin American countries have *experimental* crops of both Bt-cotton and Btcorn for precommercial evaluation.

Bt-Potatoes

In 1996 about 1% of the total U.S. potato acreage was planted to Bt-potatoes, and this rose to about 3% in 2000. The target pest for Bt-potatoes was the Colorado potato beetle (CPB) (*Leptinotarsa decemlineata*), whose adults and larvae defoliate potatoes, reducing tuber yields to the extent that potato production has had to cease in some areas. Although nonchemical methods of control are available, none are as cost-effective or practical as chemical pesticides.

CPB easily develops resistance to chemical Insecticides, and many *populations* are now resistant to a broad array of chemical types. Microbial biopesticides containing Cry3A Bt-toxins are *effective* in killing the young larvae but, in practice, are not very effective against the most *damaging* life stages, the third and fourth instar larvae and adults.

Expressing the *Cry3A* gene in the plant has considerable advantages in targeting the most vulnerable stage of the insect's life cycle, neonates, but also, if the expression levels are high enough, in controlling larger larvae and adults. Several different transgenic cultivars of potato (sold as NewLeaf varieties) express the *Cry3A* gene from *B. thuringiensis* subsp. *tenebrionis.*

Because potato is a vegetatively propagated plant, with low or no fertility, each cultivar or variety must be separately *transformed,* whereas with Bt-corn or Bt-cotton a single event can be backcrossed into several different elite cultivars or hybrids.

NewLeaf potatoes expressing Cry3A proteins were the first to be released, and control of CPB was very effective together with over 40% reduction in insecticide applications to the NewLeaf variety.

In most potato-growing areas, aphids are also a *significant* pest, not only for the damage they can do to the plant but also because they transmit harmful plant viruses such as potato leaf roll virus (PLRV) and potato virus Y (PVY).

The introduction of NewLeafPlus and NewLeafY potato varieties that have a built-in transgene protection against PLRV and PVY, respectively, as well as the Bt gene, might have made an even bigger impact on the use of Btpotatoes in areas where these diseases are prevalent.

However, large buyers of potato products have refused to buy GM potatoes and processors have followed suit, reducing the market for NewLeaf varieties despite good evidence that they provide considerable economic benefit to the farmer.

After the poor economic performance of its NewLeaf potatoes, Monsanto appears to be reluctantly *withdrawing* completely from the *transgenic* potato market to concentrate on its other more successful biotech crops.

Resistance Management and Bt Crops

One of the key concerns with deploying single *Cry* genes into crop plants is that the increased exposure will select for resistance in the target insects. This could destroy the potential for long-term control using this technology and affect other users of microbial pesticides.

Unfortunately, field resistance to microbial Bt *formulations* has already occurred in both the Indian meal worm (*Plodia interpunctella*) in stored grains and the *diamondback* moth (*Plutella xylostella*) in a number of geographically isolated insect populations attacking vegetable crops. Laboratory-selected resistance has also been *observed* in a number of species that attack Bt-crops, including *H. virescens* and more recently *H. armigera* and *P. gossypiella.*

These relatively isolated *occurrences* of resistant insects have, however, provided models for how to manage the development of resistance to Bt-crops in an agricultural setting. The *provision* of non-Bt plants or refugia nearby to generate sufficient numbers of susceptible adults is the most commonly used resistance *management* strategy. This *ensures* that any rare homozygous resistant insects selected on the Bt crop will find only fully susceptible mates, thereby *continually* diluting the resistance genes in the target insects.

For Bt-cotton, the refugia can be unsprayed or sprayed cotton or other crops that are hosts for the pest species and generate adult insects at the same time as those that might emerge on Bt-cotton. The area and location of these refugia relative to the Bt crop are critical and in Australia, at least, have been *determined* empirically for Bt-cotton from the numbers of pupae of *H. armigera* generated by crops treated in different ways.

The requirements for refugia and other resistance management procedures are legislated into the registration label for INGARD cotton. The IPM approach adopted in Australia has been *summarized.* At present, refugia *requirements* are easily achieved as the total Bt area for any one farm can only be 30% of the total cotton planted.

This area limit is likely to be lifted only when cotton with two Bt genes becomes available around 2003 or 2004. Similar refuges for Bt-cotton and Bt-corn have been *strongly* recommended by U.S. regulators in response to scientific concerns that the technology was at risk from overuse.

The effectiveness of refuge strategies is dependent on many factors *including* the biology and population dynamics of the pest species, the frequency and mechanism of resistance, the placement and *management* of the crop and *neighboring* crops, and the expression level of the transgenes.

Nontarget Effects of Bt Crops

A second concern with Bt crops, or any other insecticidal transgenic plant, is that when released on a large scale they may have unintended, or even unnoticed, effects on other organisms in agricultural or neighboring ecosystems. Because Bt-corn is thought to exude Bt-toxins into the soil, where they can persist for relatively long periods bound to soil particles, and Bt-containing biomass is regularly returned to the soil during *agricultural* production, impacts on soil insects and microbes must also be considered. Two instances of possible nontarget effects have been described.

First, Btcorn has been reported to have unexpected effects on a beneficial insect, the green lacewings that feed on the European corn borer (ECB). Green lacewings fed ECB that had eaten Bt-corn had a higher death rate and delayed development compared with the controls, and this was attributed to the poor *nutritional* quality of ECB larvae exposed to the Bt toxin.

This study has not been extended to an agricultural setting. In a second case of possible nontarget impacts of insecticidal crops, Bt-corn was believed to accelerate the demise of the *endangered* monarch butterfly (*Danaus plexippus*) in the United States.

Monarch caterpillars feed on milkweed plants that often grow near cornfields. In a laboratory simulation, milkweed leaves were dusted with Bt-corn pollen and these leaves were fed to monarch larvae. After 4 days, only 56% of the larvae survived relative to larvae fed on plants dusted with non-Bt pollen or no pollen at all. Surviving larvae were also smaller than the controls.

This laboratory study raised *questions* about the validity of the regulatory *assessment* of the environmental impacts of transgenic plants and prompted new field studies that did not confirm the *laboratory* results. The field study showed that Bt-corn would not have any adverse effects on nontarget lepidoptera such as monarch butterflies and demonstrated that the potential exposure of larvae to Bt-corn pollen was, in fact, very low.

The risks to monarch butterflies from Bt crops must be considered small compared with the risks posed by habitat destruction and must be weighed against the effects of chemical pesticides on all *environments* adjacent to cropping areas. This incident *highlights* the need for field-based *confirmation* of any laboratory study that makes a claim for benefits or risks associated with any new biotech product.

OTHER SOURCES OF INSECTICIDAL GENES FOR CROP PROTECTION

Bacillus thuringiensis and its close relatives have proved to be a valuable source of insecticidal genes. Nevertheless, after the screening of many thousands of isolates, new types of insecticidal Bt genes have been difficult to find. The commercial and *environmental* successes of Bt-crops have provided the impetus for a *widespread* search for other potent *insecticidal* genes from *microbes*, insects, plants, and even animals.

These new insecticidal genes could be used instead of Cry-toxins or used to augment Cry-toxins to strengthen resistance *management* programs for the current *generation* of transgenic crops that rely on a single insecticidal activity.

The main *requirements* for these new genes are that the insecticidal agents must be orally active and preferably encoded by relatively few genes as *transformation* technologies can still handle only a couple of genes at a time. Novel insecticidal genes have been found using mass screening or the rational approach of seeking specific inhibitors of an insect's digestive or neural physiology.

Several potential new technologies have emerged, but none of these has yet had the *commercial* impact of the Cry genes.

New Oral Toxins

Different Cry genes have been *isolated*, covering a spectrum of *insecticidal* activities, but many important pests still cannot be controlled by Cry proteins. Most mass screening efforts to identify novel *Bacillus* strains have concentrated on the *identification* of new crystal proteins and hence have been carried out with *sporulating* cultures.

· *B. thuringiensis* isolates with high activity against corn rootworms (*Diabrotica sp.*), for example, have been found only recently, but a novel screening approach has been used to discover a rootworm-active insecticidal complex *produced* during the vegetative growth phase of *B. cereus*. One *non-crystal-forming* isolate, AB78, contained a proteinaceous insecticidal activity produced during log phase growth that was absent at sporulation.

This was traced to the presence of two proteins designated Vip1A and Vip2A (vegetative insecticidal protein) that, together, appear to have activity against corn rootworms. The corresponding *Vip* genes were cloned and were found to be widespread in *Bacillus* species. Vip2 has been *crystallized* and has been shown to be an ADPribosylating toxin.

During the vegetative phase screening, a strain of *B. thuringiensis*, AB88, was also identified. This strain had high activity against many lepidopteran pests but no activity against coleopterans, and from this strain a third type of vegetative insecticidal protein, Vip3A, has been isolated. *Vip3* has no *homology* to the *Cry* genes or any other protein in the sequence databases and thus *represents* a totally new class of *insecticidal* genes.

Vip3 expressed in transgenic tobacco achieved partial protection against *Spodoptera litura*, but no extensive analyses of transgenic plants expressing this or other *Vip* genes have yet been published. The existence of the *Vip* genes will encourage a new round of screening of the existing *Bacillus* strain collections. The venom of many insect predators such as spiders and scorpions contains potent *neurotoxins*, many of which are insect specific.

These have been used to enhance the speed of kill of insect viruses but seem unlikely candidates for expression in plants because of the food safety concerns, real or *imagined*, that they would arouse in *consumers*.

Inhibitors of Digestion

The insect gut is the obvious target for orally acting *insecticidal* agents to be *expressed* in plants. The *membranes* lining the gut appear to be the target for the Cry toxins and probably the Vips, through their poreforming or lytic activities. The insect's digestive *biochemistry* is another target.

Disruption should reduce nutrient intake, resulting in mortality or at least in slowing the growth of larvae to such an extent that they are subject to a greater degree of parasitism and predation in the field. Different *components* of the digestive system can be targeted depending on whether the food source is rich in protein or carbohydrate.

Plants already appear to have adopted this as a defense strategy, as many *accumulate* high levels of proteinaceous inhibitors of digestive enzymes in their storage organs, such as seeds, fruits, tubers, and corms. A number of plants contain wound-inducible inhibitors of insect digestive *enzymes* that are switched on during herbivory.

Protease Inhibitors

To utilize the proteins present in their diets, insects rely *predominantly* on the serine proteases trypsin, chymotrypsin, and elastase. Trypsin is the dominant protease type in lepidopteran larvae. Plants *accumulate* high levels of trypsin *inhibitors* in their seed.

These are thought to act as insect antifeedants as well as nitrogenous seed reserves. A number of genes for *trypsin-chymotrypsin* inhibitors have been cloned and expressed in plants. These transgenic plants *demonstrated* antifeedant activity against a number of lepidopteran larvae.

Larval growth rates were reduced, and in some cases mortality was markedly increased. Levels of the *inhibitors* had to be over 1% of leaf soluble protein in order to afford any protection. Similar results have been reported in transgenic rice, wheat, tobacco, Lucerne, and poplar plants with a variety of serine and cysteine protease *inhibitors* from both plants and insects. For example, a gene for a trypsin-chymotrypsin inhibitor from the giant taro plant, *Alocasia mycrorrhiza*, was expressed in transgenic tobacco. This inhibitor retarded the growth of *Helicoverpa armigera*, but the larvae rapidly altered their digestive physiology to *compensate* for the presence of the inhibitor in their diet.

Although very active against *mammalian chymotrypsin*, the giant taro inhibitor turned out to be active only against *H. armigera* trypsin; its chymotrypsin inhibitor domain proved to be inactive in the insect. Insects fed on transgenic plants containing the giant taro inhibitor (or *artificial* diets *containing purified inhibitor*) adapted by elevating the levels of chymotrypsin and elastase in the midgut to counter the reduction in trypsin activity.

Similar responses have been noted for other protease inhibitors, although the *mechanisms* of adaptation can differ. This process of adaptation may be responsible for the failure of any transgenic plants *containing* protease inhibitors to reach the marketplace, although there are a couple of reports of field tolerance, e.g., to stem borers in rice expressing the cowpea trypsin inhibitor genes.

It will be important to include multiple protease *inhibitors* with differing specificities in order to develop robust insect tolerance in plants. For example, the stigmaspecific protease inhibitor from *Nicotiana alata* (ornamental tobacco) is produced as a single polyprotein that is subsequently processed into six different trypsin and chymotrypsin inhibitors and the gene confers tolerance to *H. punctigera* and *H. armigera* when expressed in transgenic plants.

Alpha Amylase Inhibitors

Some insects have diets rich in starch and utilize the enzyme α–amylase to digest the starch to simple sugars. α–Amylase inhibitors (aAIs) are produced in the seeds of many plants and may confer some insect tolerance. Seeds of many domesticated crops have been selected for reduced levels of their inhibitors of digestion, as they are *antinutritional* components for human or animal *consumption*.

This has made some grain crops more vulnerable to attack, *particularly* in storage. Field peas are widely grown across southern Australia for both human and animal feed, but the green pods are prone to attack by the bruchid beetle, pea weevil (*Bruchus pisorum*).

Some legumes are highly tolerant to attack by beetles and produce high levels of aAI, among other *antinutritional* compounds in their seeds. A gene for aAI from the common bean *Phaseolus vulgaris* was linked to a strong seedspecific promoter and used to generate transgenic field peas expressing levels of αAI as high as those in bean seeds. The inhibitor was stably expressed through to at least the T5 generation and the pea seeds were resistant to damage by pea weevil, both in the glasshouse and in the field, as well as to a number of pests of stored grain (cowpea weevil, *Callosobruchus maculatus* and azuki bean weevil, *C. chinensis*).

The seeds were shown to have no detectable antinutritional effects in animal feeding trials. The same construct in transgenic azuki beans confers resistance to three stored grain pests, *C. chinensis, C. maculatus,* and *C. analis,* but not to the South American bruchid *Zabrotes subfasciatus.* This technology therefore holds promise for *protecting* grain legumes against certain coleopteran pests.

Lectins and Assorted Insecticidal Proteins

Few insecticidal proteins have been found that are active against sap-sucking insects such as plant hoppers, leafhoppers, and aphids, yet these insects represent a significant *component* of the pest problem in many crops.

Frequently, they are vectors for serious viral diseases *devastating* world agriculture. Sugar binding proteins, or lectins, have been purified from many plants, and a number of lectins have been reported to have toxic effects on sap-sucking insects that derive most of their energy reserves from the sugars being transported in the phloem.

The mannose binding lectin from the bulb of snowdrop (*Galanthus nivalis*) *is* toxic to the peach-potato aphid (*Myzus persicae*), the glasshouse potato aphid (*Aulacorthum solani*), and the rice brown planthopper (*Nilaparvata lugens*). When the snowdrop gene is expressed in *transgenic* tobacco from either a constitutive or a phloem-specific promoter, the lectin has been shown to be ingested by the aphids, as it can be detected in their honeydew.

The gene confers some tolerance to aphids in whole plant bioassays. Wang and Guo have expressed both the gene for the Cry IAb Bt toxin and the gene for snowdrop lectin in transgenic tobacco and have generated plants showing high insecticidal activity to both *H. armigera* and *M. persicae,* suggesting that it may be possible to stack genes active against both lepidopteran and sucking pests. When three genes (*CryIAc, Cry2A,* and the gene for snowdrop lectin) were stacked in transgenic rice, protection against three important pests (a leaf folder, a stem borer, and a plant hopper) was achieved.

Similarly, a pea lectin in transgenic tobacco was thought to have an additive effect with protease inhibitors in conferring tolerance to *lepidopteran* larvae, again *highlighting* the importance of multiple components of the *defensive* system.

Snowdrop lectin in transgenic plants was also reported to have antinutritional effects on some lepidopterans, as was wheat germ agglutinin and jacalin. Many of these lectins are generally toxic, and experiments with transgenic potatoes containing the snowdrop lectin have been implicated in downstream effects on predators of the target sucking insect pests.

Subsequent analyses, however, indicate that this is due not to the toxicity of the lectin to the insect predator but to the lowered nutritional value of the affected aphids. No effects were reported for the development of a wasp parasitoid fed on *Lacanobia oleracea* larvae raised on GNA–expressing potatoes, and there was a significant reduction in plant damage, at least in the glasshouse, using the combination of transgenic plant and parasitic wasp.

However, as yet, no lectin-expressing transgenic plant has reached the marketplace. The biotin binding proteins avidin and streptavidin have also been shown to have strong insecticidal activity and have been expressed at high levels in the kernels of maize.

Although originally produced for the commercial production of these proteins, the plants show good levels of resistance to a number of stored grain pests of corn. A thorough analysis of the human food safety issues associated with avidin and streptavidin corn will be necessary before the grain can enter the food chain. Cholesterol oxidase from a *Streptomyces* species is a potent oral inhibitor of the cotton boll weevil (*Anthonomonas grandis grandis* Boheman) and has reduced activity against a number of lepidopteran species.

It is thought to act through the oxidation of cholesterol in the membranes of the midgut brush border, and low concentrations cause mortality in larvae and reduced fertility in adults. The reason for the *specificity* of the protein is unclear as both susceptible and tolerant insect species have similar cholesterol levels. Gut pH may be involved, as the pH optimum of the enzyme does not favour its activity in the high pH found in the *midguts* of *lepidopteran* larvae.

The gene for cholesterol oxidase has been cloned and expressed as enzymatically active protein in plant cells. The specificity of cholesterol oxidase makes it an attractive target for *expression* in transgenic cotton to enhance the current *conventional* approaches to boll weevil control.

However, the success of the current boll weevil *eradication* program in the United States, which relies on conventional technology, may be a contributing factor in the lack of *commercial* incentive to progress the cholesterol oxidase gene as an insect control option in cotton. Other enzymes, chitinase and *lipoxygenase*, have also been reported to confer some insecticidal activity, but this has not been demonstrated in transgenic plants.

Secondary Metabolites

Plants produce an abundance of secondary chemicals that serve as a defense against insects. In some cases, they act as olfactory or oral cues to both beneficial and pest species. Some of the defensive chemicals are being evaluated with the aim of *manipulating* the genes for their biosynthesis in transgenic plants to enhance the host plant resistance or for the biological production of *commercial* pesticides.

Thomas et al. created transgenic tobacco plants expressing the *Catharanthus roseus* gene for tryptophan decarboxylase (TDC), which converts tryptophan to the insecticidal indole alkaloid tryptamine. Sweet potato whiteflies (*Bemisia tabaci*) fed on these plants showed a dramatic decrease in fertility. However, others have reported undesirable plant phenotypes as well as elevated tryptamine levels. Alterations in metabolite profiles brought about by overexpressing key branch point enzymes, such as TDC, can have both desirable and undesirable pleiotrophic effects, as has been reported in transgenic potatoes and canola.

In potato, overexpression of TDC resulted in an altered balance of key substrates in the shikimate and *phenypropanoid* pathways, leading to reduced levels of *phenolics* and other defense compounds. These plants were more susceptible to fungal pathogens.

In canola, reductions in the available tryptophan pool resulted in reductions in the levels of tryptophan-derived indole glucosinolates as well as increased tryptamine. Complex regulation of secondary metabolic *pathways* may also have allowed Smigocki et al. to *inadvertently* elevate secondary metabolites in transgenic tobacco plants expressing the cytokinin-producing ipt gene from Agrobacterium tumefaciens driven by a wound-inducible promoter, either through the activation of cytokinin-regulated biosynthetic genes or through changes in pools of core metabolites shared between secondary metabolism and cytokinin biosynthesis.

Their plants showed a *considerably* enhanced tolerance to tobacco hornworm (Manduca sexta) and the green peach aphid (*Myzus persicae*). Transgenic plants with altered disease tolerance were generated by Hain et al. when they introduced into tobacco two genes from grapevine encoding the enzyme stilbene synthase that converts 4-coumaroyl CoA and malonyl CoA into the toxic phytoalexin resveratrol.

Plants that produced resveratrol constitutively showed enhanced tolerance to the fungal pathogen Botrytis cinerea, but this was associated with altered flower colour and male sterility, *highlighting* the importance of regulating the production of toxic defense chemicals.

Using the native grapevine genes, however, with their own highly regulated pathogen and wound-inducible promoters has allowed the production of transgenic tomatoes without the deleterious side effects.

These plants were protected from infection by the fungus Phytophthora infestans, but not by B. cinerea and Alternaria solani, even though these pathogens induced the accumulation of resveratrol. Before we can routinely engineer pest and pathogen tolerance by manipulating secondary metabolism in plants, we must develop a better understanding of the complex interactions between different metabolic pathways and their regulation.

CONCLUSIONS

Insect control through biotechnology is an *outstanding* example of the use of gene technology to enhance the efficiency and sustainability of production of broadacre crops. It is not without its risks, such as the development of resistance by the target insects and potential nontarget impacts in the environment.

There must be a concerted effort to develop new insect tolerance genes to ensure that the existing technologies are not lost by overuse in the short term. However, finding highly potent insecticidal genes that are as effective as the first generation of genes based on delta endotoxins from Bacillus *thuringiensis* is not a simple matter.

The new class of vegetative insecticidal genes from Bacillus species holds the most promise for the control of difficult *lepidopteran* and coleopteran pests, but they have yet to be expressed effectively in transgenic plants. Inhibitors of digestion used against lepidopterans and/or sucking pests have received a great deal of publicity but are yet to prove themselves commercially and will be challenged by the great adaptability of insects and the problems of antinutritional activity against humans and animals if they are used in food or fodder crops.

They are most likely to be at their best with highly *specialized* insects that are very host specific, such as some of the stored grain pests, and do not possess well-developed adaptive mechanisms to cope with a wide array of digestive inhibitors in their diets.

The next decade will be an exciting time for biotechnologists and *entomologists* as they explore the full-scale *commercial* production of transgenic insect-protected crops.

8

Chapter

TRANSGENIC HERBICIDE—RESISTANT CROPS

There has been and is an intimate, *bidirectional* relationship between molecular biology-a most basic biological science-and weed control, the most base as well as basic *agricultural* practice. Weed control, as practiced for millennia, is base because it has employed the majority of mankind on this planet since crops were *domesticated* yet has been the lowest paying mass *employment* known.

Weed control can be one of the most physically taxing tasks, yet typically more women are employed in weeding than men. Without weed control there is virtually no crop to harvest. The advent of *mechanization* (tractor plowing and *cultivating*) replaced much of the hand labor in the developed world as well as the *developing* parts of the third world.

Mechanical weed control is fraught with high energy costs, facilitates soil erosion and *compaction*, and has been largely replaced by chemical weed control using herbicides that can selectively eradicate weeds from crops. As countries *industrialize* and develop economically, cheap farm labor becomes *unavailable*, increasing the necessity for cost-effective chemical weed control.

Selectivity between a crop and its associated weeds is no mundane trait to find in a chemical; it is based on the immense biodiversity of metabolic *pathways* abounding in the plant kingdom. Too often there is no selective chemical that can control a *particular* weed in a particular crop, and the weed *infestations understandably* worsen based on simple ecological, genetic, and *biochemical* principles.

No single agricultural practice used *extensively* in the past to control weeds has remained as useful as initially presumed. After one weed problem is solved, there are other weed species that will fill the *ecological* vacuum left behind.

Thus, either weeds have evolved *resistance* to most *commonly* used herbicides or weed species that had never been controlled by the particular herbicide replace the weed species controlled. This is most apparent in monoculture, where weeds closely related to crops are becoming the greatest problems: grass weeds in grain crops, legumes in soybeans, brassicas in oilseed rape, etc.

As most *selectivities* between crop and weed are due to catabolic *degradation* of the herbicide by the crop, closely related weeds are to be expected to have catabolic pathways similar to those of the crop. This is one major reason that *transgenic* herbicide-resistant crops (THRCs) have become so useful and that *biotechnology* has been *utilized* to produce such crops as well as to find new herbicide targets.

Selectivity is *enhanced* by inserting *exogenous* resistance genes into the crops or by selecting natural mutations. This also leads to one major concern about T-HRCs, that the transgene will genetically *introgress* into related weeds.

These and other issues are reviewed in this chapter. A call for new concepts of using molecular biology for weed control that do not *necessarily* utilize HRC, with some possible examples for *consideration*, is made in the article from which this chapter is derived.

Indeed, it is highly *unfortunate* that a World Bank report dealing with how *molecular* biology can alleviate constraints to world food production has delineated only insects, pathogens, and lack of water as the major constraints where molecular biology can assist.

That report ignored weeds, even though the greatest variable input into *agriculture* is the cost of weed control, whether (fe)manual, *mechanical*, or chemical, with or without transgenics. And there are many unsolved weed problems lowering yields over vast areas of the world. If the weeds could be controlled, crop yields would increase without additional inputs.

CONTRIBUTIONS OF WEED SCIENCE TO BIOCHEMISTRY AND MOLECULAR BIOLOGY

It was already stated that there has been a *bidirectional* relationship often not *realized* between weed control and molecular biology and biochemistry. Most believe that the *relationship* has been *unidirectional* from biochemistry and molecular biology to the farmer.

This is hardly so. The dire need for developing cost-effective chemical weed control systems has led to a vast industrial investment to find and develop selective herbicides and later T HRCs. Virtually all herbicides marketed are the result of random *screening* of *chemicals* to obtain active leads, as the result of huge efforts of *procurement* and chemical synthesis.

Once a lead has been obtained, further syntheses around it are used to find *compounds* with greater activity and then selectivity.

After such *compounds* have been found and marketed, they *opportunistically* become widely used tools of the physiologists and biochemists, first to find the site of action and then as "*antimetabolites*" to further *understand* and modulate metabolic pathways.

Thus the advent of 2,4dichlorophenoxy acetic acid (2,4-D) assisted in *understanding* auxin action, atrazine and diuron (DCMU) in *understanding* photosystem II, paraquat for photosystem

I, *dinitroanilines* in dealing with tubulin assembly into microtubules, dichlobenil for cellulose biosynthesis, etc.

Herbicides are the *antimetabolites* of choice in dealing with key *enzymes* such as glutamine synthase (*glufosinate, phosphinothricin*), acetolactate synthase (ALS) (many herbicides), acetyl-coenzymeA (CoA) carboxylase (ACCase) (*many herbicides*), dihydropteroate synthase (*asulam*), enolpyruvate-shikimate phosphate (EPSP) synthase (*glyphosate*), phytoene desaturase (*many herbicides*). We know far more about the enzymes blocked by herbicides than most other enzymes in plants.

The genes for most of these enzymes have been isolated and used in transgenic programs. Such research transcended plant biochemistry and agriculture. For example, it was discovered through comparative genomics that plant and trypanosome β-tubulins were similar to each other and different from *mammalian* β-tubulin. The *dinitroaniline* herbicides then proved to be excellent *trypanocides*.

The repetitive (mis)use of single herbicides in monoculture over many years predictably led to the evolution of *herbicide-resistant* weeds. The advent of triazine resistance was crucial to the *understanding* of the role of the *psbA* gene product in the *photosystem* II binding site, leading to innumerable studies of photosynthesis, biophysics, and biochemistry correlated with molecular structure of the gene product.

Again, this transcended plant molecular biology and weeds when, based on this *agricultural phenomenon*, similar mutations were generated in photosynthetic bacteria. The mutant and natural *psbA* gene products were *crystallized* and analyzed, leading to new insights into *"drug"* (*ligand*) binding and design, as well as a Nobel Prize in Medicine. Information from herbicide resistance provided the theoretical underpinning for designing transient drought-resistant plants.

Harvey and Harper (1982) first promoted the idea that paraquat resistance can be similar to oxidative stress tolerance. This was later extrapolated to being similar to transient drought tolerance. This has allowed the development of quick pretests with paraquat to ascertain the level of transient drought tolerance of transgenic plants bearing genes designed to confer *oxidative* stress resistance.

Genes coding for *herbicide* resistance developed for *agriculture* became the selectable markers of choice for *generating* transgenics, *supplanting* antibiotic resistance, even when there is no plan for registering the herbicide for use in that crop.

The huge corporate *investment* in HRC and *Bacillus thuringiensis* (Bt) toxin-containing crops due to perceived market size resulted in the gain of much of our knowledge on promoters, organelle-specific and transit peptides, and more recently organelle *transformation*.

This corporate investment in basic plant molecular biology was greater than the public sector effort, and the spillover was great. Let us remember that it was market-driven *transgenic* research, and the market is for weed control.

NEEDS FOR TRANSGENICS NOT BEING MET

Because much of the basic and applied effort is market driven, the *predominant* weed problems being solved are those where *corporations* perceive maximal gain. Thus, the parasitic flowering *Striga* spp. that are claimed to decimate half the maize, sorghum, and legume yields of 100 million farmers in Africa are not considered a market.

This is despite the demonstration that genes already *available* allow selective control of these and similar parasites on transgenic crops. The genes are not even being made available by the *multinationals* to public sector researchers for crossing or insertion into African crop varieties.

There is a dire need for HR wheat and rice to enable the control of grass weeds that have evolved resistance to most graminicides (grass-killing herbicides) that can be used in these two crops. As these crops are *predominantly* cultivated with farmer-saved seed, especially in marginal areas, the commercial gain from seed sales does not attract the multinationals.

Again, many of the genes that could be used are already available and could be cheaply inserted. The cost of isolating genes and producing constructs that allow normal yields, as well as *ascertaining toxicological* safety, has already been incurred.

Introducing the same *constructs* in other crops is far less costly, but the corporate reluctance remains. Much hand labor and *mechanical* methods are still used for controlling weeds in vegetable crops, even in developed countries, because of a paucity of registered selective herbicides.

Such crops are especially adaptable to a transgenic approach using existing genes and herbicides. A large premium could be added to seed price when weed control costs are lowered, but the small market size and *minuscule* additional herbicide sales have *hampered* the registration of appropriate herbicides and have not enticed the development of such crops.

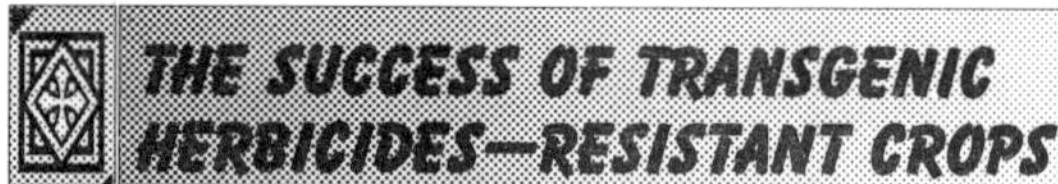

THE SUCCESS OF TRANSGENIC HERBICIDES—RESISTANT CROPS

Millions of hectares are being planted with T HRCs, with insect resistance in second place, with both traits often "*stacked*" in the same seeds to enhance their value. Farmers perceive a utility in THRCs, as they have many alternatives and still repeatedly purchase seed of THRCs.

The real values of THRCs come from instances in which there really are no viable weed control methods (*including* the *situation* due to *evolved herbicide resistances* in *weeds*) and the fact that such T HRCs could lead to more sustainable world food production.

T-HRCs are the subject of a book as well as in-depth reviews of the *molecular* aspects. The easiest way to obtain selectivity among closely related species is to engineer resistance to a general *herbicide* into the crop.

For example, it has already been shown that red rice *(Oryza sativa)* is easily controlled by glufosinate in transgenic rice bearing the *bar* gene that confers *resistance* to this herbicide. The immediate answer to multiple resistance problems in weeds of wheat in major growing areas is to engineer *resistances* to inexpensive herbicides.

Neither the chemical nor the biotechnological industries have shown *particular* interest in generating T HRCs in wheat and rice. Because too little profit is perceived to come from wheat or rice seed or even from generic herbicides, it may be necessary to have wheat and rice *engineered* by the public sector. Glufosinate resistance has been engineered into wheat, more as a marker gene than for *agronomic* utility. A request has been made for field use of glufosinate-resistant rice in the United States, which has been allowed, despite the fact that it is well known that the gene can introgress into *conspecific* red rice. BD-HR wheats and rices may be an answer to the major problems of these crops.

Insert a gene into wheat or rice conferring resistance to a *broadspectrum* herbicide and you can control weeds that evolved resistance in wheat and even closely related grasses, including red, weedy, and other wild rices.

The *transgenes* will allow overcoming the problems of resistance that have *evolved*, especially the problems of *cross-resistances* (where one evolutionary step conferred resistance to a variety of chemicals) and multiple *resistance* (where a *sequence* of evolutionary steps with different selectors conferred resistance to a variety of chemicals).

The use of nonplant *transgenes* may also allow farmers to *overcome* the natural resistances in weeds closely related to the crop. One can even choose bacterial genes for inexpensive *long-established* herbicides such as dalapon, modify them for plant codon usage, and transform them into grain crops.

Such genes have the advantage that it is harder, albeit not *impossible*, for the weeds to mimic bacteria than to mimic plants in evolving resistance. The problems of interclass cross-resistances and multiple resistances in wheat have necessitated *considering* generating BD-HR oilseed rape, especially in Australia.

Oilseed rape has become an *excellent* rotational crop, alternating with wheat in many places where wheat is grown. There are many agronomic advantages to rotating a dicot with a monocot, *especially* vis-a-vis weeds. It should be far easier to *eliminate* grass weeds in oilseed rape than in wheat, as there are more selective graminicides available for use in dicot crops.

This is usually correct except in Australia, where *Lolium rigidum* has *successfully* evolved *widespread* target site and intergroup cross-resistances as well as multiple *resistances* to all these graminicides (although not in all fields). It is *additionally* necessary to generate BDHR oilseed rape *(Brassica napus)* to allow control of closely related *Brassica* weeds including those such as *Raphanus raphanistrum.*

Here we can make the case for the need for *management* strategies with T HRCs as with any selective herbicide. Atrazine-resistant BD-HR oilseed rape was widely and exclusively used to control *R. raphanistrum* in Australia. It was generated by backcrossing the gene in from a mutant *B. campestris* that evolved in Canada.

Inevitably, there are reports that this weed has evolved resistance to triazines as well as resistance to ALS inhibitors and to diflufenican. Thus, one must engineer resistance into oilseed rape that allows control of both *Lolium rigidum* and *Raphanus raphanistrum,* with all their resistances.

To delay further resistances to the few *remaining* herbicides, perhaps gene stacking and using herbicide mixtures are necessary. Only the first generations of BD-HCRs have been released, and considerable *improvements* are to be expected.

There are far too few concrete molecular and biochemical data published about the properties of these crops, and thus there are problems in *evaluating* their properties to allow suggestions for *improvements*. Thus, some of what will be said here should be considered speculative.

Two types of genes have been used to generate herbicide-resistant crops: those whose gene product detoxifies the herbicide and those for which the herbicide target has been modified such that it no longer binds the herbicide.

One could envisage other types such as *exclusionary mechanisms* or *sequestration*, but they have yet to be found and thus not utilized. The resulting T HRCs with each type of *resistance* are rather different and thus will be discussed separately.

Metabolically Resistant THRCs

Many crops bearing *transgenes* coding for highly specific enzymes that *metabolically* catabolize herbicides have been generated. These include, for example, bromoxynil resistance crops bearing a nitrilase, *glufosinate* resistance crops bearing an *acetyltransferase*, 2,4-D-resisting crops bearing a highly specific soluble cytochrome P-450 *monooxygenase phenmidipham*-resisting crops bearing a bacterial gene, and dalapon-resisting crops bearing a dehalogenase.

Of these, only the *bromoxynil-* and *glufosinate-resistant* crops have reached *commercialization*. All of the genes used commercially are of bacterial or *actinomycete* origin, despite the fact that plants contain genes for herbicide resistance, which is the basis for most natural metabolic *selectivities* used for 45 years.

Nevertheless, plant genes conferring metabolic resistance have not yet been used commercially. There are reports on using *nonprokaryotic* genes to confer resistance, but none of this work is yet commercial, and whether they confer sufficient resistance is not clear.

A rabbit esterase gene conferred resistance to *thiazopyr* via degradation. The expression of plant and animal P-450 transgenes conferred *phenylurea* resistance. Transgenes encoding maize *glutathione* transferases increased the level of herbicide resistance.

Unlike the target site resistances that are fraught with problems, the crops *generated* with metabolic *resistances* seem to be problem free, with little metabolic load conferred by generating the small amount of enzyme needed.

The toxicology is simplified because the transgene product typically initiates a cascade of events whereby the herbicide eventually disappears. There has been an *assumption* that one cannot use catabolic *enzymes* to confer resistance to fast-acting herbicides.

This view is of doubtful relevance as biotechnologists should be able to perform as well as plants. Inhibitors of *protoporphyrinogen* IX oxidase (protox), which actually cause the *accumulation* of the *photodynamically* toxic product, induce *photodynamic* death of plants within 4-6 hours in bright sunlight.

Beans are immune to some members of this group, e.g., acifluorfen, because they possess a specific *homoglutathione transferase* and contain enough *homoglutathione* to degrade these herbicides *stoichiometrically* before they can damage the crop.

Similarly, strains of *Conyza bonariensis* contain a complex of enzymes capable of *detoxifying* the reactive oxygen species generated by the photosystem I blocker paraquat and keeping the plants alive until the paraquat is dissipated.

As almost all herbicides are degraded either in the soil or in some plant species, one should be able to find more genes for catabolic resistance to those *herbicides* and then rapidly generate *herbicide-resistant* crops with metabolic resistance rather than with target site resistance.

Target Site Resistant Crops

Biotechnology has been used to generate target site HRC crops by two means-transfer of field- or laboratory-generated mutants into crop varieties by genetic means or *transgenically*. One must assume a fitness penalty with any target site HRC.

This is simply due to the fact that if the resistant mutation was neutral or very nearly neutral there would be naturally resistant *populations preexisting* in the wild due to Sewall Wright drift. As all the mutations were found at a low frequency, one in a million or less, the resistant traits are not near neutral fitness.

This was most obvious with triazine resistance, which was crossed from weedy populations of *Brassica campestris (=B. rapa)* that evolved resistance into oilseed rape *(B. napa)*. This *psbA* gly264ser mutation is plastid inherited, allowing *researchers* to test fitness in the near-isonuclear eighth backcross, and in isonuclear reciprocal hybrids.

There was a consistent 20% productivity loss when the crop was grown alone and a much greater fitness loss when the resistant biotypes were grown in *competition* with the sensitive biotype. A 20% yield loss does not mean that such crops are without value; this *triazine-resistant* oilseed rape is widely grown in Australia because some *pernicious* weeds can be *inexpensively* controlled.

Still, the triazine-resistant varieties will probably eventually be *supplanted* by *transgenics*, which do not have the fitness penalty. Despite a plethora of papers claiming no fitness penalty in acetolactate synthase mutant and transgenic plants, elegant *experiments* by Bergelson et al. with transgenic *Arabidopsis* did indeed show that such a penalty exists.

Previous competitive fitness experiments started with transplants and/or did not measure seed output. The two most competitive phases in a plant's life cycle are establishment, when large populations of seedlings self-thin to a single plant per parent, and fertilization, when thousands of pollen grains compete on stigma and through style.

If competition is not measured seed to seed, then the fitness penalty is unknown. The natural resistance mutations to ALS and ACCase derived from maize tissue *cultures* or via pollen mutagenesis and then backcrossed into inbreds seem to have produced normally *yielding* hybrids. There have been more *problems* with the *transgenics* than the mutants, as successful as they have been in the marketplace.

The magnitude of resistance with *transgenics* is not as high as it is with the natural mutations, with both ALS and EPSP synthase target site resistances. The first single-site mutant prololser EPSP synthase transgenic plants tested were *insufficiently* resistant to *glyphosate* for field use.

Thus, considerable effort was made to increase the level of resistance and repair the huge shift in K_m toward natural substrates by both adding second site-directed *mutations* as well as enhanced promoters. The necessity to do this was the basis for the claimed invincibility of glyphosate-resistant crops from evolving resistance in weeds; it would take too many *simultaneous mutations* for resistance to evolve. This thesis was published after there was already known natural metabolic resistance in legumes as well as natural resistance due to enhanced levels of the target enzyme in *Lotus corniculatus*. These flaws in the invincibility theory were pointed out by Dyer (1994) and reiterated and updated by Gressel (1996).

The only difference that could be found between a recently evolved glyphosate-resistant *Lolium rigidum* population having a sevenfold increase in the I50 value and the wild type was the presence of a doubled level of EPSP synthase.

Lotus corniculatus with a doubled level of EPSP synthase also had a *sevenfold* increase in glyphosate resistance. This is not the only case in which it has been possible to confer *herbicide* resistance by *overexpression* of the gene encoding its target site. Glufosinate resistance was achieved in tissue culture by this means with *overproduction* of glutamine synthase.

Similarly, poplars were *transformed* for elevated glutamine synthase to enhance nitrogen utilization. The transgenic poplars are more resistant to *glufosinate* than the wild type (F. M. Canovas, personal *communication*). In addition, transgenic tobacco plants with fivefold *overexpression* of *protoporphyrinogen* IX oxidase in chloroplasts are resistant to a discriminatory dose of 20 μM acifluorfen, which severely inhibited the wild type.

Unfortunately, in the latter case there are no *quantitative* data on the magnitude of resistance. The nail in the coffin of *invincibility* came with the *identification* of glyphosate-resistant *Eleucine indica* in Malaysia. This material was resistant to far greater than typical field application rates of *glyphosate*.

It was disclosed that this material bore a target site resistance to *glyphosate*. The single mutation in the binding domain of this material was at a position equivalent to the pro 101 ser in the *Salmonella typhimurium aroA* resistance gene, the same position that was regarded as insufficiently resistant in trangenic resistant genes.

In retrospect, there is good reason to expect that transgenics will be less resistant than target site mutants bearing the same transversion. Recurrent selection of a natural mutant will select for *homozygous* resistant individuals. This cannot happen with the present generation of transgenics. They bear and express both the native and transgenic *enzymes* (although the ratios of the two have never been *published* to the best of my knowledge).

Thus, transgenic plants with target site resistance are functionally heterozygous and will remain so despite recurrent selection. Homozygosity can be achieved at present only when totally *exogenous* genes such as those for metabolic resistance are used, as they do not compete with native genes.

When the *herbicide* is applied, target site HRC must depend on the transgenic derived enzyme while the native is inhibited, perhaps even causing *phytotoxic precursors* to accumulate. There have been *continuing* problems with some glyphosate-resistant crops, *suggesting* that the critical balance of transgenic and native enzymes is not optimal.

Initial varieties of maize, about to be released 4 years ago, were retracted because late-season herbic-ide application caused pollen sterility. Similar problems of obtaining vegetative (only) *glyphosate-resistant* cotton plants continue to plague cotton growers. The period of pollen production is well known to be subject to *inhibition* by minor chemical, metabolic, or *environmental* perturbations. There have been reports of stem brittleness and cracking of untreated glyphosate-resistant soybeans, suggesting an overproduction of product leading to increased lignin formation when both the native and transgene-derived enzymes are operative. One does not know whether such glyphosate-resistant transgenic plants are transiently weakened until the herbicide is dissipated.

This period after glyphosate application is analogous to sublethal treatments of nontransgenic plants with glyphosate. When legumes are given sublethal applications of glyphosate, they are unable to produce *phytoalexins* after elicitation and are far more susceptible to disease.

A study *purporting* to ascertain whether phytoalexin biosynthesis was *compromised* after glyphosate treatment of glyphosate-resistant soybeans was artifactual. The authors measured only constitutive levels of glyceollin, without elicitation, and their *conclusions*, concerning *phytoalexins*, which are by definition elicited, are without basis. There are at least two apparent solutions to the problems arising from the functional *heterozygote* status of transgenic target site resistant plants.

One solution is to try to enhance the metabolism of the herbicide, obviating the problem. This may have been done using the gox gene coding for an enzyme-degrading *glyphosate* together with target site resistance. There are no data indicating how quickly the *transformants* degraded the glyphosate in this case. A better solution might be to begin with a "clean slate."

Target site resistant plants should be generated via replacement, i.e., in plants that have had the native gene deleted or functionally irreversibly "knocked out." This can be done by classical deletion mutagenesis with ultraviolet (UV) or gamma *irradiation*, but this causes multiple lesions and the screening for *particular* mutants is not easy. Molecular techniques show far more promise as they are more "surgical," i.e., there is less likelihood of multiple deletions along a *chromosome*, leading to complications from linked deletions. These *techniques* include T-DNA tagging and transposon *mutagenesis*.

There are an estimated 3000 genes that might be target sites of herbicides, giving mutations that will have to be rescued by the specific gene products of interest as the selectable markers. The most elegant new technique is with specific viral vectors spliced to the gene to be silenced.

After cloning into the crop, some "*black magic*" mechanism virus-induced gene silencing turns off both the viral and the *endogenous* gene. At least one of the virus vectors used is *transmitted* through seeds and by pollen, so following *generations* remain with the gene suppressed, but whether the gene is never reactivated is not certain.

After the native gene is suppressed, it should be possible to obtain *transgenics* with various levels of *transgene* expression in functional homozygotes and choose those with the optimal expression level for agricultural release. The gene used may have to be very different in sequence from the native gene as viral-induced gene silencing can suppress the native gene.

RESISTANCE MANAGEMENT—THE NEED FOR STACKED GENES

Probably >10 million ha of agricultural lands are infested with weeds that are resistant to one or more classes of diverse herbicide chemistry. Proactive resistance *management* is finally being considered; previously, there was a smug *assumption* that industry would continue to develop many new chemicals.

Now there is a realization that T-HRC is almost all there will be that is new for a long while, and measures should be instituted to delay weeds from evolving *resistance*. One way to delay the evolution of *herbicide* resistance in weeds is to stack two genes for herbicide resistance and require that the farmers use only a mixture of herbicides.

This is useful because it considerably lowers the mutation frequency for *resistance* in the weed. For example, if the frequency of resistance to one herbicide is 10^{-6} and the other 10^{-8}, the resistance to them stacked together is 10^{-14} on condition that both *herbicides* are used.

The use of stacking is very important where one wishes to preserve the ability of an excellent herbicide such as glyphosate and one has a pernicious weed with a *propensity* to evolve resistance, e.g., *Lolium rigidum* in Australia. There are two hazards that must be assessed with glyphosate and other BD-HR wheats: the risk of grass weeds such as *Lolium rigidum* evolving resistance to the herbicide and the risk of *introgression* of the gene into related weeds.

If glyphosate resistance is to be engineered into wheat, it should be stacked with a gene coding for resistance to a second unrelated *graminicide*. The herbicide mixtures should always be used when such wheat is cultivated.

Glyphosate used alone will clearly further engender evolution of *glyphosate* resistance, and/or bring about a shift in weed spectra toward weeds that have never been controlled by glyphosate. The use of stacked BDHR wheat and herbicide mixtures should delay the resistance of *Lolium* to glyphosate.

The risk of *introgression* of stacked genes into wheat-related weeds will be discussed later. When stacked resistance genes and herbicide mixtures are used, it is possible that there will be cases of enhanced weed control by the mixture.

Still, some mixtures may be contraindicated vis-a-vis resistance *management*. Simply combining herbicides with different modes of action will not result in delaying *resistance* if the efficacy and temporal activity *characteristics* of the mixed herbicides do not match. Both mixing partners must effectively inhibit the weeds most sensitive to the *vulnerable* herbicide because the greater selection pressure weed species are the most likely to evolve target site resistance.

Resistance could quickly evolve in a weed species that is naturally resistant to one of the *herbicides* in a mixture. The components of the mixture need to have similar persistence or the mixing partner with a low mutation *frequency* must have longer persistence than the vulnerable one with a high mutation frequency of resistance.

Otherwise, there will be a period when only the vulnerable partner is present, and it will select for resistance in the target weed as if there were no mixture at all. This would be the case when a persistent resistance-vulnerable ALS inhibitor is mixed with a short-lived phenoxy herbicide.

Unlike crops, which have been selected to *germinate* uniformly shortly after planting, seeds of many weed species display many flushes of *germination* during a cropping season. If a resistance-prone weed species has multiple flushes during the season and the vulnerable herbicide has a longer period of activity than the mixing partner does, then the *vulnerable* herbicide selects for *individuals* resistant only to it after the mixing partner has dissipated.

A mixture that is not well matched for persistence can still be effective if all the weeds *germinate* over a short period of time and both herbicides outlast the *germination*. The ideal mixing partner should have three other properties in addition to equal persistence:

1. It should have a different target site of action from the vulnerable herbicide.
2. The mixing partner should not be degraded in the same manner as the vulnerable herbicide. For example, if the vulnerable herbicide is degraded in the crop by a glutathione transferase, the mixing partner should have no chemical site that can be attacked by the same enzyme.
3. Another useful attribute in a mixing partner would be to possess negative cross-resistance, i.e., where individuals resistant to the vulnerable herbicide are more susceptible to the mixing partner than the wild type. This would actually reduce the frequency of resistant alleles in the weed population. This strategy was first proposed for herbicides on the basis of laboratory data, and *information* on the existence of negative cross-resistance has been published at the whole plant level.

INTROGRESSION OF TRANSGENES FROM CROPS TO WEEDS

We have been warned that THRCs can lead to the evolution of "superweeds" that will inherit the earth. The rapid commercial release of such crops has often been without broad-based scientific scrutiny with the most competent experts being involved, and there is little published *physiological, biochemical, ecological, genetic,* and agronomic data to scrutinize.

This leads to a certain degree of skepticism among scientists, which contributes to the public *questioning* the needs, utility, risks, and values associated with the use of T HRCs. The severe pressures by detracting groups on policy makers make it politically incorrect to pursue public sector research in this area, which prejudices the ability to perform *experiments* to obtain accurate *information* about the risks.

These pressures also prevent *generating* crops needing resistance to *herbicides* where the agrochemical or seed industry perceives little profit. Herbicide-resistant rice and wheat can be of great benefit only if used with care to prevent or mitigate gene transfer to related feral and wild rices and related weeds of wheat such as *Aegilops cylindrica.*

Whereas the wild and feral rices are widely distributed, *A. cylindrica* has a relatively narrow distribution, although it can be quite pernicious. No solution in agriculture has been forever; farmers have always had to deal with evolution. More sophistication will be needed than is presently being used with transgenic wheat and rice to mitigate *introgression* delaying such *evolution.* Discussions of T-HRCs have rarely dealt with the risks from a weed biology perspective.

The main risk stated by the detractors is claimed to be that of the T-HRCs becoming "volunteer" weeds (in following crops) or their introgressing traits into a wild relative, rendering it weedier: the superweeds of the mass media. An attempt at such an *assessment* based on weed science was made using a defined set of uniform criteria in a decision tree format.

Decision trees, by requiring discrete answers to sequential, stepped questions, lower the bias in arriving at conclusions vis-a-vis the risks deriving from a given hazard. Conversely, there are wild species that are unlikely ever to become weeds unless they evolve a large number of weedy traits.

Unfortunately, too many risk studies do not *differentiate* between weedy relatives of crops and wild relatives. Risk *assessment* must be performed on a local or regional basis, as the risks from the same T-HRC will vary greatly from one agricultural ecosystem to another.

A second assessment should be done (but has not been done in the past) about the effects of introgression from *transgenic* crops on weed flora of countries that import bulk *unprocessed* commodities such as wheat and oilseed rape. The risks of *introgression* have been assessed on a case-by-case basis by regulatory *authorities*.

The Canadians delineated criteria before even having to evaluate plants with novel traits, whether or not transgenic, and then specifically evaluated oilseed rape in the context of these criteria. In a series of documents they further evaluated oilseed rapes resistant to *imidazolinone*, glyphosate, and glufosinate.

The decision process was based on their perception of the risks to the regional agricultural ecosystems in western Canada, without considering other regions that may be *importing* the crops. *Internationally*, the OECD (*Organization* for *Economic Cooperation* and Development) and UNIDO (United Nations Industrial Development Organization) are *developing* a series of *consensus* documents on the biology of various crops (with regard also to related weeds) so that there is a common starting point to evaluate each cropping situation.

Most of the stated hazards of interspecific introgression from T-HRCs are based on *unpredictive* laboratory *experiments*, which prove that introgressions could occur. Thus, they show that the hazard exists but give little indication of risk: how quickly such transfers will occur in the field or how fit recipients will be to cope with *competition* in a multfactorial situation.

The time factor is not *inconsequential*; if resistance introgresses to produce resistant populations more slowly than natural mutational evolution of resistance, what is the significance of introgression?

Vertical, Horizontal, and Diagonal Gene Transfer

Two types of gene transfer are widely discussed: (1) vertical, within a species, and (2) *horizontal*, transfer among unrelated species, usually by asexual means. Biology is not as clear-cut; there can be some sexual transfer between plant species in the same genus and closely related genera.

These are *typically* included in *discussions* of introgression as *horizontal* gene transfer. Horizontal gene transfer via plasmids is common in prokaryotic organisms. Because extrapolations are often made from these rare cases of gene transfer among closely related species to "*prove*" that all horizontal transfers are possible, I suggest terming these special interspecific cases in plants as "*diagonal*" gene transfer, denoting the gray area where they exist.

Vertical and diagonal transfer *possibilities* are obvious to any biologists, but *horizontal* transfers, in eukaryotes, with their potentially disastrous *implications* for *agriculture* are not. The possibilities of true *horizontal* transfers are *extrapolated* from the intergeneric and interfamilial plasmid-mediated transfer of traits among *microorganisms*, which have allowed transfer of antibiotic resistance (*analogous to herbicide resistance*) among unrelated pathogens.

The claim continues that because plasmids are often used as vectors in the genetic engineering of crops, interfamilial transfers will become commonplace or at least inevitable. This claim does not stand up to *epidemiological* experience with organisms such as *Agrobacterium tumefaciens* and *A. rhizogenes.*

The plasmids used for laboratory gene transfers from these *Agrobacterium* spp. naturally infect a broad range of dicots, using the plasmid as part of the infection process. If such interfamilial transfers were to occur via *Agrobacterium,* they would have been seen over the past 50 years with naturally occurring herbicide resistances.

There are no known cases where such genes have transferred *interfamiliarly* from any crop to weed via *Agrobacterium,* despite the great selective advantages that such weeds would have and the ubiquity of *Agrobacterium* in the environment. The more than 10 million hectares of herbicide-resistant weeds that have appeared in the past 30 years can all be traced to *evolution* resulting from mutant selection, not to plasmid-mediated *horizontal* gene transfer.

In addition, an extensive survey of the GenBank database found few *Agrobacterium* DNA sequence pieces in any of the plant genes, which would have been expected in the millions of years of cohabitation. This matching task took hundreds of hours of computer time.

Horizontal gene transfer need not be discussed further; diagonal gene transfer is a hazard for which the risks must be estimated in particular cases.

Generalizing from Hazards to Risks

Because of the genetic variability of crops and weeds and the chemical *variability* in herbicides having different effects and modes of action, one cannot make easy *generalizations* about the risks of introgression of resistance.

Each case needing a prediction of the risk of *introgression* must be evaluated on its merits, often after basic biological, genetic, and *epidemiological* studies. More important, other issues must be considered:

1. What is the benefit to agriculture of introducing resistance into a certain crop, especially in management of evolved herbicide resistance in weeds?
2. What are the possibilities of, and implications of, having herbicide resistance pass from the crop into a weedy or wild species?
3. What are the possibilities of and implications of having the THRC becoming a volunteer resistant weed in agricultural ecosystems or become an alien weed in ruderal or more pristine ecosystems?

The final decision on risk/benefit ratio is *ultimately* a balance between science, economics, local benefits, local values, pressure groups, and local politics. The politicians often misuse or ignore science for clearly political decisions.

Still, there is good reason that the criteria for risk assessment for T-HRCs should be uniform, using universal criteria and processes of examination.

Risks of Introgression of Transgenes to Related Weeds

In most of the world there can be virtually no risk of transgenes carrying herbicide resistance moving from crop to related weeds in such major crops as maize, soybeans, potatoes, and cotton. Outside the centers of origin, there are no related weeds or even remotely *interbreeding* wild species that could become weeds.

Clearly, *experimentation* would be required in the centers of origin to assay the risk, but these centers represent a minuscule portion of the areas where these crops are grown. Genes from wheat easily introgress into the genomes of some related wild species, wild species that are related to the progenitors of domestic wheat.

There is much *information* on introgression of genes from hexaploid wheat into *Aegilops cylindrica,* a very problematic weed in the western plain states and the Pacific northwest of the United States. This species shares a D genome with *hexaploid* wheat, and homologous *recombination* occurs naturally under field conditions.

It would theoretically be much harder to obtain transfer resistance from AABB tetraploid (durum) wheat to this species, as durum lacks the D genome. Thus, homeologous recombination (*crossing over between related but dissimilar chromosomes*) would have to occur when herbicide-resistant durum is used.

Genes for various traits have been transferred from many wild grasses to domestic wheat, especially from the genus *Aegilops.* Many *Aegilops* species are in fact considered to be *Triticum* species. The only other *Aegilops* sp. besides A. *cylindrica* known to have a wheathomologous genome is A. *squarrosa = Triticum tauschii.*

Only *homeologous recombination* can occur between hexaploid and durum wheats with the other less-related species. It takes much more than a single gene, even one for herbicide resistance, to turn a wild species into a weed. The risks of *introgression* of transgenes from wheat to these wild species are very low, even though breeders have moved them.

Many intergeneric hybrids generated by breeders do not occur in the field; natural alleles have not passed from wheat to wild, related but mainly ruderal species and vice versa. The breeders have to resort to forced crosses and then use techniques such as embryo rescue in tissue culture to save the hybrid embryos that would otherwise abort. Most oilseed rapes cultivated *are Brassica napus,* a recent tetraploid derived from the CC genome of *B. oleracea* and the AA genome of *B. campestris = B. rapa.*

Thus, the only weed where *homologous recombination* can occur is *B. campestris.* Still, homeologous recombination is known, especially in the laboratory, with many related species. *Interspecifically* this required hand pollination after emasculation of the weed, male sterility or self-incompatibility in the weed, massive amounts of crop pollen, and/or embryo rescue of the rare progeny, which are mostly sterile or runts.

Initially, the general fear of T-HRCs precluded *performing* such *experiments* in the field, especially in Europe, where the public fears are greatest. This hysteria prevents obtaining field data that might *substantiate* or more likely allay the fears of introgression.

A large-scale field experiment in Australia found no *introgression* from oilseed rape to the related *Raphanus raphanistrum.* The significance of laboratory introgression studies to the field situation was evaluated by Kareiva et al. (1996). The older epidemiological or apocryphal reports are actually more relevant to risk analysis than many of the artificial laboratory experiments; the older results could indicate that such transfers can occur in the field as well as the time until *predominance* and the competitive advantage (if any) of such introgressions.

Few studies dare to estimate comparatively how long it will take to have resistance introgress and predominate in field weed populations versus how long it would take resistance to evolve by natural selection versus the expected *commercial* lifetime of the herbicide.

It has already been shown that transgenic *glufosinate* resistance can be transferred genetically from rice to red rice. How easily this will occur in the field is unclear, as rice is predominately *selfpollinated*, before flower opening. Less is clear about the other rice species.

Rice is a species for which there is far too little field information despite considerable information in the breeders' and *cytogeneticists'* laboratories. Cultivated rice *Oryza sativa* has an AA genome, as does the red and many feral forms of weedy rice that are also *Oryza sativa*.

Genes readily move between the cultivated and feral forms despite rice being *predominantly* self-pollinating. There are many wild and weedy rice species, one of which, *O. rufipogon*, has an AA genome and is considered a major weed of rice. Another major weedy rice, *O. officinalis*, has a CC genome.

There are many other diploid and tetraploid wild (but not weedy) rices bearing genomes through the alphabet from AA to HHJJ. It is possible to transfer genes from many of these wild and weedy species to rice, which is how the breeders introduce new traits, despite the chromosomal incompatibilities. This often requires embryo rescue and/or intermediate crosses through bridge species.

The significance of this to field problems is unclear. The taxonomic *differentiation* among these species is also rather unclear. In many places where weedy rices are even major problems, it is not known whether the weeds are the conspecific red and feral forms or the other species.

Indeed, studies have shown that the material in genetic resource *depositories* has been misclassified. Much of this ambiguity will be clarified by modern molecular *taxonomic* techniques using DNA *fingerprinting*, so that better predictions can be made of risk in different locales.

Assaying Introgression in the Field

There are ways to ascertain the rapidity of gene movement without causing lasting damage to agriculture and/or the *environment*: simply insert a gene *conferring* resistance to a rarely used herbicide. There would be little consequence of the herbicide becoming unusable due to the resistance *disseminating* into the wild, as herbicides are not used on wild *populations*.

Another tracing system could be used with acetolactate synthase (ALS) resistance. At present, if a weed becomes resistant to any ALS herbicide, it cannot be known whether it evolved resistance naturally by mutation or was introgressed through *cross-pollination* with a nontransgenic THRC. The highly mutable ALS gene (10^{-6} natural resistance frequency in populations) quickly evolves naturally in weeds.

Engineering the same ALS allele either with a two-base-change coding difference from the natural resistance allele or with different introns would allow easy *differentiation* between mutational events and introgression. This would indicate the rate of evolution due to *introgression* versus the rate of evolution from natural mutation.

Triazine resistance has been found to be *maternally* inherited in many species, so one might assume it will never introgress from crops to weeds. Maternal inheritance is not absolute; 0.4% pollen transfer of triazine resistance was found with genetic markers in weeds and 0.5% for tentoxin resistance in tobacco.

Maternal *inheritance* of chloroplast-encoded traits is typical, but there are many cases in higher species, including some crops where such traits are *biparentally* inherited. Corriveau and Coleman (1988) developed a rapid cytological assay to screen for *biparental* inheritance, which they did not find in the major *agronomic* crops but did find in sweet potato, chickpea, vetch, alfalfa, common beans, and geranium. In all, they found evidence for biparental inheritance in 14% of the 192 plant species assayed.

Their evidence and the genetic evidence they cite would not have found the 0.4% paternal *inheritance* described by Darmency (1994b). Thus, it will be necessary to ascertain frequencies of paternal *inheritance* with each crop situation where maternal *inheritance* is predominant. There is a good chance that more pollen transmission will be found with herbicide resistance, and the estimates will be more accurate.

Herbicide resistance is a better selectable marker than those previously available to the geneticists dealing with chioroplast inheritance, and because of the field size *experiments*, the numbers of plants tested will be much larger than had been possible. Polymerase chain reaction (PCR) *amplification* of chioroplast primers *discriminates* between *Brassica napus* and *B. rapa = campestris* in the —0.6% natural hybrids that occur between the two species.

A low number of hybrids were *examined*, and all were indicative of maternal inheritance. It would have been far more interesting if they had used chloroplast DNA encoded triazine resistance, using a *semidominant* nuclear marker to verify the hybrid nature of random field crosses of both species. The analysis would be far easier and could be confirmed by PCR *amplification. Susceptible* weeds growing among THRCs will not introgress the resistance genes if the herbicide is used; dead weeds do not have sex, but the genes could introgress into nearby unsprayed weeds.

Seed set on *emasculated* plants from oilseed rape was measured 1.5 km from the pollen source, but can the progeny compete or survive in feral populations without a selector? Without emasculation of the recipient, resistant pollen fertilized 24% of *conspecific* plants in the immediate vicinity but <0.027% just 10 m away.

If THRC seeds carry over as volunteers to other crops where related species are serious weeds, gene exchange might happen through this route and long-distance dispersal becomes *unnecessary*. Many weed scientists were *surprised* that the Canadian authorities allowed the field use of ALS inhibitors, glyphosate, glufosinate, (and soon) *bromoxynil-engineered transgenic* oilseed rapes.

The surprise was due to the known introgression of herbicide-resistant genes into weeds, *including* the problematic *Brassica campestris = B. rapa. Brassica campestris* has been *domesticated* to become various crops in many places (Polish oilseed rape, turnip, Chinese cabbage, and pak choi). The more ancient conspecific wild form as well as the feral forms are pernicious weeds in other areas.

While *botanically* identical, they have very different *morphotypes*, with very different phenologies, biologies, and competitiveness. Most of the *B. campestris* crop types are easily controlled in fields, and as easily controlled volunteer weeds they have never left *agricultural* or ruderal areas.

Their botanically but not phenotypically identical weedy twin can be very *problematic* in *agroecosystems* and was a predominant weed in grains before the advent of selective herbicides. It is hard to predict what will become of the feral *populations* of Polish oilseed rape, which still remain ruderal.

They could evolve to become more weedy. Deleterious weed gene *introgression* from feral *populations* is common into both commercial oilseed rapes, lowering yield and oil quality. A major use of herbicide-resistant oilseed rapes is to facilitate control of its wild relatives.

The Canadian *authorities* subjected *nontransgenic* ALS-resistant oilseed rape derived by *mutagenesis* to full regulatory scrutiny before release to the market. Their decisions allow unrestricted field *cultivation*, while noting the likelihood of introgression into *B. campestris* and stating that the worst case would be the loss of the particular herbicide to control such weeds.

The decision, partly based on release studies, stated that introgression would not increase weediness of the crop or related weeds outside agriculture. *B. campestris* is the weediest of species related to oilseed rape and the one species with demonstrated field transfer of genes, but not quite as readily as initially presumed.

No formal or informal *monitoring* system was instituted. This is *unfortunate* as much has been written on how *comparatively* easy it is to eradicate small pest populations and how impossible it is after they have reached a critical size, yet few learn these lessons. Instead, a survey has shown widespread *introgression* of herbicide resistance traits among the various volunteer *herbicide-resistant* oilseed rape populations in western Canada.

Many volunteer populations already contain all the three released herbicide *resistances,* to *ALSinhibiting* herbicides, glufosinate, and glyphosate resistances.

The regulatory system cannot preclude *reintroducing* triazine-resistant varieties, and possibly could not prevent the use of 2,4-D-resistant varieties if such were generated from known transgenes because each case is considered on its own merits.

There soon could be *"volunteer"* weed populations of oilseed rape in *subsequent* crops in rotational cycles that cannot be *controlled* by any herbicides available in the farmers' arsenal.

There is clear reason to consider requiring the use of certified seed for all plantings along with a *requirement* that the certified seed contains a single herbicide-resistant gene, unless there is a premeditated reason for stacking and a requirement for the use of herbicide mixtures.

The question of how quickly *resistance* genes will move from *B. nap us* to *B. campestris* may be moot, as Polish oilseed rape *(B. campestris)* with various herbicide resistance genes has also been released in western Canada.

The crop as a volunteer weed could become a problem, especially if it also becomes multiply resistant via cross-breeding to all four herbicides introduced in various varieties.

PREVENTING AND MITIGATING INTROGRESSION FROM THRCS TO WEEDS

There are various failsafe mechanisms that can be used to prevent or mitigate the risk of introgression, when and if it does occur. These vary from *management* practices (weed-free zones around transgenic crops) to techniques that involve breeding or more *biotechnology*.

Those using a *transgenic* approach are discussed here, but other approaches such as using apomyxis are also conceivable.

Gene Placement Failsafes

The particular placement of a transgene in crop genomes can affect its movement to other varieties and species.

Chromosomal

Wheat and oilseed rape are composed of multiple genomes derived from different wild sources. In any given locale it is possible that only one of the genomes of the crop is identical to that of a related weed, allowing easy gene transfer. As the D genome of wheat is compatible with the D genome of *Aegilops cylindrica* and the B genome of oilseed rape with many brassica weeds, transgenes easily introgress from them to wild species.

One can perform the cytogenetic localization to ensure that the transgene is on the incompatible A or B genomes of wheat or the C genome of oilseed rape and then ascertain whether there is no *homeologous introgression*, i.e., crossing over between the *nonhomologous chromosomes*.

There is evidence, though, for a considerable extent of homeologous *introgression* between oilseed rape and *B. campestris*, so there is no utility in this type of failsafe in oilseed rape, but there is little information for assessing *homeologous* wheat *introgression* into *Aegilops cylindrica*.

Hybrids

A simple failsafe can be found with hybrid crops. If a dominant transgene for herbicide resistance is placed in the male sterile line in close linkage with the male sterility gene, there will be no possibility of *introgression* in crop production areas.

Care will have to be taken only in the seed production areas when the male sterile line is restored. Such areas must be kept free of related weeds, a typical *precaution* in seed production generally practiced before the advent of transgenics.

Plastome or Chondriome

If the transgene for herbicide resistance is placed on the *mitochondrial* or plastid genomes, as has been done in tobacco, there should be limited possibility of gene flow, due to the *maternal inheritance* of these genomes. Species such as tobacco that are often claimed to have no paternal *inheritance* often have about 0.1-0.5% pollen transfer of traits.

The risk of transgenes being established in related populations is far greater with herbicide-resistant traits where the herbicide exerts *selection* pressure, than traits such as *production* of medicinals, with other traits in between.

Largescale experiments should be performed with such crops to ensure that the level of paternal transfer of traits is sufficiently low to justify using this strategy, and the risk analysis must consider the *transformed* traits.

Transient Transgenics

It would be conceivable to insert certain metabolic traits (e.g., catabolic herbicide resistance) on RNA viruses or in endomycorrhizae that are expressed in the plant but are not carried through meiosis into reproductive cells. One would have to transfect the crop every *generation*, but the transgenes could not spread sexually.

Transgenetic Mitigation (TM)

Genetic *engineering* can be used to mitigate any positive survival traits *transgenes* may confer. If the herbicide resistance gene engineered into the crop is flanked on either side by a TM gene in a tandem construct, the overall effect would be deleterious to weeds *introgressing* the construct from a crop. This is based on three premises:

1. Tandem constructs of genes act genetically as tightly linked genes and their segregation from each other is exceedingly rare.
2. There are traits that are either neutral or positive for a crop that would be deleterious to a typical or volunteer weed, or to a wild species.
3. Because weeds are strongly competitive among themselves and have large seed outputs, individuals bearing even mildly deleterious traits are quickly eliminated from populations. Even if one of the TM alleles mutates, is deleted, or crosses over, the other flanking TM gene will remain, providing mitigation.

TM traits that could be used are best visualized when observing the differences between crops and weeds. This is best illustrated with two cases: (1) wheat and weedy relatives and (2) oilseed rape *(Brassica napus)* and feral and weedy Polish rape/wild radish *B. campestris = B. rapa*, as summarized in the following.

Traits for Transgenetic Mitigation

Seed Dormancy

Weed seeds typically have secondary dormancy with seeds from one harvest *germinating* throughout the following season and over a number of years. This evolutionary trait is considered to be a risk-spreading strategy that *maximizes* fitness while reducing losses due to sib competition. Staggered secondary dormancy prevents all the weeds from being controlled by a single agronomic procedure.

However, crops have lost secondary dormancy as a result of domestication. Genetically abolishing secondary dormancy would be neutral to both crops but deleterious to their related weeds. Tillage, crop rotation, and preplant use of herbicides, all standard practices, would control the *uniformly* germinating TM weed seeds lacking secondary dormancy in rotational crops.

Ripening and Shattering

Weeds disperse their seed over a period of time and much of the ripe seed "shatters" to the ground, ensuring continuity. A proportion of the weed seed is harvested with crop seed, *contaminating* the crop seed and facilitating weed dispersal to wherever the crop seed will be grown.

Weeds have evolved morphological and phenological "*mimicries*" to the crop seed, *necessitating* continual evolution and refinement of techniques to remove the *contaminating* weed seed. Recently domesticated crops such as oilseed rape still suffer from shattering. In addition to the loss of yield, the shattering of crop seeds results in their becoming a volunteer weed, especially in oilseed rape.

Uniform ripening and *antishattering* genes would be detrimental to weeds but neutral for crops that ripens uniformly and not shatter and positive for oilseed rape, which still has a shattering problem.

Dwarfing

Crops have been selected for height, to outgrow weeds. Weed evolution kept apace, selecting for taller weeds. The advent of selective *herbicides* to kill weeds allowed genetic dwarfing of these crops, with more seed harvest and less straw.

Various new systems of genetically engineered height reduction are being introduced. These include genes related to hormone production as well as to shade avoidance. Shade avoidance is *advantageous* when competing with other species but not in a weed-free crop stand where only siblings are competing.

The overexpression of specific phytochrome genes prevents *recognition* of shading, and thus the plant remains short. This is *advantageous* for a crop and could also be used where the present dwarfing genes prevent obtaining the highest yields. Dwarfing would be disadvantageous for a weed that must compete with the crops; it would be shaded over by the crop.

Balancing Primary and TM Traits

If the primary transgenic trait confers an advantage to a weed, how much will TM traits actually mitigate that advantage? Weeds are not only highly *competitive* with crops, they are *competitive* with weeds of other species as well as within their own species.

Weeds typically produce thousands of seeds in steady-state conditions to replace a single plant, suggesting extreme *competition* to be the replacement; the selection for the highest competitive fitness is intense. Other transgenes can be considered for *mitigating* the risks of *integration* with other crops. These include the following characteristics:

1. Eliminating seed coat characters that allow weed seeds to pass through animal digestive tracks intact and then be dispersed.
2. Genes promoting partitioning to roots would be advantageous to cultivated root crops such as beets but detrimental to related crops such as annual wild beets.
3. Genes that prevent premature flowering (bolting), i.e., promote biennial growth, would be excellent for carrots, celery, cabbage, lettuce, beets, and related crops but would be highly deleterious to related weeds.
4. Antiflowering genes would prevent introgression of genes from potatoes into their wild

Andean relatives and prevent volunteer potatoes arising from true seed.

After a weed introgresses a transgene and then stabilizes (*eliminates cytogenetic incompatibilities*), the trait will quickly spread through a population, even if it has a marginally positive fitness advantage. Conversely, one can balance the *disadvantage* of TM traits against the advantage of the primary trait.

This must be done in both the presence and absence of the *herbicide*, as herbicide resistance provides an advantage only when the herbicide is used. Indeed, when the herbicide is not present, the transgene resistance trait can be disadvantageous; as *demonstrated* with an ALS resistance transgene. Each TM trait should work in a balance with the primary trait, and it might be necessary to have more than one TM trait in a construct to obtain balance.

The risks of introgression can be further decreased by combining TM traits with a cytogenetic failsafe, where these are available. Even if one or two TM genes were to confer some *unforeseen* and *unforeseeable* advantage in the future, this would be akin to evolving *resistance* to a herbicide.

The first case would be reviewed and a decision could be made whether the situation warrants removing the TM *transgenic* crop from market to prevent the *occurrence* of further cases. The only aspect that is predictable is the *segregation* of tightly linked genes, and that is why flanking the primary gene on both sides could be used.

The *segregation* of a gene would be visible, *allowing* any such material to be removed from the breeding population.

TM Genes Are Available to Mitigate Movement of Resistance

Some possible traits for TM constructs just exist as named genes that are inherited, others are also mapped to positions on various *chromosomes*, and a few are actually *characterized* as *sequenced* genes. Thus, not all TM traits have genes that are immediately available for insertion in tandem constructs.

Still, there can be many different ways for a plant to confer a TM trait, and thus more than one gene might be available.

Secondary Dormancy

Unfortunately, *Arabidopsis*, the typical source of genes, has already been *sufficiently domesticated* that it is unlike *cruciferous* weeds; the laboratory strains no longer have strong *secondary* dormancy. A mutant that is insensitive to abscisic acid and lacks *secondary* dormancy was found in a wild, *undomesticated Arabidopsis* strain.

Shattering

Physiologically, one way to avoid *premature* seed shattering is to have uniform ripening. Early maturing seeds of oilseed rape on *indeterminate, continuously* flowering varieties typically shatter. Determinacy, with its single uniform flush of flowering is one method to prevent shattering, but this often shortens the season, reducing yield.

The *hormonology* of the abscission zone controls whether *shattering* will occur, and it is possible that if cytokinins are overproduced, shattering will be delayed. As with *secondary* dormancy, no *sequenced* genes are yet at hand except for cytokinin *overproduction*.

Dwarfing

Many of the genes used for breeding dwarfism seem to have an unknown function. Still, many genes are known that control height.

Gibberellins

Preventing the biosyntheses of gibberellins reduces height, which is the basis of many chemical dwarfing agents used *commercially* on wheat. The three enzymes and genes *controlling* various steps in gibberellin biosyntheses are known and have been cloned. *Arabidopsis* mutations bearing *mutations* in any of them are dwarfed, and the dwarfing is *reversible* by *gibberellin* treatment.

Overexpression of a gene coding for *entkaurene* synthase, causing *cosuppression*, mimicked the mutant *phenotype*. In addition, a GA receptor gene has been isolated that confers gibberellin *insensitivity* when a truncated form is transformed into grains (GAI) and thereby induces dwarfing.

Some processes such as flower stalk bolting are controlled by specific gibberellins; in radish, GA, and GA, are *responsible*. It may be necessary to *characterize* the genes coding for the *monooxygenases* and *dioxygenases* that are *responsible* for the later steps. Some of these genes have been isolated as well.

Brassinosteroids

This group of hormones also causes *elongation* of stems in many plant species, and their absence results in dwarf plants. A 22 d-hydroxylase cytochrome P-450 has been isolated that controls a series of these steps in *brassinosteroid biosynthesis* and plants lacking the enzyme are dwarfed. Plants are also dwarfed when they produce normal levels of these growth regulators but are mutated in the bril gene coding for the receptor. In addition, *suppressive overexpression* of a sterol C24-methyl transferase in the pathway also causes dwarfing.

Shade Avoidance

Various forms of the pigment phytochrome interact to detect whether a plant is being shaded. The engineering of *suppressive overexpression* constructs of one of these *phytochromes* led to plants that did not elongate in response to shading.

CONCLUDING REMARKS

One can and should envisage many other ways besides T-HRC in which genetic engineering can be used to replace partially or augment herbicides in *controlling* weeds. Thus, it is unfortunate or deplorable (*depending* on one's *outlook*) that because of an antichemical bias among some of the authors of the World Bank report, weeds were not among the constraints to agriculture that could be overcome by biotechnology.

With weeds not listed, many biotechnologists do not realize the problems facing *agriculture* and will not be stimulated to support and study the positive aspects and drawbacks of the first generation of T HRCs and then innovate new solutions.

Thus, one can quote Confucius: "If language is incorrect, what is said is not meant. If what is said is not meant, what ought to be done remains undone." If weeds are not considered a constraint, biotechnological solutions will not be found to deal with them.

9 Chapter

TRANSGENIC PLANTS INCREASING TOLERANCE TOWARDS OXIDATIVE STRESS

A variety of 7stresses (such as chilling, ozone, high light, drought, and heat) can severely damage crop plants with consequent high yield losses. A common factor in all these adverse conditions is the occurrence of oxidative stress.

Oxidative stress can be defined as the enhanced *accumulation* of active oxygen species (AOS) within several subcellular compartments of the plant. The AOS can react very rapidly with DNA, lipids, and proteins, with cellular damage as a result.

Under normal growth conditions, AOS are efficiently *scavenged* by both *enzymatic* and nonenzymatic *detoxification* mechanisms. Nevertheless, during prolonged stress conditions, this defense system becomes saturated and cellular damage is inevitable. The key players in the defense system are superoxide dismutases, ascorbate peroxidase, and catalases.

These antioxidant enzymes directly eliminate AOS. This chapter gives an overview of transgenic plants with modulated *antioxidant* enzyme levels (focusing on superoxide dismutases, ascorbate peroxidase, and catalase) that are produced to test the potential use of *antioxidant* enzymes in improving stress tolerance during adverse *environmental* conditions.

OXIDATIVE STRESS

The AOS are generated as side products of regular cellular metabolism, but most of the AOS are formed by dysfunction of enzymes or electron *transport* systems as a result of a stress situation. In the cell, AOS are mainly produced in the *organelles* with high *oxidizing metabolic*

activities or with intense electron flows. Together with the electron transport chain of *mitochondria, chloroplasts* are hence the main sites of AOS production in plants. During the reduction steps to H_2O, several AOS can be formed. Incomplete reduction of O_2 or, *alternatively, acceptance* of either electrons or excess energy by O_2 leads to the *formation* of superoxide radicals (O^-_2) and hydrogen peroxide (H_2O_2).

Other sources of AOS *production* are the microbodies. In the *glyoxisomes*, H_2O, is produced during fatty acid degradation in the glyoxylate cycle. In the peroxisomes, photorespiration is responsible for H_2O_2 production. Superoxide is a *moderately* reactive, short-lived AOS with a half-life of *approximately* 2-4 μsec.

The O^-_2 cannot cross biological membranes and is readily *dismutated* to H_2O_2. Alternatively, O^-_2 can reduce quinones and transition metal complexes of Fe^{3+} and Cu^{2+}, thus affecting the activity of *metal-containing* enzymes.

On the contrary, *hydroperoxyl* radicals (HO;) that are formed from O_2 by *protonation* in aqueous solutions can cross the *biological* membranes and subtract *hydrogen* atoms from polyunsaturated fatty acids and lipid hydroperoxides, thus initiating lipid *autooxidation*.

H_2O_2 is moderately reactive and a relatively long-lived molecule (1 msec) that can diffuse some distances from its site of production. It may *inactivate* enzymes by *oxidizing* their thiol groups. Enzymes of the Calvin cycle as well as copper/zinc (Cu/Zn) and iron (Fe) *superoxide* dismutases (SODs) are also inactivated by H_2O_2.

Although neither O_2 nor H_2O_2 seems particularly harmful at *physiological concentrations*, their *toxicity* in vivo is enhanced by a metal ion-dependent *conversion* into hydroxyl radicals (OH), one of the most reactive species known in chemistry: $O^-_2 + H_2O_2 \rightarrow O_2 + 2OH$ (*Haber-Weiss reaction*).

Hydroxyl radicals can react *indiscriminately* to cause lipid peroxidation, the *denaturation* of proteins, and the mutation of DNA. Fortunately, plants have the capacity to cope with these aggressive agents by *eliminating* them with an AOS-scavenging system.

Under moderate stress conditions, the produced radicals can be efficiently scavenged. During periods of more severe stress, however, these *scavenging* systems become saturated with the increased rate of radical production. The presence of excessive AOS results, for instance, in damage to the *photosynthetic* apparatus, bleaching of leaves by *oxidation* of the pigments *resulting* in severe yield losses.

The AOS are *excessively* produced under a wide variety of stresses (such as drought, heat, salt, pollution, chilling, and ozone stress). These, at first sight unrelated, stresses all have in common the electron leakage from electron transport chains in *chloroplasts* and *mitochondria*.

And Friend

In certain situations, the plant uses AOS in a *beneficial* way. The AOS play an important role in the induction of protection *mechanisms* during biotic and abiotic stresses. The best known example is their role in the activation of resistance responses during *incompatible* plant-pathogen interactions.

Upon infection, an NADPH oxidase of the plasma membrane is activated, producing superoxide radicals. Superoxide radicals are, through *spontaneous dismutation* or SOD activity, converted into H_2O_2. The defensive properties of H_2O, are situated on several levels.

1. High levels of H_2O_2 are toxic for both pathogen and plant cells. Killing the plant cells *surrounding* the infection site inhibits spreading of a (biotrophic) pathogen.
2. H_2O_2 can serve as a substrate in peroxidative cross-linking reactions of lignin precursors and induces cross-linking of cell wall proteins. A reinforced plant cell wall slows down the spreading of the pathogen and makes new *infections* more difficult.
3. Because H_2O_2 is relatively stable and diffusible through membranes (in *contrast* to *superoxide*), it is a good *candidate* to act as a signal molecule during stress responses. H_2O_2 induces several pathogen defense genes (coding for *pathogenesis*-related proteins and *phytoalexin* production) and a programmed cell death pathway.

These different effects of H_2O_2 are thought to be regulated not only through the level and timing of H_2O_2 induction but also through *interactions* with other potential signals, such as salicylic acid, *superoxide,* and nitric oxide.

The role of H_2O_2 as a molecular signal for the induction of gene *expression* may not be limited to plant-pathogen interactions. Studies of maize *hypocotyls* and potato and mustard seedlings have shown that H_2O_2 mediates *subsequent* cold and heat tolerance, *respectively.*

In barley, H_2O_2 treatment broke dormancy of seeds. Hence, AOS production is vital to plant development and in defense against pathogens, but it needs to be tightly controlled in order to avoid cellular damage.

OXIDATIVE STRESS DEFENSE MECHANISMS IN PLANTS

To limit cellular damage caused by *excessive* AOS levels, plants have evolved a broad variety of nonenzymatic and enzymatic protection mechanisms that *efficiently* scavenge AOS. The best-known *nonenzymatic antioxidants* are ascorbate, glutathione, α-tocopherol, and carotenoids.

They are present in *relatively* high concentrations within plant cells. For a detailed overview on these components, the reader is referred to Alscher and Hess.

Because *hydroxyl* radicals are too reactive to be directly *controlled,* aerobic *organisms* prefer to eliminate the less reactive precursor forms, such as *superoxide* and H_2O_2, and hence prevent the formation of *hydroxyl* radicals.

Superoxide dismutases scavenge superoxide radicals, whereas catalases and *peroxidases* remove H_2O_2. Catalases consume the bulk of H_2O_2. Ascorbate peroxidases remove H_2O_2 that is not accessible for catalase, because of their higher affinity and their diverse subcellular locations.

Other enzymes that are involved in the removal of AOS are monodehydroascorbate reductase, dehydroascorbate reductase, *glutathione* reductase, and glutathione *peroxidase.* However, these *enzymes* will not be described in detail in this chapter. For an overview of these enzymes the reader is referred to Noctor and Foyer.

Superoxide Dismutases

Superoxide dismutases (SOD; superoxide: superoxide *oxidoreductase;* EC 1.15.1.1) can be considered key enzymes of the *antioxidative* stress defense mechanism. They directly determine the cellular *concentrations* of O^-_2 and H_2O, because they dismutate O^-_2 into O_2 and H_2O_2.

$$2H^+ + 2O_2^- \xrightarrow{SOD} H_2O_2 + O_2$$

Apart from a few *exceptions,* SODs are present in all aerobic organisms and in all subcellular *compartments* that have to deal with AOS. They are classified *according* to their metal cofactor as isozymes containing Cu/Zn, Fe, and manganese (Mn).

The FeSOD and MnSOD proteins are structurally similar, whereas the Cu/ZnSOD family is structurally unrelated. The SODs catalyze the *disproportionation* of *superoxide* through an *oxidation-reduction* cycle of the prosthetic Cu, Mn, or Fe cofactor.

Experimentally, the three SOD types can easily be *distinguished* via in situ gel staining. Incubating the gels with KCN or H_2O_2 allows *discrimination* between the different classes. The Cu/ZnSOD is *characterized* as being sensitive to both H_2O_2 and KCN; FeSOD is sensitive only to H_2O_2, whereas MnSOD is resistant to both inhibitors.

However, an FeSOD from rice was shown to be resistant to both inhibitors. Besides their differential *sensitivity* toward inhibitors, these enzymes also have a distinctive subcellular distribution. The amount and relative *abundance* of SOD isozymes vary within each organism.

Developmental control and *environmental* stresses that generate AOS (*ultraviolet,* ozone, air pollutants, low *temperatures,* salt stress, drought, heat shock, pathogen infections, etc.) can induce plant SOD activities. The MnSOD is found in the mitochondria of all eukaryotic cells, including plants; Cu/ZnSODs are found in the cytosol, *peroxisomes,* and *chloroplasts* of higher plants.

Multiple Cu/ZnSOD isoforms are also present in the extracellular fluids of Scots pine. Until now, FeSODs were found only in prokaryotes and in the chloroplasts of plants.

Ascorbate Peroxidase

Peroxidases are *ubiquitous* enzymes found in plants. Besides the *peroxidases,* whose *oxidation* products play mainly physiological roles (*lignification, cross-linking of cell wall matrices*), a second class is also part of the AOS defense system.

Ascorbate peroxidases (APXs; EC 1.11.1.11) destroy harmful H_2O_2 via the ascorbate-glutathione pathway in *chloroplasts* and cytosol of plants, algae, and some cyanobacteria. Also, APX activity has been identified in insects and purified from bovine eye tissue.

The ascorbate-glutathione pathway provides protection against oxidative stress by a series of coupled redox reactions, *particularly* in photosynthetic tissues but also in *mitochondria* and peroxisomes. The APX eliminates H_2O_2 by using ascorbate as an electron donor in an oxidation-reduction reaction. Ascorbate is then oxidized to *monodehydroascorbate* (MDHA).

$$2\ \text{ascorbate} + H_2O_2 \xrightarrow{APX} 2\ \text{MDHA} + 2H_2O$$

Ascorbate is regenerated from MDHA in the chloroplast membrane by ferredoxin or in the stroma by MDHA reductase at the expense of NADPH. The MDHA can also spontaneously dissociate into ascorbate and *dehydroascorbate* (DHA), which is rereduced by DHA reductase (DHAR).

The DHAR uses reduced glutathione as an electron donor. Oxidized *glutathione* is then recycled by NADPH-consuming *glutathione* reductase (GR). The APX is directly involved in the defense response against oxidative stress. In pea and radish, APX activities are induced by Fe excess and salt and drought stresses. Winter-acclimated pine needles contain up to 65-fold more APX than summer needles, whereas in maize APX (together with SOD) is *constitutively* higher in a chilling-resistant than in a sensitive line.

After anoxic stress, APX activity rises in wheat roots and rice seedlings. Also in wheat, correct temporal expression of APX is an important factor for efficient seed *germination*. APX activity increases during *germination* in parallel with the rise of ascorbate levels. Based on the available sequence data, seven different APXs are distinguished in plants: two soluble cytosolic forms, three cytosol *membranebound* types including a *glyoxisome-bound* form, one *chloroplastic* stromal, and one thylakoid membrane-bound APX.

The various isoforms differ in several molecular and *enzymatic* properties, such as molecular weight, electron donor specificity, lability in the absence of *ascorbate*, pH optimum, and ascorbate and H_2O_2 affinity. In general, the chloroplastic isoforms are very specific for ascorbate as electron donor, whereas the cytosolic APX can also oxidize pyrogallol.

Catalases

Plants, unlike animals, have multiple forms of catalase (H_2O_2:H_2O_2 oxidoreductase; EC 1.11.1.6) that are mainly found in *peroxisomes* and *glyoxisomes*. Catalase activity was also found in the mitochondria of maize. Catalases directly consume H_2O, or oxidize substrates (R), such as methanol, ethanol, *formaldehyde*, and formic acid.

$$2H_2O_2 \xrightarrow{\text{catalase}} 2H_2O + O_2$$

$$H_2O_2 + RH_2 \xrightarrow{\text{catalase}} 2H_2O + R$$

There are some striking similarities in the *organization* of the catalase gene family in different species. Our laboratory showed that catalases can be divided into three classes according to their expression. The transition from glyoxisomes to leaf *peroxisomes* during seedling development is associated with the *disappearance* of class III catalases and the induction of class I catalases.

In maize, however, both class I and class III are expressed in seeds, indicating that the class I catalase has a dual function in maize. Class I is most prominent in *photosynthetic* tissues, where they are involved in the removal of photorespiratory H_2O_2,. Class II catalases are highly expressed in vascular tissues, where they might play a role in lignification, but their exact biological role remains unknown.

As mentioned before, class III is abundant only in seeds and young seedlings and its activity is linked to the removal of excessive H_2O_2 that is produced during fatty acid *degradation* in the glyoxylate cycle in the *glyoxisomes*.

Because catalase *isozymes* are rapidly induced by ultraviolet B (UV-B), ozone, and also chilling, they may play a direct role in stress protection

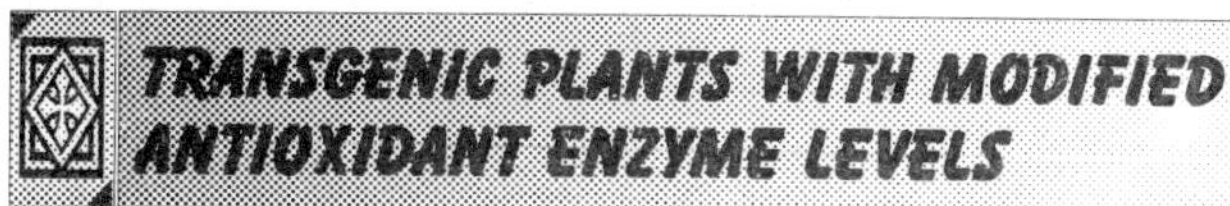

TRANSGENIC PLANTS WITH MODIFIED ANTIOXIDANT ENZYME LEVELS

Because of the involvement of AOS in a wide variety of *environmental* stresses, antioxidant enzymes are *interesting* molecular targets for the production of new plant varieties that can cope with these stresses. Several antioxidative stress enzymes have been genetically *engineered* into plants to assess their potential capacity for *enhancing* oxidative stress tolerance.

The beneficial effects observed in some of these transgenic plants can lead to *interesting agronomic* applications. The following section gives an overview of the state of the art concerning transgenic plants with modified levels of *antioxidant* enzyme levels.

Transgenic Plants with Elevated Superoxide Dismutase Levels

The first report on *transgenic* plants *overproducing* SOD was, however, not promising. Transgenic tobacco plants with 30- to 50-fold increased SOD activity levels due to the production of a petunia chloroplastic Cu/ZnSOD were not more resistant against methyl viologen (MV).

The tolerance toward *oxidative* stress is easily tested in vitro with MV (also known as paraquat), which is a light-activated herbicide. In the light, MV becomes an electron acceptor from photosystem I (PSI), *subsequently* reducing dioxygen to O_2.

In this way, the herbicide strongly enhances the formation of superoxide radicals and is a fairly good mimic of the superoxide-forming process that occurs in vivo in *illuminated* chloroplasts. The MV also accepts electrons from the respiratory electron transport chain in the *mitochondria* and forms superoxide radicals in the dark too.

Transgenic tomato plants with two- to fourfold increased SOD levels by producing the same chloroplastic Cu/ZnSOD were not better protected against *photoinhibitory conditions* known to increase *oxidative* stress (high light, low *temperatures*, and low CO_2 *concentrations*). Pitcher et al. showed that the same transgenic tobacco plants were not protected against ozone stress.

Although the activity levels of enzymes involved in H_2O_2 scavenging (APX, GR, etc.) were not measured in both cases, the lack of induced tolerance is *plausibly explained* by the inability of the plants to cope with the elevated levels of H_2O_2 that were produced by the enhanced *dismutation* of superoxide radicals.

Transgenic potato plants *overproducing* tomato cytosolic or chloroplastic Cu/ZnSOD lacked a chlorotic and wilting phenotype that was seen in wild-type plants after dipping their shoots in 100 μM MV. In culture medium with 10 μM MV, root *cultures* from the same *transgenic* potatoes grew at rates similar to those in control medium.

In contrast to the very high overproduction of SOD reported in the *transgenic* tobacco plants, these *transgenic* potato plants had only a modest increase in Cu/ZnSOD activity.

In this way, too high *accumulation* of H_2O_2 is avoided, preventing promotion of *hydroxyl* formation by H_2O_2 and O_2 interaction. A correlation between MV tolerance and chilling tolerance was found in transgenic tobacco plants that overproduce a *chloroplast-localized* Cu/ZnSOD from pea at twofold higher levels than the endogenous FeSOD.

In agreement, moderate cytosolic *overproduction* of a pea Cu/ZnSOD in transgenic tobacco confers partial resistance to ozone-induced foliar necrosis. Up to sixfold *enhancement* of SOD activity led to 30 to 50% less visible foliar damage. The beneficial effect of the transgene could, however, be detected only in older leaves (leaves 3 to 5).

In the youngest leaves (5 and 6), no difference between transgenic and wild-type plants could be observed. Because Cu/ZnSODs are sensitive to H_2O_2 it is also possible that some of the introduced Cu/ZnSOD activity is *inhibited* by its own end product.

In this way, MnSOD, which is insensitive to H_2O_2, was introduced as a better candidate for *engineering* oxidative stress tolerance.The MnSOD from *Nicotiana plumbaginifolia* has indeed been more consistently reported to confer resistance to *oxidative* stress. Transgenic tobacco plants *overproducing* the nuclear-encoded mitochondrial MnSOD in either *mitochondria* or chloroplasts (by replacing the *mitochondrial* transit sequence with a chloroplast transit peptide) were less sensitive to MV.

Overproduction of MnSOD in the *mitochondria* rendered the plants more tolerant to MV in dark but not in light incubations with MV. By contrast, MnSOD *overproduction* in the *chloroplasts* made the plants more tolerant to MV in both dark and light incubations.

The SOD *overproduction* in the *chloroplasts* also led to the induction of other *antioxidant* enzymes (FeSOD, APX, DHAR peroxidase) and higher *glutathione* and ascorbate levels. Enhanced SOD activity in the mitochondria had only a minor effect on ozone tolerance in transgenic tobacco. However, *overproduction* of SOD in the *chloroplasts* resulted in a three- to fourfold reduction of visible ozone injury.

In addition to the fact that MnSOD is resistant against H_2O_2, the subcellular *location* may probably play an important role in *determining* whether positive or negative effects arise from SOD *overproduction*. Targeting SODs to organelles with a higher risk of AOS production seems more efficient than cytosolic *overproduction*.

Because during most abiotic stresses the chloroplast is the main site of AOS production, it is considered the target organelle for protection against oxidative stress. Because of their original presence in plant chloroplasts, FeSOD proteins are theoretically better *candidates* for *overproduction* in the chloroplasts. Under *conditions* in which H_2O_2 *accumulation* is not the limiting factor, the biochemical properties of the FeSOD proteins should be better adapted to function optimally under the specific conditions within the chloroplast.

This characteristic was indeed shown by *overproduction* in transgenic tobacco of the mature FeSOD from *Arabidopsis thaliana* coupled to a chloroplast transit peptide. Transgenic FeSOD protected both the plasmalemma and PSII against *superoxide* generated during *illumination* of leaf discs impregnated with MV. *Overproduction* of a mitochondrial MnSOD in the chloroplasts protected only the plasmalemma, but not PSII, against MV.

This difference was attributed to the higher membrane affinity of FeSOD, allowing this enzyme to *scavenge* superoxide radicals at the site of their formation, i.e., near PSI. The potential of SOD *overproduction* in stress *engineering* strategies has been reported for three crops, cotton, alfalfa, and maize.

Transgenic cotton plants that produce chloroplast-localized MnSOD are more tolerant against chilling-induced oxidative stress. Transgenic alfalfa plants with twice the amount of total SOD-overproducing *N. plumbaginifolia* MnSOD in both the mitochondria and the *chloroplast* were tested for increased tolerance against oxidative stress by incubating leaves with the herbicide *acifluorfen*.

Acifluorfen is a *photobleaching*, p-nitrodiphenyl ether herbicide that promotes accumulation of the chlorophyll precursor *protoporphyrin*; in the light it generates singlet oxygen that causes *peroxidation* in the tonoplast, *plasmalemma,* and chloroplast envelope. Increased resistance against acifluorfen correlated with increased freezing stress tolerance.

One transgenic plant, *propagated* by cuttings, had increased regrowth capacities compared with *nontransgenic* plants when subjected to sublethal freezing *temperatures* from -8°C to -16°C. When viability was measured by electrolyte leakage or by tetrazolium staining, differences between *transgenic* and wildtype plants were minor or nonexistent, despite *differences* in winter survival among the plants.

Two other experiments with two transgenic alfalfa plants producing MnSOD indicated the value of *engineering* oxidative stress tolerance to improve *environmental* stress tolerance in crop plants. For the first time, transgenic plants *overproducing antioxidant* enzymes were also tested in a natural field environment.

The transgenic plants tended to show reduced injury from water deficit stress as determined by chlorophyll *fluorescence, electrolyte* leakage, and regrowth from crowns. Over a 3-year field trial, vigor and survival of transgenic plants were significantly improved. It should be noted that the preceding *experiments* were done by using only a few transgenic plants obtained by *transformation* of an alfalfa cultivar with poor agronomic *performance* and originally not well adapted to winter conditions.

McKersie et al. expanded their original observations by transforming two elite alfalfa plants that are adapted to the field environment, and they *examined* many more independent transgenics under both *laboratory* and field conditions.

This detailed assessment confirmed the earlier observation that transgenics had a greater survival and yield (total shoot dry matter production) in the field. Increased winter survival was also correlated with increased SOD levels in transgenic alfalfa plants *overproducing* FeSOD but not with any beneficial effects on photosynthesis, growth, or oxidative stress *tolerance* in leaves.

This correlation can be *explained* by the increased superoxide-scavenging capacity in the root, thereby enhancing recovery from primary freezing injury. Another more attractive *explanation* relates to enhanced levels of H_2O, produced by SOD *overproduction.*

In addition to its potential toxicity, H_2O, is well recognized to act as a signal molecule in several defense responses. Altered H_2O_2 levels might induce an *acclimation* process that induces a general defense response to tolerate better the adverse *environmental* conditions during winter survival. We evaluated transgenic maize pants that *overproduce* an *N. plumbaginifolia* MnSOD or an *A. thaliana* FeSOD *complementary* DNA (cDNA) fused to a chloroplast transit peptide from pea under control of the cauliflower mosaic virus 35S (CaMV35S) promoter.

The *recombinant* MnSOD was correctly targeted to chloroplasts and its enzymatic activity could be distinguished on SOD activity gels. One transgenic line showed enhanced tolerance to MV. The growth *characteristics* of transgenic maize lines were followed during growth at ambient (22-25°C) and chilling temperatures (15-17°C) in growth cabinets.

Although the transgenic lines in all experiments had a growth advantage compared with the wild-type lines, no statistically significant increase in growth could be observed. To extrapolate the in vitro oxidative stress tolerance to improved growth effects during *environmental* stress conditions, such as chilling, we are currently *evaluating* the initiated field trials at different locations in Europe

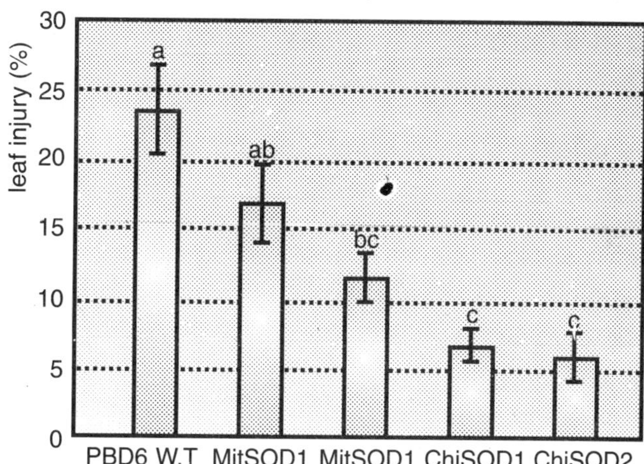

Figure 9.1: Leaf injury in transgenic versus wild-type tobacco plants after 1 week of ozone fumigation. The values given show the mean ± standard error of the mean for wild-type plants (PBD6 W.T.), transgenic plants overproducing SOD targeted to the mitochondria (MitSODI and MitSOD2), and transgenic plants overproducing SOD targeted to the chloroplasts (ChlSODI and CNSOD2). Means with the same letter are not significantly (P < 0.05) different.

to scale up the experiments and to check the behavior of the transgenic plants under natural *environmental* stress conditions.

Immunolocalization experiments revealed that in transgenic maize the recombinant MnSOD is mainly (although not exclusively) located in the chloroplasts of the bundle sheath cells. The low levels of MnSOD in the mesophyll cells could be attributed to a different expression capacity of the CaMV35S promoter, but posttranscriptional or *posttranslational* regulation of the recombinant MnSOD cannot be excluded.

Wilson et al. have also shown the vascular-specific activity of β-glucuronidase (GUS) in leaves of maize plants *transformed* with a CaMV35S-GUS f0on. Because *endogenous* SOD and APX activities are restricted to the bundle sheath cells, whereas GR and DHAR activities could be detected only in the mesophyll tissue of maize, a clear partitioning of the AOS defense system between the mesophyll and bundle sheath cells must be present.

This differential localization correlates with the need for NADPH of the respective enzymes. Because NADPH is limited in the bundle sheath cells, GR and DHAR activities are rate limited in this *compartment*. This differential *distribution* of *antioxidants* is, of course, crucial for maize plants to deal with oxidative stress.

The overproduction of AOS scavengers within each cell type could restore this natural imbalance and, hence, confer a higher tolerance to maize plants against chilling-associated oxidative stress. The exclusive presence of the transgenic MnSOD in the bundle sheath cells probably influenced the expected *protective* effect of MnSOD in the *transgenic* maize plants during chilling stress.

Transgenic maize lines *overproducing* an A. *thaliana* FeSOD in the chloroplasts also suffered less from paraquat damage than controls as indicated by decreased *membrane* leakiness and by higher *photosynthetic* activity.

In contrast to the MnSOD lines, the transgenic FeSOD maize plants also exhibited a significantly increased growth rate at low *temperatures* (as estimated from fresh weight and summed leaf length determinations). These and previous results in tobacco suggest that FeSOD is a better candidate enzyme to protect plants against oxidative stress.

The reason could be the *difference* in *suborganellar* location between the *overproduced* MnSOD and FeSOD. Because of their chloroplastic and mitochondrial origin, respectively, FeSOD and MnSOD might have *different* properties. Van Camp et al.

showed that in tobacco the transgenic FeSOD is at least partially bound to the chloroplast membrane, whereas transgenic MnSOD behaves more like a stromal enzyme. This differential *subcellular* location might provoke different protective effects against oxygen radicals.

Transgenic FeSOD might be able to bind electrostatically to the chloroplast membrane in the vicinity of the site of radical production, resulting in increased *protective* properties.

Transgenic Plants with Modulated Ascorbate Peroxidase or Catalase Levels

Overproduction of an *A. thaliana* APX in tobacco chloroplasts provided almost complete protection of the PSII reaction center against *aminotriazole. Aminotriazole* inhibits catalase and in this way provokes accumulation of H_2O_2. Tolerance to MV was slightly better, but tolerance to eosin (*a singlet oxygen generator*) or chilling-induced *photoinhibition* was not enhanced.

Transgenic tobacco plants overproducing an A. *thaliana* peroxisomal APX were protected against aminotriazole but not against MV (causing mainly AOS *formation* in the chloroplast). These data show that H_2O_2 formed in the peroxisomes can diffuse and affect *photosynthetic activities* in the chloroplast. Protecting plant cells against oxidative stress during *photorespiratory* conditions can hence be done by scavenging H_2O_2 at the place of production in the *peroxisomes* or by providing the *chloroplast* with extra H_2O_2-scavenging capacity.

In an *ozonesensitive* transgenic tobacco, a 10-fold increase in *chloroplastic* APX activity was not effective against cellular injury caused by ozone stress. Overproduction in tobacco chloroplasts of the other major H_2O_2 scavenger, catalase, led to *tolerance* against MV and drought stress conditions.

By *combining* superoxide *scavengers* and H_2O_2 scavengers, even better results can be envisaged, the most spectacular results having been reported in insects. In *Drosophila melanogaster,* the overproduction of SOD and catalase resulted in a delay of aging and greater longevity, whereas *overproduction* of either of the two enzymes alone had only minor effects.

Transgenic tobacco overproducing an *Escherichia coli* GR or a rice Cu/ ZnSOD were fivefold more resistant against ion leakage caused by MV treatments. Crossings between both transgenic lines were highly tolerant to MV *concentration* of 50 p.M, whereas control plants were sensitive to MV *concentrations* as low as 1 μM. Underproduction of antioxidative stress enzymes often increases *sensitivity* to the *experienced* stress.

Tobacco plants with decreased APX or GR activity, obtained by antisense *technology,* are more susceptible to ozone stress and MV, respectively. Transgenic plants deficient in catalase (class I) can be grown only under low light conditions (<100 μcool m^2 sec^{-1} photosynthetic photon fluence rate).

When exposed to higher light intensities, these plants developed white necrotic lesions on the leaves after 1 to 2 days. Lesion *formation* was induced by *photorespiration* because damage was prevented under elevated CO_2.

Stress analysis revealed that Catl-deficient plants were more sensitive to paraquat, salt, and ozone stress, indicating that Catl is a key *component* of several stress defenses.

PERSPECTIVES

The production of crop plants that can cope with adverse *environmental* conditions is a very important research objective within the agroindustry. Improved *production* rates of crops during stress situations, such as drought and chilling, or resistance against pathogen attacks will certainly improve the life quality of the *ever-growing* world population in the next century.

The rationale for the production of stress-tolerant crop lines is to reduce the yearly losses due to adverse environmental conditions or to expand the growing range to currently less favorable regions. The strategy that was *surveyed* in this chapter is the study (and eventual modification) of the *antioxidants* in different crop species.

Besides the production and evaluation of transgenic lines, we should also focus on a more detailed characterization of the plant AOS-scavenging machinery. From this basic research, valuable information will be gained that can be applied to future *engineering* strategies.

In maize, SOD activity is apparently different between bundle sheath and mesophyll cells, which could be a main cause of the chilling susceptibility of maize. Specific enhancement of SOD activity in the mesophyll cells could lead to chilling-tolerant maize lines.

The isolation of novel isoforms of AOS enzymes in plants will also provide better insight into its defense mechanisms. The molecular characterization of several *chloroplastic* APXs in A. *thaliana* clearly shows that the AOS-scavenging enzyme families in plants are larger than *previously* thought.

With the help of genome-wide transcript *profiling methods*, such as cDNA-amplified fragment length *polymorphism* and microarray technology, or through the outcome of several genome and cDNA sequence *initiatives*, new isoforms of the different AOS-scavenging enzyme *families* will certainly be discovered. There is evidence for a dual role for H_2O_2.

At higher *concentrations* it can promote cell death, but at lower levels it serves as a signal molecule to induce stress defense responses that can eventually lead to *acclimation*. Controlled modulation of H_2O_2 levels is, hence, an interesting second route to identify and improve the *oxidative* stress signal transduction pathway(s), leading to broader and more *sustainable* resistance.

As described before, such a situation in which altered H_2O_2 levels induce stress *tolerance* might already exist in SOD-overproducing plants. Together with the *identification* of novel *antioxidant* isozymes, a better *characterization* of signal *transduction pathways* involved in oxidative stress tolerance will certainly open new *opportunities* for the engineering of stress tolerance in plants.

10 Chapter

MODIFIED OILS

The importance of oils and fats in human nutrition is well documented. Lipids form a vital *component* of many cell constituents and are an important source of energy. Oils and fats also contribute significantly as a *functional* ingredient in *improving* the sensory characteristics of numerous processed food products.

About 70% of edible oils are derived from plant sources (about 50 million tonnes/annum), and there are three major groups of *oil-producing* crops. These are temperate annual oilseeds (soy, rapeseed, *sunflower*, and peanut), about 60% of the total vegetable oil production; perennial tropical crops (oil palm, coconut, and babassu nut), about 25% of total oil production; and crops such as cotton and corn where the embryo is a by-product of processing.

This latter group accounts for about 10% of total vegetable oil production. The *remaining* 5% of total vegetable oils are derived from miscellaneous niche crops such as olive (3%), linseed (1%), and sesame (1%). Many oils are also used for nonfood *applications* (about 2% of total *production*). The plant oils most *commonly* used for industrial purposes include coconut, castor, linseed, and soy.

The *predominant* source of industrial fatty acids, however, is tall oil, a by-product of the wood pulp and paper mill industry. The utility of a given oil in a food or industrial *application* is *determined* primarily by acyl composition of the storage triacylglycerol (TAG). For most edible oils the acyl composition of the TAG is *qualitatively* the same as that of the *membrane* lipids.

That is, the same five acyl groups palmitate (16:0), stearate (18:0), oleate (18:1), linoleate (18:2), and linolenate (18:3) occur in both lipid classes, often in the same molar ratios. The degree of fatty acid *desaturation* determines both the melting range and the thermal stability of the oil. Industrial oils such as castor, which is rich in *hydroxy-fatty* acids, often contain fatty acids with functional groups other than methylene-*interrupted* double bonds.

These functional groups determine the reactivity and cross-linking ability of oils used for such applications as paints and coatings. The number of different fatty acids used for industrial purposes, however, is currently quite small compared with the number available (over 300 different types) from nature. Thus, a review of plant seed oil modification is really a review of the fatty acids that make up the oil.

Here we discuss the potential for extending the range of domesticated crops, such as soybean and rape, for novel industrial and food purposes by producing new and useful fatty acids in these crops.

SHORT- AND MEDIUM-CHAIN SATURATED FATTY ACIDS

There are basically two classes of oilseed species with high levels of saturated fatty acids in their oil. The classes are divided by the presence or absence of saturated fats at the *sn 2* position of their TAG. Coconut oil is the best known example of an oil with >90% of its acyl chains saturated (C8:0 to C16:0, predominantly *C12:0*) and thus containing saturated fats at the *sn-2* position.

In this species both the fatty acid *elongation machinery* and the acyl transferase (LAPAAT) that transfers acyl chains to the *sn-2* position are modified. Other examples of these types of oils can be found in many plants including the Lauraceae, *Myristicaceae*, and Lythraceae, which have *predominantly* medium-chain (C10:0 to C14:0) acyl chains in all three *sn* TAG positions in their seed oil.

In most oils saturates are not found at the *sn-2* position of TAG because normal LPAAT cannot use saturated acyl chains as substrates. Thus, the second class of oilseed *accumulates* saturated acyl chains only up to about 60% of the total oil. In these oils the specificity of LPAAT has excluded 16:0 and 18:0 acyl chains from the *sn-2* position of TAG.

Examples of these oils are cocoa butter (30% 16:0, 30% 18:0) and oil palm mesocarp (40% 16:0). The major biochemical *determinant* for seed oils containing *mediumchain* (C8:0 to C16:0) fatty acids is now known to be the presence in the developing seed of a specialized acyl-acyl carrier protein (ACP) *thioesterase* that can redirect the common fatty acid synthase complex to produce medium-chain fatty acids, which are then incorporated into TAG formation.

This has been elegantly shown by the work of the Calgene group, who first purified and cloned a medium-chain fatty-acyl-ACP thioesterase from developing California bay seeds. *Overexpression* of this enzyme in seeds of both *Arabidopsis* and canola *redirected* fatty acid *accumulation* in the TAG of both seeds to accumulate up to 40% laurate. Since then, complementary DNAs (cDNAs) encoding other *mediumchain* thioesterases have been cloned from a variety of plants whose seeds are enriched in medium-chain fatty acids, most notably *Cuphea sp.*, coconut, and elm.

It is now clear that all of these are members of the *fat B* gene subfamily. The production of

A simplified pathway of TAG Biosynthesis

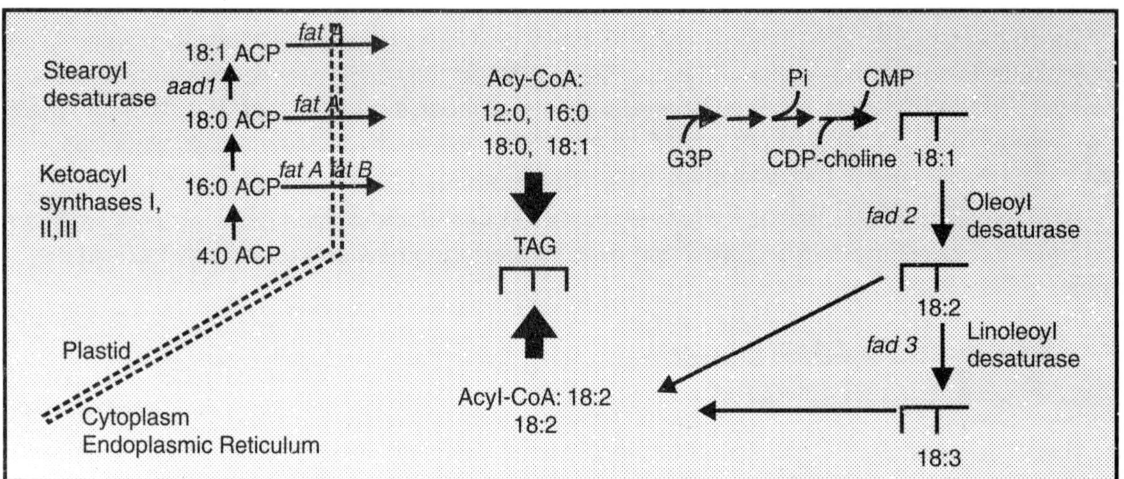

Figure 10.1: A simplified pathway of triglyceride biosynthesis. Fatty acid biosynthesis from C2 to C16:0, C18:1 occurs in the plastid. Critical steps affecting oil quality are the stearoyl desaturase and the thioesterases. The remaining steps in TAG biosynthesis are located in the smooth endoplasmic reticulum. The oleoyl and linoleoyl desaturases are the most critical extraplastidic steps affecting oil quality.

medium-chain fatty acids (C8:0 to C14:0) in developing seeds of, for example, *Cuphea* is catalyzed by the seed-specific expression of these novel *fat B* enzymes. Although the specialized *fat B* enzymes are necessary and sufficient for medium-chain fatty acid production, as with plants with unusual desaturases, other modifications are required to *optimize* short-chain production in vivo.

In *Cuphea sp.* it has been shown that the fatty acid synthase was also modified to produce shorter chain fatty acids. These workers suggested that, in *Cuphea wrightii, the* short-chain β-ketoacylsynthetase (*kas A*) somehow increased the efficiency of the medium-chain alkyl-ACP thioesterases. This hypothesis was supported by the work of Dehesh et al., who isolated embryo-specific *kas A* cDNAs from C8:0- and C10:0-producing *Cuphea* species and functionally tested the encoded polypeptides in seeds of transgenic canola.

In *transgenic* seed extracts, the medium-chain elongation reaction had increased resistance to cerulenin, and in double constructs with the C8:0/C10:0-specific *thioesterases,* the medium-chain fatty acid production was increased relative to TE-only transformants. A *schematic* of the pathway of triglyceride *biosynthesis* is shown in Figure elsewhere in this chapter, showing the critical *enzymatic* steps that affect fatty acid and hence TAG quality.

LONG CHAIN SATURATED FATTY ACIDS

Two major targets for fatty acid modification of edible oils are increased *monunsaturates* (18:1) with a concomitant decrease in polyunsaturates (18:2, 18:3), combined with a reduction in total saturates (16:0, 18:0).

This would yield more a chemically stable oil (high 18:1) with reduced total saturated fat content. Another important target has been to increase the total 18:0 and 18:1 content of the plant oil so that it has an acceptable solid fat *functionality* for use in *margarine* and other *confectionery applications* but without the perceived deleterious health effects of partially hydrogenated oils rich in *trans-fatty* acids. It has been shown that the *fat B* class of acyl:ACP thioesterases control the release of 16:0 into the cytoplasm, making it available for TAG biosynthesis. Thus, inactivation of *fat B* should give a low 16:0 phenotype. Conversely, overexpression of *fat B* should give a high 16:0 phenotype.

The insertion of the first double bond into fatty acyl chains is a plastidic reaction catalyzed by a soluble *desaturase* enzyme, stearoyl-ACP desaturase (AADI). Inactivation of the *aad 1* gene should result in a high 18:0-coenzyme A (CoA) pool in the cytoplasm and a resultant high 18:0 content of seed TAG. Oleoyl-CoA is also *incorporated* into membrane *phosphatidylcholine* (PC), where it is desaturated to linoleoyl-PtdCho by a *membrane-bound* 5-12 desaturase encoded by *a fad 2* gene.

Inactivation of the *fad 2* gene should give a high 18:1 phenotype. High-oleic mutants of corn, peanut canola, and sunflower have been described, with an 18:1 ranging from 60 to 90%. The high-oleic sunflower is *particularly* noteworthy because it is a *dominant* mutation in a structural *fad 2* gene. Interestingly, no good high-oleic mutant of soybean has yet been found by chemical mutagenesis despite intensive *screening* by both private and public breeders.

In contrast to most high-oleic mutants, which are primarily recessive mutations, *transgenic* soy lines in which the seedspecific expression of *fad 2* has been inactivated result in a *consistently* high oleic (>80%) content of the seed oil. This phenotype is not affected by environment and has no yield penalty.

Low-saturate mutants of soy also exist, primarily due to altered *fat B* activity, but again they are recessive and are the result of mutations in several genes. Transgenic soy lines in which the *fat B* thioesterase activities are suppressed have a 50% reduction in total 16:0 and are dominant. Again, both high-16:0 (inactive *kas 2*) and high-stearate (reduced *aad* 1 activity) mutants of soy exist.

The high-16:0 mutants (>40% 16:0 in seed oil) are relatively stable across different *environments,* although the mutants are recessive. Transgenic soybean plants *overexpressing fat B* also produce >40% 16:0 in the seed oil but as a dominant trait. The high (20-30% 18:0) stearate mutant of soy, by contrast, has severe phenotypic *consequences* associated with the trait including poor *germinability* and loss of vigor.

These characteristics were overcome in both transgenic soy and canola in which one or more endogenous seed-specific *aad 1* genes were inactivated in the *transgenic* seeds. The resultant oil in both cases was enriched in stearate (35-40% 18:0) and the *vegetative* tissue of the *transgenic* plants was normal. In both cases, however, the seed *germination* was impaired, possibly because of the presence of 18:0 in the membrane phospholipids as well as the TAG.

Sunflower, by contrast, has a high-stearate mutant (25% 18:0) that appears to be normal in all other respects. Further, transgenic sunflowers that contain 35% 18:0 in the TAG (seed-specific suppression of *aad 1*) *germinated* normally, although the seed oil content was reduced. There is also a report of a *specialized* thioesterase involved in the production of stearate in the seeds of mangosteen (*Garcinia mangostana*). Stearate is the *predominant* fatty acid (45-50% of total fatty acids) in this seed. When the *mangosteen thioesterase* gene (*fat A*) was expressed in canola seeds, stearate levels of 20% were observed.

 MONOUNSATURATED FATTY ACIDS

Oleic acid (Δ9 18:1) is a component of most common plant oils, ranging from about 20% in soybean to over 80% in some mutant varieties of canola and sunflower. The Δ9 *desaturase* enzyme described earlier normally inserts a double bond at the Δ9 position of stearoyl-ACP to form oleoylACP.

There are, however, a number of naturally occurring oils that contain *monounsaturated* fatty acids with double bonds in positions other than the n-9 carbon from the carboxyl group. For, example, seeds of the Umbelliferae species such as carrot and coriander contain oils rich in petroselenic acid (Δ6 18:1).

This unusual *monounsaturate* is the result of the activity of a seed-specific plastidial Δ4 desaturase that converts palmitoyl-ACP to Δ4 *hexadecanoyl*-ACP, which is then elongated to petroselenoyl-ACP.

Thus, this soluble desaturase has both a different substrate (*chain length*) specificity and different regiospecificity from the canonical stearoyl-ACP desaturase, yet based on its primary amino acid sequence it is clearly a member of the same gene family. This gene family (*aad 1*) includes a number of other members that vary from the standard Δ9 18:0-ACP in their substrate specificity, regiospecificity, or both.

Additional examples include the Δ6 18:0-ACP desaturase from *Thunbergia alata* and Δ9 16:0-ACP desaturases from *Doxantha spp.* and from *Asclepia syriaca*, all of which have >70% amino acid sequence *similarity* to Δ9 18:0-ACP desaturases.

It has been shown thut mutations in as little as five amino acids can produce changes in both substrate specificity and *regiospecificity* of an acyl-ACP *desaturase*, for example, converting a Δ6 16:0-ACP desaturase into a Δ9 18:0-ACP desaturase. Despite this strong *conservation* of primary sequence in the *aad 1* gene family, it is necessary but not sufficient to express the coriander Δ4 palmitoyl-ACP desaturase in a standard oilseed (e.g., soybean, sunflower) in order to produce large amounts of *petroselenic* acid instead of oleic acid.

This is because the *Umbelliferae* species producing this fatty acid have a *modified* fatty acid biosynthetic pathway adapted to produce this fatty acid. Adaptations include a modified *kas A* gene product resulting in a condensing enzyme with specificity for Δ4 *hexadecanoyl*-ACP and a modified *fat B* gene encoding a petroselenyl-ACP *thioesterase*, plus other additional variants including *acyltransferases*, ferredoxins, and possibly ACPs.

These observations demonstrate both the complexity of the *evolutionary* process that has resulted in divergent oils and the technical challenges of producing novel fatty acids in oilseed plants. Very long chain *monounsaturated* fatty acids (VLCFAs, 20-26 carbons) are found in the storage oils of some plants, such as members of the Cruciferae family, and in epicuticular and storage wax esters.

Most unsaturated VLCFAs are the result of the elongation of oleoyl-CoA by a membrane-

Simplified pathway of plant long chain polyunsaturated fatty acid biosynthesis

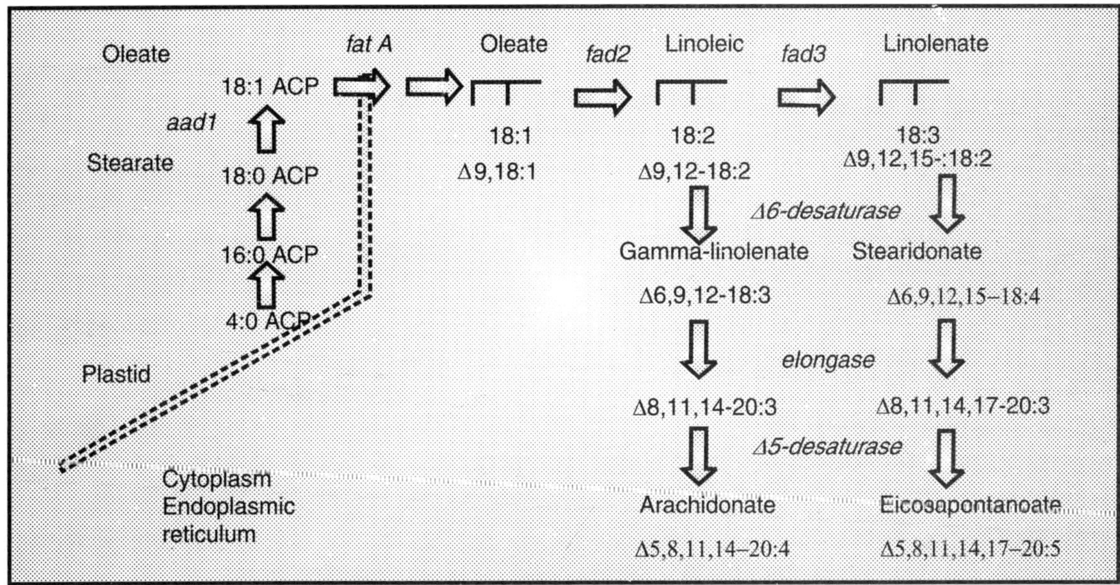

Figure 10.2: Higher plant pathway of long-chain PUFA formation from linoleic and a-linolenic acids. A simplified schematic showing the extraplastidic pathway of arachidonate and eicosapentaenoate from stearate. The minimum amounts of enzyme activities are shown with no cross talk between the two pathways.

bound elongase complex. Waxes, esters of long-chain alcohols and fatty acids, are *abundant* in plants as a cell wall component to give *hydrophobicity*, resistance to fungal attack, and light *absorption* and reflection.

Jojoba (*Simmondsia chinensis*) is the only angiosperm known to *accumulate* liquid waxes in its seeds as an energy store. Up to 60% of the seed dry weight consists of linear wax esters of ω-9 *monounsaturated* C20, C22, and C24 fatty acids and alcohols. TAG is absent. From earlier biochemical data it was inferred that an acyl-CoA-based chain elongation was responsible for the long-chain acyl chains of jojoba wax.

This was confirmed by the Calgene group's purification and cDNA cloning of all three components, a jojoba β-ketoacyl-CoA synthase, a fatty acyl reductase, and a wax synthase proposed as necessary for wax synthesis. In transgenic *Arabidopsis* seed *expressing* all three of these cDNAs, large quantities of short-chain liquid wax accumulated, representing up to 70% of the seed oil.

It has thus been *demonstrated* that not only are these three enzyme activities necessary and sufficient for seed wax formation but also this pathway can efficiently divert carbon from TAG in vivo. An *Arabidopsis* gene (*fae 1*) related to the jojoba condensing enzyme (β-ketoacyl-CoA synthase) has been cloned by insertional mutagenesis.

Fae 1 was shown to complement *Arabidopsis* mutants that have reduced 20C fatty acids and increased oleic acid and to produce VLCFAs when expressed in tobacco. It seems probable based on these observations that a single *condensing* enzyme controls the elongation of C18 to C20, C22 acyl CoAs in VLCFA-producing seed. *A fae 1* homologue has also been cloned from *Limnanthes* and has been expressed in soybean seeds.

The result is the formation of C20 and C22 saturated fatty acids at the expense of palmitic acid (16:0). When coexpressed with the *Limnanthes* $\Delta 5$ desaturase, 20:1 is formed at about 20% relative abundance. These results illustrate that the specificity of the *elongation* step of acyl-CoAs appears to be *determined* entirely by the *fae* I gene product and that the *Limnanthes fae I* gene product has specificity for saturated fatty acids, unlike the *monounsaturated* specificity of the *Arabidopsis fae 1.*

POLYUNSATURATED FATTY ACIDS

The 18-carbon polyunsaturated fatty acids (PUFAs) linoleic and α-linolenic acids are essential components of plant membranes (18:2, 18:3). PUFAs are also substrates for the *lipoxygenase-mediated* production of various volatile compounds *including* methyl jasmonate. This is an area of active research because the volatiles produced are important both as signaling agents in response to pathogen attack and as flavoring components in the area of food and fragrance chemistry.

The PUFAs α-linoleic and linolenic acids are widely *distributed* in nature. In addition, γ-linolenic acid (GLA) is found in the seeds of a few plant species (borage, evening primrose, black currant) as well as *cyanobacteria* and fungi. Longer chain n6 PUFAs such as *arachidonic* acid (ARA 20:4n-6) are found in *microorganisms* such as the fungus *Morteriella alpina* and the marine diatom *Porphyridiom cruentum.*

The related n-3 LC-PUFAS eicosapentanoic acid (EPA 20:5n-3) and *docosahexanoic* acid (DHA 22:6n-3) are found in marine *microorganisms* and in fish oil. Both linoleic and α-linolenic acids are essential fatty acids in the human diet because the $\Delta 12$ and n-3 desaturase activities necessary to convert oleic acid to these fatty acids are lacking in most *mammalian* microsomes.

The dietary PUFAs (18:2, 18:3) are used primarily in mammals as precursors for the *eicosanoids* including *prostaglandins* and leukotrienes. Because of the known beneficial effects associated with the intake of LC-PUFAs in the diet of both infants and adults and the limited natural sources *commercially* available, there has been much interest lately in the possibility of producing ARA, EPA, and DHA in plant seed oils, where they do not normally occur.

In higher eukaryotes, the major long-chain PUFA arachidonate (ARA 20:4n-6) is derived from linoleic acid (18:2, and EPA (20:5n-3) and DHA (22:6n-3) from α-linolenic acid (ALA). The metabolic pathways for longchain PUFA formation have been known for some time, but until recently none of the proteins had been identified.

The pathways of very long chain PUFA synthesis in fungi and marine algae involve a series of sequential reductions and elongations that resemble the production of long-chain fatty acids such as erucic acid in plants like *Arabidopsis* and rapeseed. With the advent of modem genomic techniques and the existence of known desaturase and elongase protein sequences, it was possible to search cDNA EST databases of PUFA-containing organisms using conserved desaturase and elongase domains.

In this way, Δ5 and Δ6 desaturases and the 18:3 n-6 elongase from the ARA-accumulating filamentous fungus *Morteriella alpina* were identified. Using similar approaches, orthologues of the Δ5 desaturase and the 18:3n-6 elongase have been *identified* from *C. elegans* and human cDNA EST databases *respectively*. Rapid functional *identification* of putative cDNA clones was carried out by *expression* in yeast.

This technique enabled *identification* of individual positive cDNA clones and led to the possibility of producing these very long chain PUFAs in the oil of transgenic plants. Earlier work on the expression of a δ-6 desaturase from a *cyanobacterium* in transgenic tobacco showed no accumuation of GLA or OTA in seeds.

In contrast, coexpression of *M. alpina* Δ6 and Δ12 desaturases in canola seed resulted in a GLA content of about 40% of the seed oil fatty acids. Similarly, seed-specific expression of the borage Δ6 desaturase in transgenic soy seed resulted in a similar total GLA content in the seed oil (*S. Coughlan, unpublished results*).

The differences between canola and soy seed may be related to the higher amount of 18:2 naturally present in soy oil (50%) compared with canola oil (20%). With the cloning of all of the individual components of the eukaryotic pathway of LC-PUFA *formation*, the technical challenges remaining are those of metabolic pathway engineering.

For example, it will be necessary to co-express up to six different enzymes *simultaneously* in a developing oilseed in order to produce DHA from a-linolenic acid in transgenic plants. Finally, it should be noted that some marine *microorganisms* (bacteria and diatoms) have a completely different pathway of LC-PUFA formation using polyketide synthases.

VARIATIONS ON THE METHYLENE-INTERRUPTED DOUBLE BOND

As discussed earlier, the polyunsaturated fatty acids of plant membrane phospholipids and of the most common plant oils are *predominantly* linoleic and α-linolenic acids. These are 18-carbon fatty acids with two or three methylene-interrupted double bonds.

A wide variety of plants have oils *containing* fatty acids with other types of functional groups or *non-methyleneinterrupted* bonds, and many of these fatty acids are the result of the activity of diverged members of the phospholipid A12 desaturase (*fad 2*) gene family. The first diverged *fad-2* genes to be identified were the genes encoding 12-hydroxylases from *Ricinus communis* and *Lesquerella fendleri*. These enzymes catalyze the *introduction* of hydroxy groups into fatty acids.

Heterologous expression of these diverged *fad 2* cDNAs in transgenic *Arabidopsis* seeds resulted in the production of up to 20% hydroxylated fatty acids in the seed oil. Also observed were a concomitant increase in oleic acid, which is a common by-product of heterologous expression of diverged *fad 2* cDNAs, and an accumulation of the novel fatty acid in membrane phosphatidylcholine.

One interpretation of these observations is that the novel fatty acid is not being properly channeled from the PC to TAG after the functional group has been inserted. Thus, the whole cycle is slowed down and there is a backup of oleoyl-CoA waiting to be incorporated into PC for desaturation. Thus, it is likely that additional diverged enzymes exist in the species producing these unusual fatty acids to ensure the appropriate *channeling* from the membrane *phospholipid* into the storage lipid. To obtain levels of these unusual fatty acids in transgenic oilseeds comparable to those in the native plant, it will be necessary to understand the metabolic pathway and to coexpress the additional enzyme *activities* into the transgenic oilseed together with the diverged *fad 2.*

Candidates for these activities include novel phospholipase(s), acyl CoA synthases, and the *acyltransferases* including the newly described PDAT (*phospholipid:diacylglycerol acyltransferase*) class. The *Lesquerella* hydroxylase is actually a bifunctional enzyme with some omega-6 desaturase activity, and only a few amino acid *substitutions* are necessary and sufficient to change the hydroxylase to desaturase activities of the enzyme.

These *similarities* in primary amino acid sequence between *fad 2* desaturases and *fad 2* hydroxylases led to homologybased searching for other *fad* 2-related genes in oilseed species *containing* unusual fatty acids in their oil. This approach led to the *identification* of *fad* 2-related epoxygenases from *Vernonia galamensis* and *Crepis palaestrina* and a fatty acid acetylenase from *Crepis alpina.*

These enzymes catalyze the formation of epoxy groups and acetylenic triple bonds, respectively, into fatty acids. More recently, *fad* 2-related conjugase cDNAs from *Momordica charantia, Impatiens balsamica,* and *Calendula officinalis* have been identified. Conjugated fatty acids are polyunsaturated fatty acids with nonmethylene-interrupted double bonds.

Momordica is rich in a-eleostearic acid (18:3 Δ9cis, *lltrans, 13trans*). *Impatiens* is rich in a-parinaric acid (18:4 Δ*9cis, lltrans, 13trans,* 15cis) and *Calendula* in calendic acid (18:3 Δ*8trans, l0trans, 12cis*). Finally, the plant sphingolipid desaturases represent a possible ancestral fusion of an N-terminal cytochrome b_5 with a Δ6-desaturase first described in borage (*Boragio officinalis*) seeds. Borage seeds, in common with a few other plants such as evening primrose (*Oenothera biennis*) and black currant (*Ribes nigrum*), contain oils rich in γ-linolenic acid.

Given the primary sequence homology between the ubiquitous plant *sphingolipid* desaturases and the borage Δ6 desaturase, it seems probable that the borage-type Δ6 *desaturases* represent enzymes that have diverged in substrate *specificity* from the 08/06 sphingolipid desaturase family. Curiously, the borage Δ6 desaturase is extremely effective at producing up to 50% GLA in transgenic soy seed but not in transgenic *Arabidopsis* or canola seeds.

COMMERCIAL PRODUCTION OF NEW OILS FROM TRANSGENIC PLANTS

In all the preceding examples in which fatty acid metabolism has been *manipulated* in *transgenic* plants, the abundance of novel fatty acid content in the resulting seed oil varies depending on the type of fatty acid produced. Very *significant* amounts of short-chain, *monounsaturated* and *polyunsaturated* fatty acids have been produced in transgenic plants.

In contrast, fatty acids containing unusual functional groups are produced in transgenic plants in amounts considerably less than that of exotic plants that normally produce them. The differences in the relative *accumulation* of different fatty acids in transgenic plant oils are not yet fully understood. Thus, a key technical goal that remains is the ability to produce any given novel fatty acid as a large proportion of the seed oil.

Additional hurdles to the commercial production of novel oils includes any possible negative impact of the *transgenes* on seed yield and the costs associated with gaining worldwide regulatory approval to grow and produce the new crop (currently running into many millions of dollars).

The ability to sell these new oils for a premium over commodity oil that is large enough to cover these costs is essential to convert the many technical *achievements* described in this chapter into commercial successes.

Chapter 11

PLANTS AS IMMUNOTHERAPEUTIC AGENTS

Since the first reports 20 years ago, genetically engineered plants with improved traits, pest and herbicide *resistance*, etc., have produced significant agricultural revenues. In contrast, the development of plants as bioreactors to produce transgenic proteins for *pharmaceutical* use is in its infancy. Numerous *immunotherapeutic* proteins, antibodies, and vaccines have been produced; however, a limited number have made their way into clinical trials.

The most advanced product in human clinical trials is a secretory *immunoglobulin* A (IgA) antibody composed of four polypeptide chains that inhibits the binding to teeth of *Streptococcus mutans,* the major oral pathogen. This chapter will *summarize* recent work *demonstrating* the potential of plants to synthesize and assemble complex proteins suitable for human *therapeutic* use.

PLANT BIOREACTORS FOR IMMUNOTHERAPEUTIC PROTEINS

The first transgenic plants were reported in 1983. Since then, many *recombinant* proteins have been expressed in several important agronomic species of plants including tobacco, corn, tomato, potato, banana, alfalfa, and canola.

Recent work *suggests* that plants will be a facile and economic bioreactor for large-scale production of industrial and *pharmaceutical recombinant* proteins.

Genetically engineered (transgenic) plants have several advantages as sources of proteins compared with human or animal fluids or tissues, *recombinant* microbes, transfected animal cell lines, or *transgenic* animals.

These include

Efficiency of the *transformation* technology and speed of scale-up

Correct assembly of multimeric antibodies (unlike bacteria)

Increased safety, as plants do not serve as hosts for human *pathogens*, such as human *immunodeficiency* virus (HIV), prions, and hepatitis viruses

Production of raw material on an *agricultural* scale at low cost

Reduced *capitalization* costs relative to *fermentation* methods

Depending upon the promoters used, *transgenic* proteins will be *sequestered throughout* the plant or in specific parts of the plants (e.g., seeds) or specific organelles within a given plant cell. Much of the early work utilized strong generic promoters, such as the cauliflower mosaic virus 35S promoter giving *widespread* protein *expression* in green biomass.

For example, De Wilde et al. (1998) showed that in *Arabidopsis,* antibody or Fab fragments bearing *conventional* leader sequences accumulate at the sites where water passes on its radial pathway toward and within the vascular bundle.

A large proportion of these proteins are transported into the apoplast of *A. thaliana,* possibly by the water flow in the *transpiration* stream. In contrast, numerous laboratories have shown transgenic protein accumulation in seeds of tobacco, corn, soybean or barley. Table elsewhere in this chapter presents a listing of expression levels of several major *immunotherapeutic* proteins in transgenic plants.

The most widely studied proteins have been antigens for use in oral vaccines and antibodies for passive *immunotherapy*. Plants are attractive expression vehicles for each of these applications.

Table 11.1: Immunotherapeutic Proteins Synthesized in Transgenic Plants

Recombinant proteins	*Plants*	*Protein production levels*
sIgA Anti-S. *mutans*	Tobacco	200-500 (μg/g)
HBsAg	Tobacco	0.01% TSP
Norwalk capsid protein	Tobacco	0.23% TSP
Norwalk capsid protein	Potato	10-20 (μg/g)
E. coli	Potato	3-4 (μg/g)
LT-B		
Cholera toxin	Potato	30 (μg/g)
CT-B		
Mouse GAD67	Potato	150 (μg/g)
TSP-total soluble protein		

ISSUES REGARDING TRANSGENIC PLANT EXPRESSION OF IMMUNOTHERAPEUTIC PROTEINS

Production Costs

Cost benefits of plant production are enormous. For example, Kusnadi et al. (1997) calculated the cost of producing a *recombinant* protein in various agricultural crops. The cost estimate was based on the commodity price of the crop, the fraction of total protein in the crop, and the not *unreasonable* assumption that the *recombinant* protein *accumulated* to 10% of the total plant protein.

Although crops with more protein content (e.g., soybeans 40% versus potatoes 2%) are more cost-effective, these costs are 10- to 50-fold less than those for protein produced at a high level in *Escherichia coli* (20% total protein).

Depending upon the use of the protein and the requirements for purification for in vivo *pharmaceutical* use, purification costs will obviously augment final product costs; however, at the hundred kilogram to metric ton level, plant-produced proteins will provide obvious savings.

Glycosylation of Transgenic Plant Proteins; Plant Antibody Glycosylation

Cabanes-Macheteau et al. (1999) reported the first detailed analysis of the *glycosylation* of a functional *mammalian* glycoprotein expressed in a transgenic plant. The structures of the N-linked glycans attached to the heavy chains of the monoclonal antibody Guy's 13 produced in transgenic tobacco plants (plantibody Guy's 13) were *identified* and compared with those found in the *corresponding* IgGi of murine origin.

As in mouse antibodies, both *N-glycosylation* sites located on the heavy chain of the plantibody Guy's 13 are N-glycosylated. However, the number of Guy's 13 glycoforms is higher in the plant than in the mammalian expressed antibodies.

In addition to highmannose-type N-glycans, 60% of the oligosaccharides N-linked to the plantibody have beta(1,2)-xylose and alpha(1,3)-fucose residues linked to the core Man3GlcNAc2. These oligosaccharide linkages, not found on *mammalian* N-linked glycans, are potentially *immunogenic* and raise the possibility that plantibodies containing N-linked glycans may have limited scope as parenterals or even when applied topically or orally, *particularly* in patients with severe food allergies.

Food allergans bearing beta(1,2)-xylose and alpha(1,3)-fucose have been linked to specific IgE in serum and to biological activity, i.e., histamine release, in allergic patients. In contrast, the mere presence of serum IgE against *crossreactive* carbohydrate *determinants*, which include the beta(1,2)-xylose and alpha(1,3)-fucose linkages to the core Man3GlcNAc2 of plant glycans, has been shown to be a poor predicter of clinical allergy.

These results preclude generalities about the potential toxicity of plantibody glycans in humans. When the mouse plantibody (*mouse amino* acid *sequence and plant glycans*) was used to immunize mice, there was no, or only a minimally detectable, serum immune response.

Thus, in the mouse at least, a "*self*" primary protein structure, decorated with plant N-linked glycans, can be nonimmunogenic. This plantibody has been applied *topically* in the mouth of humans with no detection of human antimouse antibodies. *Humanization* of plantibody primary structures may go a long way to obviate the immunogenic potential of plant glycans, and further genetic *engineering* may, if necessary, alter the glycan structures themselves.

Most dramatically, aglycosyl antibodies can be created by altering the peptide recognition sequence for N-linked *glycosylation* (asn-X-Ser/Thr). Highmannose glycosylation, which does not contain the core-linked xylose and fucose residues, may be favored by the addition of a C-terminal KDEL sequence and the *subsequent* targeting of plantibodies to the *proximal* endoplasmic reticulum. Alternatively, the specific fucosyl or xylosyl *transferases*, which operate in the trans-Golgi, may be targeted for silencing.

Gene Silencing: A Potential Problem of Plant Expression

Levels of transgenic protein accumulation reported in the literature generally represent the highest levels found in primary *transformants*. It is becoming increasingly clear that stability of *expression* is just as important as absolute levels of expression.

Many laboratories have noted the common occurrence of *transgene* silencing in plants, in which transgenes can become inactivated either during development or in subsequent generations. Two types of gene silencing have been observed in plants: *transcriptional* gene silencing (TGS), in

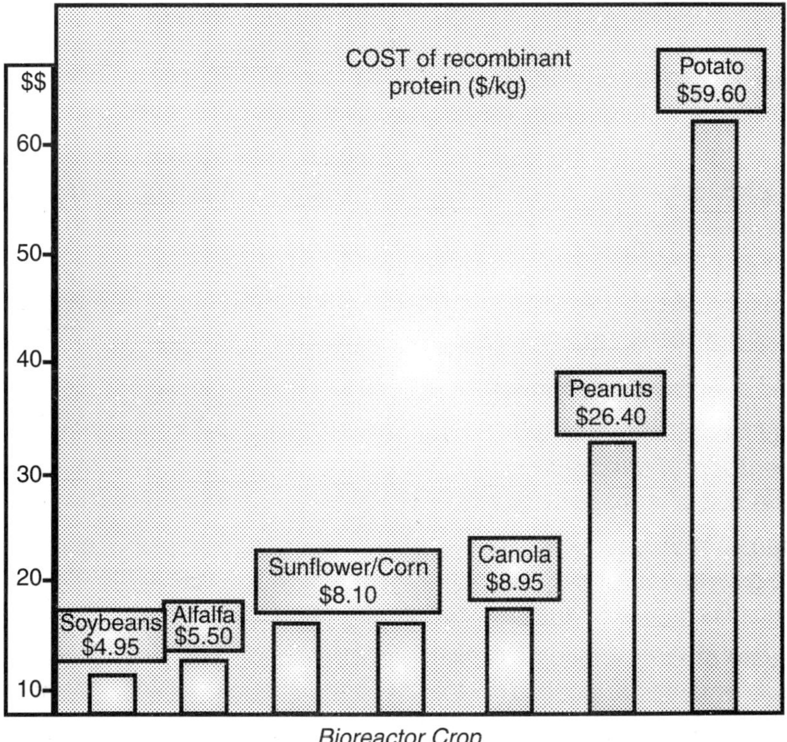

Figure 11.1: Relative cost of protein production in various agricultural crops.

which promoters become silenced and *transcription* is reduced, and *posttranscriptional* gene silencing (PTGS), in which *transcription* continues unabated but *transcripts* are rapidly degraded.

The exact mechanisms of both types of gene silencing are still being discovered, but there are common features to both. For instance, the presence of *homologous* sequences is frequently involved. If repeats are present within transgenes, or if transgene sequences are *homologous* to endogenous genes, silencing is more frequent. Methylation of DNA may be involved.

In TGS, the promoters of silenced genes are *hypermethylated.* In PTGS, it is the coding regions that tend to be methylated. de Neve et al. found both types of silencing in a careful examination of five different *homozygous* transgenic *Arabidopsis* lines expressing either IgG or Fab. Silencing seems to be positively correlated with level of expression and with copy number of the transgene.

That is, transgenes present in multiple copies or expressed from strong constitutive promoters are more likely to be silenced. This suggests some possibilities for reducing the occurrence of silencing. Silencing may be less of a problem with tissue-specific or weak *constitutive* promoters, although this may be *antithetical* to the desire for high levels of expression.

The introduction of multiple copies can be reduced by the use of *Agrobacterium,* which tends to result in fewer transgene copies than biolistic *transformation.* Flanking transgenes with matrix attachment region (MAR) sequences has been shown to reduce the occurrence of gene silencing.

This probably works by preventing formation of antisense transcripts by *transcription* from flanking endogenous genes into the transgene. Viral *supppressors* of silencing have been used quite effectively to prevent or reverse PTGS. When plants that are transgenic for a viral protein known as helper component protease (HC-Pro) are crossed with plants in which a transgene is silenced, expression is restored in progeny containing both transgenes.

It should also be possible to use HC-Proexpressing plants as the starting material for transformation with a gene of interest. Finally, a number of mutants have been isolated in *Arabidopsis* that lack either TGS or PTGS. Some of these mutants appear to be normal in every respect except the inability to silence transgenes.

It may eventually be possible to isolate similar mutations in plants that are more practical for the production of transgenic proteins.

Purification and Process Development

The potential for cost reduction when using *genetically* engineered green plants as bioreactors, instead of *conventional pharmaceutical* factories engineered with concrete and steel, is a powerful argument for the use of transgenic plants to produce recombinant proteins.

The commercial-scale production of proteins from transgenic plants generally requires one to envisage the growth and processing of tons of biomass to achieve the economy of scale that would fully exploit the inputs of sunlight, soil, water, and fertilizer.

The *processing* of large amounts of biomass also anticipates large numbers of patients or consumers, large amounts of purified protein needed for each patient or consumer, lower than anticipated levels of *expression,* and losses during processing. The realities of commercial-scale production benefit from a demand for simplicity early on in the development of a large-scale process.

Bench-scale or laboratory-scale procedures often employ the *pampering* conditions that are necessary for a proof of concept but are too complicated and *expensive* for large-scale efforts. For instance, because of issues regarding toxicity and expense, it is preferred not to use protease inhibitors beyond the bench scale.

Reagents such as ammonium sulfate are frowned upon because of the *disposal-associated* costs, as are organic solvents because of their toxicity and *flammability*. Efforts to avoid the purchase and maintenance of centrifuges will eventually be gratefully acknowledged by *maintenance* personnel.

In addition, and more *fundamentally*, it is important to realize that a commercial process will not be executed by rocket scientists, each with extensive postdoctoral training, but by more ordinary and, while no less dedicated, almost certainly less well-trained and educated people (i.e., they cost less).

Thus, simplicity in the number, as well as the type, of components in a process is *paramount* to reduce not only costs but also errors. Minimalist *approaches* to large-scale process development will often be rewarded even though they may appear simplistic.

We found that grinding transgenic tobacco in water alone gave up to 70% of the *expected immunoglobulin* compared with tobacco ground in a buffer, poised at a specified pH, containing six components in addition to water; each component had been chosen for a particular, *biochemically* sound, reason.

Table 11.2: Antibody-Derived Molecules Produced in Transgenic Plants

Mab form (no. of chains)	*Antigen*	*Plant species-comment*
Single domain (dAb) (1)	Substance P (neuropeptide)	*Nicotiana*
Single chain Fv (1)	Phytochrome	*Nicotiana*
Single chain Fv (1)	Artichoke mottled crinkle virus coat	Nicotiana-viral protection
Single chain Fv (1)	Abscisic acid	*Nicotiana-wilty* phenotype
Single chain Fv (1)	Root-knot nematode	*Nicotiana*
Single chain Fv (1)	Beet necrotic yellow vein virus	*Nicotiana benthamiana*
scFv	Several	*Nicotiana*, KDEL augment expression
Fab; IgG (k) (2)	Human creatine kinase	*Nicotiana Arabidopsis*
IgG (k) (2)	Transition-state analogue	*Nicotiana*
IgG (k) (2)	Fungal cutinase	*Nicotiana*
IgG (k) and IgG/A	*Streptococcus mutans* adhesin	*Nicotiana* hybrids (2)
Secretory IgA/G (4)	*S. mutans* adhesin	*Nicotiana*
IgM/(G) (2)	NP (4-hydroxy 3-nitrophenylacetyl) (Hapten)	*Nicotiana*

Yet this was evidence which suggested that perhaps not all of the *components* were vitally important, and we now use a two-component buffer at a specified pH. Commercial-scale production of *recombinant* proteins from plants will also benefit from the *technology* and *equipment* commonly used in the food and beverage industry.

Grain mills and coleslaw slicers will doubtless be useful off-the-shelf *machinery* for the initial *processing* of seeds and leafy tissue. The *beverage industry* has always been concerned with the clarification of juices and their phenolic content and is a source of knowledge and *equipment*, both new and used.

The chef's trick of delaying the browning of cut fruit by the addition of lemon-acidulated water has led us to formulate buffers to inhibit the "*tanning*" of proteins in tobacco extracts. Two constituents of stem and leaf extracts that require special consideration are *membranes* and cell walls.

The green color of stem and leaf extracts indicates the presence of chlorophyll and the *suspension* of *thylakoid* membranes. These and other membranes must be removed to allow filterability at or below a pore size of 0.45 μm.

This level of filterability helps to ensure, but does not guarantee, the good behavior of the extract during subsequent chromatography and serves to remove bacterial sources of *contamination*. The cellulose-containing debris, which forms a large part of the insoluble portion of extracts, can be used as an endogenous "filter aid" during the initial *clarification* to remove these membranous components.

Phenolics are a major concern when extracting most stems and leaves, and one's efforts are rewarded by their early removal. They may interact with proteins and other extract *components* via *hydrophobic* interactions, salt bridges, hydrogen bonding, and by *additional* reactions to nucleophilic centers.

These interactions can dramatically and *irreversibly* alter the properties of proteins. Fortunately, the majority of released phenolics are *generally* small in size, as well as water soluble, and may be removed by tangential-flow *ultrafiltration/diafiltration*, which also serves to concentrate the considerably larger proteins of interest.

In addition, other incompatible, water-soluble secondary metabolites, such as neonicotine

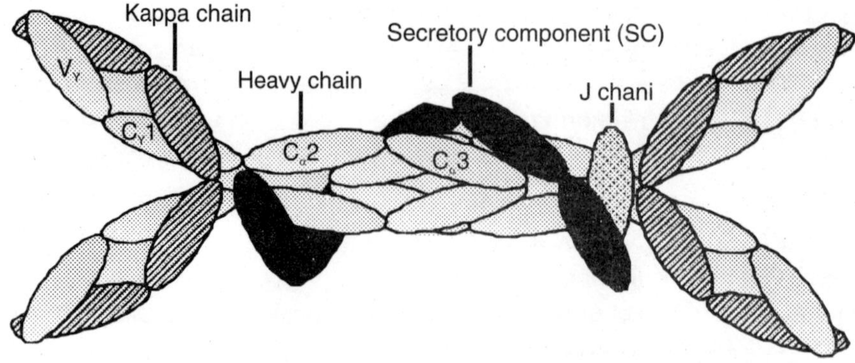

Figure 11.2: The structure of secretory IgA.

SIgA Transcytosis

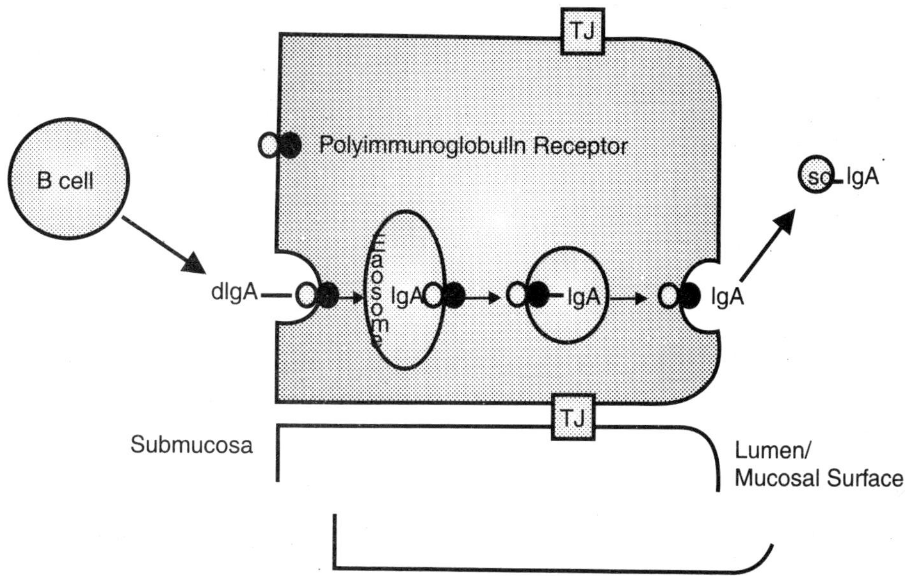

Figure 11.3: SIgA is produced by two cell types. Submucosal lymphoid tissue produces dimeric, IgA, which diffuses to the serosal side of the mucosal epithelial cells, where it binds to the polyimmunoglobulin receptor. Secretory component (SC) is proteolytically derived from the polyimmunoglobulin receptor.

(*anabasine*) and nicotine from tobacco, may be removed by *ultrafiltration/diafiltration*. After such clarification and concentration steps, *recombinant* proteins can be assumed to behave *independently* and with regard to the *peculiarities* of their own biochemistry.

In other words, they are now ready for chromatography. Residual phenolics may still dictate the degree of cleanup necessary before *chromatography* on an *expensive* protein A or protein G affinity column is allowed; these are economic considerations common to any *purification* process. One additional note of caution: because the processed plant or seed was probably grown in dirt, or some similarly unclean stratum, one may anticipate the presence of a diverse bioburden.

Contamination of product with *endotoxins* and *mycotoxins* can be *minimized* by rapid *processing* and early filtration, but process development must also always recognize the necessity to eliminate compounds as well as the necessity to purify, concentrate, and stabilize a product of interest.

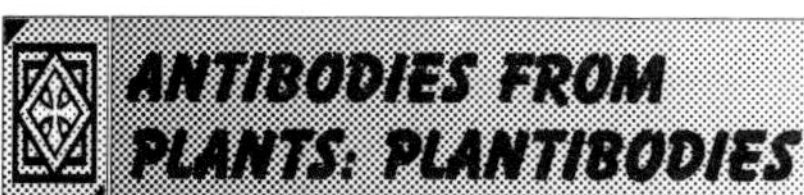

ANTIBODIES FROM PLANTS: PLANTIBODIES

Although antibodies were first expressed in plants in the mid-1980s by two German graduate students, the first report was published in 1989. Since then, a diverse group of "*plantibody*" types and forms have been prepared.

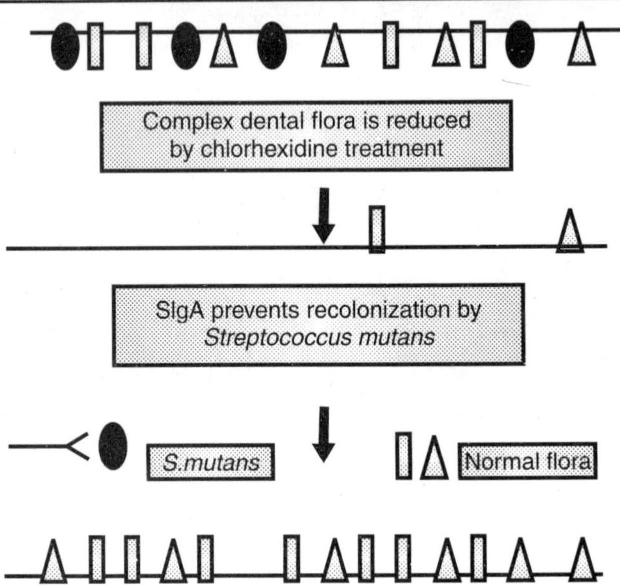

Figure 11.4: Proposed mechanism of CaroRx: the concept of ecological niche. After all flora have been reduced using oral antiseptic, chlorhexidine, a short treatment course with CaroRx provides an opportunity for normal flora to replace S. mutans.

Originally, foreign antibody genes were introduced into plant cells by *nonpathogenic* strains of the natural plant pathogen *Agrobacterium tumefaciens* and *regeneration* in tissue culture resulted in the recovery of stable transgenic plants.

Although this initial work to generate multichain proteins required crossing of plants expressing each chain, more recent studies have shown that multiple chains can be introduced via a single biolistic *transformation* event, greatly reducing the time to final assembled plantibody.

SIgA: A Novel Antibody Isotype

This laboratory has focused on the production of secretory IgA (SIgA) plantibodies. At the present time, plants offer the only large-scale, *commercially* viable system for production of this unique form of antibody. SIgA is the most abundant antibody class *produced* by the body (>60% of total *immunoglobulin*).

SIgA is secreted onto mucosal surfaces to provide local protection from toxins and pathogens. The SIgA is composed of four different protein chains: heavy and light *immunoglobulin* chains that form the antigen-binding *hypervariable* region, a J chain that *dimerizes* two IgA molecules (SIgA has four *antigen binding* sites), and a secretory component that is derived from the mucosal epithelial cells.

Dimeric IgA containing J chain derived from submucosal B cells binds to the epithelial cell *polyimmunoglobulin* receptor (PIG^R) that transports the IgA to the mucosal surface. Binding triggers *transcytosis* to the mucosal surface, where a protease releases a portion of the PIG^R called secretory component *conveniently* used to bind the SIgA.

The secretory component protects the dimeric IgA from proteases and *denaturation* on the

Table 11.3: Plant-Produced Human Therapeutics (-1998)			
Protein	***Target***	***Organization***	***Stage***
SIgA	Caries	PLANET Biotech	Phase II
IgG	Cancer	NeoRx/Monsanto	Phase I/II **(cancelled due to unexpected gastrointestinal toxicity) (unpublished)**
E. coli LT	*E. coli* diarrhea	Boyce Thompson	Phase I/II

mucosal surface. Previously it was not possible to obtain therapeutic quantities of this class of *immunoglobulin.* The recent availability of large amounts of secretory IgA plantibodies opens up a number of novel therapeutic opportunities for disorders of the mucosal immune system.

These include therapies for intestinal pathogens such as hepatitis viruses, *Helicobacter pylori,* and *enterotoxigenic E. coli,* and cholera; respiratory pathogens such as rhinovirus and influenza; and *genitourinary* sexually transmitted diseases (e.g., herpes simplex virus) and contraception. To date, three *immunotherapeutic* products produced in plants have entered the clinic.

These products, listed in Table elsewhere in this chapter, include two antibodies and an oral vaccine. Clinical studies of the anti-EPCAM plantibody (*codeveloped* by NeoRx and Monsanto) were *discontinued* due to significant gastrointestinal side effects. The *anti-Streptococcus mutans* antibody is currently in phase II trials.

CLINICAL STUDIES OF CARORXTM, AN ANTISTREPTOCOCCUS MUTANS SIGA TO PREVENT DENTAL CARIES

The most clinically advanced SIgA plantibody, called CaroRx, recognizes and inhibits the binding of the major oral pathogen, *Streptococcus mutans,* to teeth. In preliminary work, a series of in vivo passive immunization ex-periments was carried out in 84 human subjects using murine anti-S. *mutans* antibodies.

Topical application of anti-*S. mutans* antigen SA I/II monoclonal antibodies (MAbs) prevented colonization of artificially implanted exogenous strains of *S. mutans* as well as natural recolonization by indigenous *S. mutans.*

In these studies the pathogenic *S. mutans* was replaced by endogenous flora. The presence of the complement activating and phagocyte-binding sites on the Fc fragment of the MAb was not essential for activity because the $F(ab)_2$ portion of the MAb was as protective as the intact IgG; however, the Fab fragment failed to prevent *recolonization* of *S. mutans.* Prevention of recolonization was specifically restricted to *S. mutans,* as the proportion of other organisms, such as *S. sanguis,* did not change significantly.

The surprising feature of these experiments was that protection from recolonization by *S. mutans* lasted up to 2 years (*J. Ma, personal communication*), although MAb was applied for only 3 weeks and functional MAb was detected on the teeth for only 3 days following the final application of MAb. All studies indicated that this form of *immunotherapy* appears to be safe and well tolerated.

The long-term protection could therefore not be accounted for by persistence of MAb on the teeth but may be due to a shift in the microbial balance in which other bacteria occupy the ecological niche vacated by *S. mutans*, resulting in resistance to *recolonization* by *S. mutans*. The antigen-binding V regions of the best murine Mab identified by Ma and Lehner, Guy's 13, has been used to create an SIgA plantibody produced in tobacco-designated CaroRx.

Levels of production of CaroRx in tobacco are up to 0.5 mg/g fresh weight. Future plans call for production of CaroRx in corn and other cereal grains. CaroRx has been produced and purified from tobacco under GMP conditions for clinical testing in the United Kingdom and the United States.

CaroRx was engineered with an additional IgG CH2 domain to facilitate purification of the antibody by protein G affinity chromatography. A Poros T" protein G affinity purification was used to obtain >95% pure CaroRx from green plant tissue. Clinical evaluation of CaroRx in a pilot phase II trial has been completed at Guy's Hospital.

In this trial a functional comparison was made between CaroRx and the parent IgG monoclonal antibody Guy's 13. BIACORE analysis revealed that the affinity of the antibodies for purified *S. mutans* SA 1/II was similar (KD = 0.5-1.3 X 10^{-9} M); however, CaroRx had fourfold higher avidity (*functional affinity*), a not unexpected result given the tetravalent binding of the SIgA. Using an experimental design similar to that used to demonstrate activity of the parent Mab, CaroRx gave specific protection against colonization by oral streptococci for over 4 months.

In addition to this therapeutic end point, *pharmacokinetic* studies showed that in the human oral cavity, CaroRx survived for >3 days versus 1 day for the IgG antibody and multiple serum antibody samples were negative for human antimouse (HAMA) or antirabbit antibodies.

There was no evidence of local or systemic toxicity of the topically applied plantibody. These initial clinical studies demonstrate that topically applied anti *S. mutans* SIgA plantibody (CaroRx) is safe (no HAMA, no local or systemic toxicity) and prevents colonization by *S. mutans*, the major cause of human dental caries.

Planet Biotechnology, Inc., has submitted an IND (*investigational* new drug *application*) to the U.S. Food and Drug Administration (FDA) and phase I/II *confirmatory* clinical trials began at the School of Dentistry at the University of California in San Francisco in Autumn 1998.

12

Chapter

TRANSGENIC PLANTS WITH INCREASED TOLERANCE AGAINST VIRAL PATHOGENS

Compared with fungi and bacteria, plant viruses are the third important pathogens on cultured plants. They rely *completely* on host cells for replication and gene *expression*, and that is why numerous attempts to cure infected plants by chemical treatment have been *unsuccessful*.

Therefore, plant virologists have focused their research on quarantine measures (diagnosis, establishment of virus-free cultures), control of virus vectors (insects, fungi, and nematodes), and resistance breeding. Genetic traits of wild and cultivated plant species *introduced* by classical crossings have become the most sustainable *instruments* to protect plants from viruses.

These tools are now being augmented by gene *technological* engineering. Molecular biology has identified and characterized known resistance genes and created new resistance traits. Classical genetics and molecular biology have developed fruitful *interactions* and rely on each other for *long-lived* defense strategies. In contrast to animals, plants do not have a real immune system to combat invading viruses.

Whereas animals encounter viruses from the outside of the cell, plants receive viruses by wounding or direct injection into the cytoplasm. As a rule, plant viruses stay within symplastic tissues during further spread through plants without the need to cross membrane borders.

Exceptionally, those plant viruses have evolved *mechanisms* to bud out through membranes that multiply in their insect vectors. Natural as well as artificial resistance mechanisms have to *acknowlege* these *peculiarities* of plant viruses.

Definition of Terms

"Resistance" and "tolerance" have specific meanings in plant virology

in contrast to other areas of plant pathology. Unfortunately, the terms are often *intermingled* in the literature. It is, therefore, necessary to define the terms more precisely, at least to *understand* this review, following the principles of Matthews' classical textbook on plant virology.

Table 12.1: Definition of Terms Following the Principles of Matthews' Classical Textbook on Plant Virology

1.	*Nonhosts* (immune plants)	Viruses do not replicate in protoplasts, cells, or plants. After inoculation they might be disassembled but do not multiply, e.g., due to lack of essential host factors. (The term "immune" is frequently used in a general meaning and might be misunderstood; plants do not have a real immune system and the failure to multiply in nonhosts does not rely on an equivalent mechanism.)
2.	*Hosts* (infectible plants)	Viruses can infect and replicate in protoplasts.
2.1.	*Resistant* plants	Viruses remain confined to the primary infected cell(s). Further spread is suppressed either by lack of compatible host transport factors or by defense reactions (e.g., hypersensitive response).
2.2.	*Susceptible* plants	Viruses replicate and spread systemically through the plant.
2.2.1.	*Sensitive* plants	Plants react with more or less severe symptoms.
2.2.2.	*Tolerant* plants	Viruses do not induce obvious symptoms.
2.2.3.	*Recovery*	Some organs recover from infection either because they become accidentally virus free or because they develop a somaclonal resistance.

In spite of widespread misuse of terms in the literature, for practical applications it is crucial to assign the genetic traits accurately. In case of uncertainty, "protection" might be used instead of resistance, leaving open whether viral multiplication, spread, or symptoms are ameliorated.

DEFENSE RESPONSES OF PLANTS

Following inoculation, plants activate a broad spectrum of responses, either general ones after several types of stress, pathogens and wounding, or specific ones that require the *recognition* of a *particular* pathogen.

Both reaction types may be linked or act separately and determine whether the virus is *virulent* (the host susceptible) or *avirulent* (the host resistant). The resulting interaction is mostly the outcome of a race between virus *multiplication* and the velocity of defense.

General Responses

As with other pathogens, viruses encounter an oxidative burst early, followed by the transcriptional activation of pathogenesis-related (PR) proteins, accumulation of phytoalexins, and a systemic signal *mediated* by salicylic acid, leading to *systemically* acquired *resistance* (SAR) in *noninoculated* tissues or organs.

No evidence is available that PR proteins interact directly with plant viruses, and it is believed that the broad defense reaction is rationalized by the evolutionary experience that a virus seldom comes alone in nature.

A further general response has been attributed to ribosome-inactivating proteins (RIPs), which accumulate in certain plants to high levels in an inactive pre-form that is rendered active during wounding to destroy the *translational* machinery. Several *components* of the general response

Table 12.2: Examples of the Relation between Host Resistance (R Genes) and Virus (*avr* Genes)

Host species	*R gene*	*Virus*	*avr gene*
Arabidopsis thaliana	RCY1	Cucumber mosaic	Coat protein
A. thaliana	HRT	Turnip crinkle	Coat protein
Capsicum chinense	L3	Pepper mild mottle	Coat protein
Lycopersicon esculentum	Tm2	Tobacco mosaic L	ORF(30kDa) (movement protein)
L. esculentum	$Tm2^2$	Tomato mosaic	ORF(30kDa) (movement protein)
L. esculentum	Tm-1	Tobacco mosaic	Helicase-like domain in ORF 126/183 (replicase)
Nicandra physaloides	?	Potato A	6K2 and VPg (protein linked to the 5' end of genomic RNA)
Nicotiana clevelandii, *N. edwardsonii*	ccdl	Cauliflower mosaic	Gene VI (viroplasma protein, transactivator of translation)
N. glutinosa	N	Tobacco mosaic	Helicase-like domain in ORF (126/183kDa) (replicase)
N. sylvestris	N'	Tobacco mosaic	Coat protein
N. tabacum Samsun nn	?	Tomato aspermy	TAV2b (suppressor of PTGS)
Phaseolus vulgaris	?	Bean golden mosaic	BV1 (movement protein)
Solanum acaule	Rx	Potato X	Coat protein
Solanum stoloniferum	Ry	Potato Y	Nla proteinase (function?)
Vigna unguiculata	Cry	Cucumber mosaic	ORF 2a (replicase)

system have been *manipulated* in order to obtain *protection* against viruses but so far with only limited success.

Virus-Specific Responses

As Flor elaborated for fungi, genetic traits of a pathogen coevolve with the respective host resistance genes in a pairwise manner. This gene-forgene concept also holds true for plant viruses. Gene products of a virus are recognized by a host and lead to a defense response.

The viral genes are then said to be avirulence (*avr*) genes, although they fulfill different functions in the context of the viral life cycle. Almost all viral genes may function as *avr* genes by triggering a host response. Breaking resistance is most frequently caused by mutations in *avr* genes, and during classical breeding the main task has been to cope with this challenge by *introducing* new resistance genes into crop plants, *essentially* by crossing wild *predecessors* and cultivated plants.

The *avr* gene products elicit host responses on different levels. One example, *extreme resistance*, inhibits viral *multiplication* in the *inoculated* plant cells and in protoplasts. The fact that this genetic trait is *terminologically* considered resistance and not *immunity* is merely based on the observation that other strains of the same virus multiply readily in single cells. A second and

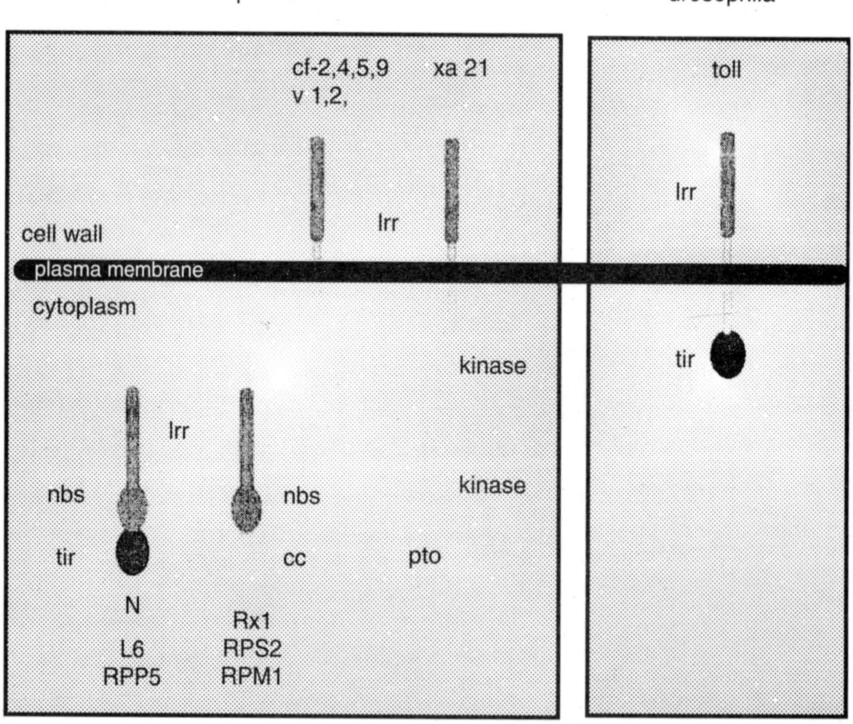

Figure 12.1: Similarity of plant resistance gene products and the signal receptor Toll of Drosophila. The proteins are composed of modular domains: leucinerich repeats (LRRs), kinase, Toll/interleukin-1 receptor (TIR), nucleotide-binding site (NBS), and coiled coil (CC) domain. The following resistance genes are compared: against Cladosporium fulvum (Cf), Verticillium dahliae (Ve), Xanthomonas oryzae (Xa), Pseudomonas syringae (RPS, RPM, Pto), Melampsora lini (L6), Peronospora parasitica (RPP), tobacco mosaic virus (N), and potato virus X (Rx).

most common example, the *hypersensitive reaction* (HR), allows *multiplication* in the inoculated cells and limited spread in the tissues, but then infected parts die and further infection is impaired.

It has been *questioned* whether resistance is solely due to this "suicide for survival", and at least in some cases *resistance* can be uncoupled from cell death. Extreme resistance and *hypersensitive* reactions are currently the best known barriers for viral infections; others are being investigated to elucidate additional *mechanisms* in the near future.

In particular, *apoptosis*, the *programmed* cell death of single cells thereby preventing necrosis of tissues, might be an interesting candidate. This mechanism has been *intensively* studied in animals and might also be responsible for resistance traits in plants.

Most virus-specific host responses rely on the general signal *transduction* cascades of *eukaryotic* cells, but for plants signal perception between virus and host takes place mostly inside the cell (in the symplast).

Recovery

The word "symptom" originates from the Greek *o-uµTrTwµa*, which means "chance, transient peculiarity". Correspondingly, symptoms may disappear during the infection process. Some shoots may escape from infection just by chance; others may develop virus-specific resistance that does not allow reinfection by the same virus, but unrelated viruses are *propagated* without problems.

This recovery *phenomenon* gave rise to intensive research and led to the discovery of virus-induced gene silencing, discussed later.

 HOST RESISTANCE GENES

Numerous genes conferring resistance to viruses have been characterized by classical genetics and *localized* to certain chromosomes. The two best analyzed examples will be reported here in greater detail to exemplify current *experimental* strategies to transmit virus resistance from wild to domestic plants.

One of the most fascinating outcomes of this research was the discovery that resistance genes directed against *pathogens* as diverse as fungi, bacteria, and viruses produce effector proteins with similar molecular architectures.

N Gene

The N gene is the classical example of virus resistance associated with a hypersensitive reaction. It is specifically directed against *tobacco mosaic virus* (TMV). After its discovery in *Nicotiana glutinosa*, it was introgressed into the Samsun cultivar of *N. tabacum*. The "N" refers to necrosis on foliage leaves a few days post inoculation (dpi).

The development of local necrotic lesions restricts systemic spread of TMV in a *temperature-dependent* manner. Above 28°C, **HR** is suppressed and TMV can infect further tissues. Decreasing the temperature then again induces systemic necrosis in large areas, as far as TMV has spread. Exploiting this peculiar feature of the dominant *N* gene, it was possible to clone and sequence a virus resistance gene for the first time by a combination of *transposon* tagging and positional cloning. An isolated genomic clone *harboring* the *N* gene was *transferred* to the susceptible cultivar

N. tabacum cv. Petite Havana SRI and to *Lycopersicon esculentum*, proving that this clone was *necessary* and *sufficient* to establish TMV specific resistance. The *N* gene encodes a protein in which one of the domains shows high similarity to the *Drosophila Toll* gene and the interleukin-1 receptor of mammals (named the TIR domain), indicating that it might participate in the general signal *transduction* pathway of eukaryotic cells.

It contains further domains with a nucleotide binding site (NBS) and with leucinerich repeats (LRRs). Both signatures are *commonly* found in animal receptor proteins that perceive and transmit signals from outside the cell at the plasma membrane. In the case of the *N* gene product, however, no *transmembrane* anchor is present.

Therefore, it is suggested that the N gene protein recognizes TMV inside the cell. The *N* gene is composed of five exons and four introns, which are alternatively spliced. Interestingly, a larger transcript is *constitutively* expressed before and after TMV inoculation.

The alternative, shorter transcript is induced during infection. To provide resistance, both transcripts have to be expressed, leading to the assumption that two versions of N proteins cooperate in signal transduction.

Consequently, it is necessary to transfer the genomic clone rather than a complementary DNA (cDNA) clone to new species to obtain resistance. Using such transgenic plants as indicators, the avirulence gene of TMV, the helicase domain of the 126-kDa and 183-kDa protein, could be defined very precisely.

Rx Gene

The Rx gene of *Solanum acaule* is directed against *potato virus X* (*PVX*). It confers extreme resistance, which works at the single-cell level. The *corresponding avr* gene is the coat protein gene of PVX. For the molecular analysis, the Rx locus was defined by classical and bacterial artificial chromosome (BAC) mapping. Using *cobombardment* of BAC clones with reporter constructs of virulent or avirulent modified PVX strains, the *Rx* gene could be identified and transferred to susceptible potato and a heterologous plant species (*N. benthamiana*).

The two transformed plant species exhibited extreme resistance against *avr* PVX but not against a resistancebreaking strain. These results proved that the isolated gene was necessary and sufficient for the strain-specific resistance against PVX. The Rx gene with three exons and two introns encodes a protein of 937 amino acid residues (107.5 kDa), which revealed *surprising* similarities with HR-inducing receptor proteins of the NBS-LRR class.

Although an HR is not observed during normal infection of an *avr* PVX on an *Rx* plant, reinvestigation of this relation showed that if the coat protein of *avr* PVX was ectopically expressed under the control of 35S CaMV promoter in an *Rx* gene-containing plant, HR was *obviously* induced. Moreover, the avr coat protein of PVX was expressed from a TMV vector in NN tobacco also containing the *Rx* gene.

Extreme resistance was found in this interaction but no N-mediated HR, suggesting that *Rx* is epistatic to HR. The *Rx* prevents the multiplication of PVX inside the cell but has no influence on the transport of the virus. Double-grafting *experiments* showed that *avr* PVX moved from an infected wild-type rootstock through an *Rx* gene-containing scion to a second wild-type scion, inducing *symptoms* only in the latter

These experiments indicate that the signal-inducing interaction between the *avr* and *R* gene does not occur in all cells of a plant. In summary, currently available *evidence* suggests that a continuum between extreme resistance, the micro-hypersensitive response, and the fully developed local or systemic HR exists in plants. The question is whether the defense reaction is triggered early or late in the infection process.

Avr Genes as Tools for Resistance Breeding

The discovery that even proteins responsible for extreme resistance can induce HR under certain conditions allowed the *development* of a versatile tool for the *identification* of unknown resistance genes as far as the viral *avr* genes of interest are delimited.

Using an *Agrobacterium-mediated* transient expression assay, further *Rx* loci were cloned and sequenced. The same assay was used to answer a reciprocal question, to identify an *avr* gene if the *resistance* gene is known. Ry provides extreme *resistance* in potato against *potato virus Y* (PVY). However, because no resistance-breaking strains of PVY are known, it was unclear which viral gene is the elicitor.

Agrobacterium-mediated transient expression assays assigned the NIa proteinase domain to the *avr* gene and provided evidence for the necessity of an intact catalytic center for HR induction. Although it cannot be completely ruled out that the structure of the center is responsible for virus recognition, the *experimental* results promote the intriguing hypothesis that the proteolytic function of this domain is essential.

 PATHOGEN-DERIVED RESISTANCE

Classical Cross-Protection

In the early days of plant virology, a phenomenon was observed and called "cross-protection": Preinoculating a plant with a mild virus can protect it from a subsequently inoculated severe and related virus. Classically, such *experiments* were used to determine the relatedness of two viruses.

Although this phenomenon formally resembles that of *immunization*, it differs *significantly* in that the effect is obtained only if the mild virus continues to multiply. This circumstance implies that viruses are disseminated continuously when this strategy is used.

Because the term "mild" or "severe" does not define the virus proper but refers to a relationship between pathogen and host, the classical approach contains the possible impact of creating new diseases on other plants. In consequence, the application of such techniques has remained limited, although prominent success has been obtained against *Citrus tristeza virus* and *Papaya ringspot virus*.

The classical approaches using cross-protection and their respective risks have been reviewed in detail. A variation on this theme is the use of satellite viruses or satellite RNA as protective agents. These small entities need a helper virus for *multiplication*, and they gained special interest because they modulate symptom expression.

Dependent on the combination of helper virus, satellite, and host plant, symptoms may be increased or ameliorated. As with cross-protection, the effect of satellites depends on their multiplication and, in principle, involves the same risks. Nevertheless, the approach has been utilized with some success using *preinoculation* of a mild combination of helper virus and satellite. Envisioning the advantages as well as the safety impacts of this strategy, it was consequently a challenge to scrutinize whether the useful properties of a virus could be dissected from the harmful ones.

Pertinent questions were whether parts of the viral genomes are sufficient for the protection and whether viral protein or RNA is responsible for the effect. Starting in the 1980s, molecular biology has answered these questions unequivocally and opened new, unprecedented areas of resistance that have also revolutionized our understanding of basic gene regulation in eukaryotes on the level of epigenetics.

During this period it became obvious that cross-protection can be obtained on a variety of routes including viral proteins and RNA. In summary, cross-protection came out to be a more general term.

Protein-Mediated Protection

Several viral proteins can mediate cross-protection. Some provide protection only to the closest relatives, others to a broader community of related viruses. Among the strategies using expressed viral proteins, two have been predominantly proved successful: expression of functional coat proteins or of defective proteins from genes with dominant negative mutations.

Coat Proteins

One early idea to explain cross-protection focused on the assembly of virus particles. For TMV it has been shown that disassembly of invading particles starts by the interaction of virions and ribosomes. This cotranslational *disassembly* needs a partial free 5' end of the viral RNA for first recognition events, which is normally obtained by removal of five to seven coat protein molecules according to the thermodynamic equilibrium between viral particles and components inside the cytoplasm.

It should, therefore, be possible to shift the *equilibrium* to the formation of stable particles by increasing the amount of coat protein within the cells. The elevated level of coat protein could be produced by a preinoculated virus or, more *conveniently*, by ectopic expression of the coat protein in transgenic plants.

In fact, this concept proved to be successful not only for TMV as the first virus but also for a vast variety of viruses. In the light of the additionally found RNA-mediated protection (see later), it was questioned whether the effector in the case of coat protein expression was protein or RNA. The role of coat protein, however, has been confirmed by several lines of evidence.

1. The coat protein-mediated resistance can be overcome by inoculating naked viral RNA.
2. Mutations in the coat protein genes that affect assembly also abolish protection.
3. The protection occurs only for viruses with proteins that might coassemble to mixed-coat virions (phenotypic mixing).
4. Virus particles are stable for hours in protoplasts transgenic for coat proteins, whereas they are disassembled within a few seconds in wild-type protoplasts.

All these data have led to the conclusion that although RNA-mediated effects might overlap,

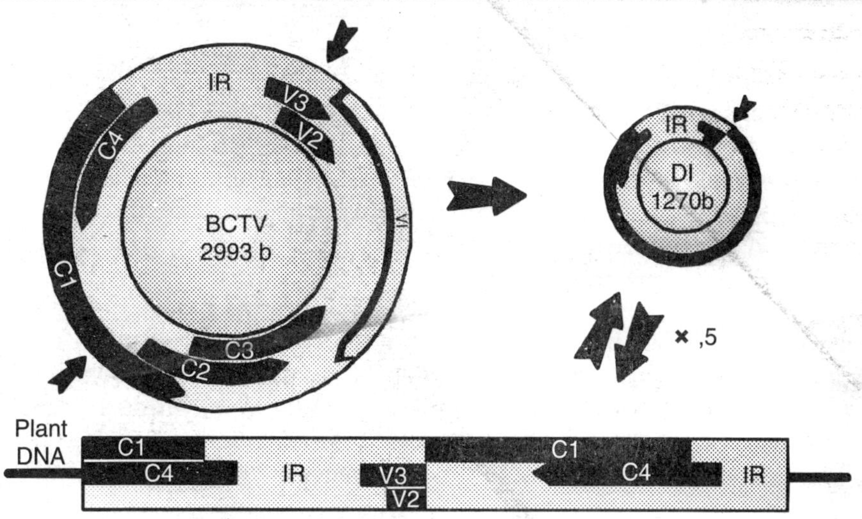

Figure 12.2: Defective-interfering (DI) DNA of beet curly top geminivirus (BCTV) to protect plants from virus infection. Open reading frames are named according to their complementary (C) or viral (V) orientation. IR assigns the intergenic region harboring viral promoters and the origin of replication. Bitmers (x1.5) were integrated into plant chromosomes, which are transreplicated upon infection with the cognate virus (BCTV).

particular cases are based on the presence of the correct coat protein. These cases are usually recognized by a correlation between the amount of expressed coat protein and the degree of protection. With one exception, this strategy was reliable for RNA- but not for DNA-containing viruses. Stimulated by plant virologists' work, it was also applied to animals.

Dominant Negative Mutations

A second idea has been raised by the perception that several viral proteins are *multifunctional* and are therefore composed of multiple domains. Such domains must cooperate, e.g., for RNA binding and RNA *polymerization* or for RNA binding and plasmodesmata gating.

It was predicted that if one of the functions of the domains was inactivated and the mutated protein still formed complexes with the RNA, the mutation might be dominant over the wild-type gene (dominant negative mutations).

Conceivably, most work *concentrated* on replicase-mediated protection because it was anticipated that the earliest defect during viral *multiplication* should be the most useful one.

Nevertheless, every viral protein might be prone to such an effective *modification*. The role of nonstructural viral proteins in protecting plants has been extensively reviewed, and it has been shown that RNA- as well as DNA-containing viruses may be impaired by this strategy.

In addition to the interaction of viral proteins with each other, in certain cases the binding of a viral with an unrelated protein was useful for protection.

Potyviruses need viral proteinases for the processing of their large preprotein. This function can be blocked in transgenic plants by ectopic expression of a cysteine proteinase inhibitor, providing broad resistance against distinct potyviruses.

RNA-Mediated Protection

During early work on protein-mediated cross-protection, some transgenic constructs behaved unexpectedly. While expressing low or no proteins, they nevertheless provided some degree of protection. In these cases no correlation between protein concentration and protective effect was observed, and sometimes, in control experiments, an *untranslatable* messenger RNA (mRNA) *serendipitously* appeared to be the effector molecule. This initial evidence founded the hypothesis that RNA by itself might mediate protection.

Antisense and Sense RNAs

An alternative idea finally led to a similar conclusion. To block translation of viral RNA by means of hybridization, antisense RNA was expressed in various plants. Surprisingly, in some cases not only antisense but also sense RNA, from a control construct, provided *protective* effects. The inhibition of viruses by sense constructs resembled a *simultaneously* discovered phenomenon perceived by plant molecular biologists and has been termed "cosuppression":

If several copies of the same gene or of the same promoter were artificially integrated into plant *chromosomes*, their expression was not increased but abolished. Antisense as well as sense RNA strategies have, *subsequently*, proved to be useful in certain cases but, even more important, have opened a new field of research that is now called "silencing" (see later), emphasizing the role of RNA in *protection* against viruses.

Interfering Replicons

During natural virus infections replicons may accumulate that are derived from the master virus but have a smaller size or are predominantly unrelated to the helper virus (satellites). Moreover, some replicons appeared to be *recombination* products of a helper virus nucleic acid and unrelated sequences. These additional replicons might enhance the effect of the virus, ameliorate the symptoms, or behave neutrally.

When they interfere with virus multiplication or symptom *development*, they are called defective interfering (DI) nucleic acids.

Defective Interfering (DI) Nucleic Acids

DI nucleic acids have been observed for RNA- and DNA-containing viruses. DI-DNA molecules of geminiviruses have attracted special interest. Geminiviruses encapsidate single-stranded circular DNA and replicate in nuclei.

Over the past three decades they raised worldwide devastating epidemics, *predominantly* in tropical and *subtropical* countries but also in the United States (*beet curly top virus*, BCTV) and around the Mediterranean sea (*tomato yellow leaf curl virus*, TYLCV). Their genomes consist of either one component (genera *Mastre-*, *Curto-*, and *Topocuvirus*) or two *components* (most of the genus *Begomovirus*), which are called DNA A and DNA B.

DI-DNA has been investigated in more detail for BCTV, with a set of half and smaller size DNA circles from a single genomic component, and for *African cassava mosaic begomovirus*, which *accumulates* smaller molecules derived from the DNA B component. All these DI molecules harbor the origin of replication and parts of predominantly the left halves of the genomic components.

They usually do not contain intact open reading frames with the exception of BCTV-DI, possessing the small ORF C4 influencing symptom expression. Integrating tandem copies of DI-DNA into plant chromosomes does not disturb the development of plants, and DI-DNA is not replicated because the viral replication initiator protein (AC 1 or C 1) is lacking.

Upon *challenge* by the cognate virus, DI-DNA replicates and *symptoms* are ameliorated, leading to a recovery after longer time periods of infection. During this process, DI-DNA accumulates and full-length viral DNA is reduced compared with infection of control plants.

It has been suggested that down-regulation of viral *multiplication* is caused by the competition of DIDNA with viral DNA for *replication* complexes, but it is not completely excluded that intact proteins (C4), defective proteins (SAC 1, ABC 1) as dominant-negative effectors, or RNA-mediated processes participate in the protection.

In this context it is interesting to note that smaller DI-DNA may replicate to even higher levels, but such an increase did not lead to enhanced inhibition. DI-DNA is packed into half-size particles and the amount of DI molecules is elevated after serial passages to further plants, rendering this strategy *especially* useful for field applications.

A limitation results from the necessity to recognize a specific origin of *replication* by the compatible replication-associated (Rep) protein of the cognate virus to induce DI-DNA multiplication. Therefore, DI-DNA can act only against closely related viruses that are able to transreplicate each other.

Satellites

Satellites are small, a few hundred nucleotides in size, RNA (satRNA) or DNA (satDNA) molecules that are transreplicated by a helper virus. Some of them, *encoding* their own coat protein for packaging their RNA, are called satellite viruses.

The other satellites might also contain small open reading frames (ORFs) of unknown function. Satellites modulate *symptom* expression of their helper virus, either increasing or decreasing severity. Their particular effects are governed by the triangular *interrelationship* between virus strain, satellite, and host genotype.

Expression of putative proteins from ORFs of satRNAs has been prevented by site-directed *mutagenesis* without abolishing *symptom* modulation. Therefore, it is believed that the secondary structure determines the effect rather than the coding capacity of the RNA. It was shown in model plants that satRNA expressed from transgenes can confer some protection against the helper virus effects.

For field application this approach was frequently questioned, especially because of the variability of possible effects upon coinfection with other viruses or because satRNA might be transferred to other nontarget hosts. Nevertheless, this strategy using either classical *coinoculation* techniques or transgenic means has been successfully applied in Asia, resulting in a considerable reduction of yield losses.

GENE SILENCING

Silencing of genes is a long known process providing programmed differential gene expression during the individual development of all organisms. It can occur at different levels, repressing genes in prokaryotic operons, combining sets of transcription factors in eukaryotic cells, or condensing chromatin structures. In addition to these regulatory means, it was already perceived in classical genetics that certain genes can be suppressed (phenocopied) and that such suppression can be inherited (paramutation, imprinting). It was proposed that this type of silencing might rely, at least for some examples, on the interaction of *homologous* sequences (ectopic pairing of homologous chromatin) followed by the inactivation of the particular gene, perhaps through *methylation*.

However, whether methylation, which is regularly seen in such genes, is the cause or the result of silencing remains to be shown. From a historical point of view, one of the most *fascinating* chapters of molecular biology was the perception during the past 10 years of how results of completely unrelated areas of research have converged to throw light on the puzzle of *silencing* mechanisms.

Phenomena called "cosuppression" for transgenic plants, "virus-induced gene silencing" for plant viruses, "RNA interference" for *Drosophila* and *Caenorhabditis*, and "quelling" for *Neurospora* turned out to rely on common molecular pathways. Summarizing the evidence, homology-dependent gene silencing (HDGS) may occur on two different levels: *transcriptional* gene silencing (TGS) based on promoter inactivation, *methylation*, and chromatin remodeling and posttranscriptional gene silencing (PTGS) caused by sequencespecific destruction of transcripts.

The removal of sequence-specific RNA in PTGS was shown to be based on the presence of homologous interfering double-stranded RNA (dsRNA). Some evidence suggests that a feedback loop of regulation from PTGS to TGS exists. Originally, these mechanisms were thought to control the copy number of genes to protect the genome from too many mobile genetic elements and viruses.

Currently, however, the possibility arises that similar *mechanisms* are also involved in the programmed *differential* gene activation during ontogeny.

Transcriptional Gene Silencing (TGS)

The TGS process is an unpredictable one in which multiple copies of a gene or a promoter influence each other, leading to the inactivation of a particular gene. In experiments it is recognized by a lack of steady-state transcripts and the absence of the particular transcript in nuclear run-on assays.

Frequently, it is associated with increased methylation of the promoter and the gene. TGS may be present in the whole plant or in sectors of various organs. The pattern of TGS may be inherited by the next generation (imprinting) and reverted to an active state of *transcription* under certain conditions.

Posttranscriptional Gene Silencing (PTGS)

The PTGS process relies on the multiplicity of genes; their inactivation is also *unpredictable*, as for TGS, but the effective homology must reside within the transcript. Experimentally, it is detected by reduced steady-state amounts of RNA as in TGS but the presence of nuclear run-on transcripts.

Moreover, the appearance of small RNA molecules (21-25 nt) of both polarities is diagnostic for PTGS. PTGS is not present throughout the whole life cycle of a plant but appears late during *development* in individual plants of silencing lines.

Virus-Induced Gene Silencing (VIGS)

The first evidence for VIGS came from the observation of recovery from symptoms after inoculating a potyvirus on transgenic plants containing a potyviral gene. The recovered shoots remained protected from a second infection with the same virus but were susceptible to others.

The interpretation of this observation became a heuristic idea, namely that effector molecules, presumably *complementary* RNA, had been generated to signal virusspecific inhibition. In a similar approach it was shown that viroids can also trigger gene silencing, *underscoring* that the effector molecule might be RNA. Interestingly, these peculiar experiments with viroids led to inactivation of its *homologous* transgene, associated with methylation of the DNA copy.

In other cases VIGS did not change the *transcription* but induced PTGS, which was best shown for PVX, a virus that replicates exclusively in the cytoplasm. Transgenes, e.g., glucuronidase (GUS), were silenced by PTGS if the plant was infected by a chimeric PVX containing the GUS gene, too. Conversely and surprisingly, a plant transgenic for GUS became resistant to this hybrid PVX.

Systemic Acquired Gene Silencing (SAS)

Once established at some site, the silencing signal may spread throughout the plant, which is most convincingly demonstrated by grafting experiments. A silenced rootstock can transfer the signal to an unsilenced scion.

This effect is maintained as long as the homologous gene is present in the recipient plant. Which molecules trigger SAS is still unclear. It has been suggested that the gene-specific small RNAs participate in the signal *transduction*, but recent grafting *experiments* have questioned this idea. Alternatively, longer dsRNA might induce SAS, but evidence for this *assumption* is still lacking.

Mechanistic Aspects of Posttranscriptional Gene Silencing

The mechanism of PTGS has been elucidated in different organisms, converging to a fundamental concept during the last few years. The trigger for PTGS is dsRNA (blunt end or with a few protruding 3'nucleotides) *homologous* to a target RNA.

Several genes are involved in this process in plants, animals, and fungi coding for a ribonuclease (RNase) III-type enzyme cutting dsRNA, an RNA-dependent RNA polymerase (RdRp), a helicase, and a protein with homology to a eukaryotic initiation factor (eIF2C).

These factors interact in (trans-)gene silencing, whereas for viruses a viral RdRp may replace or modulate the *analogous* host enzyme. One key enzyme is now called DICER because it chops small pieces of about 22 by (siRNA, for short interfering RNA) *proceeding* from the ends of dsRNA with a type III-like RNase activity.

The protein contains two RNase III domains, a putative helicase domain, and a PAZ domain, which is possibly responsible for protein-protein interaction with other factors. According to the currently discussed model, siRNA remains bound to DICER, is melted by a helicase, and *subsequently* guides the sequence-specific nuclease to homologous RNA of (+) or (–) orientation.

In this reaction, target RNA is cleaved in the middle of the recognized 22-nt sequence, leading to a periodicity in the digested RNA similar to that of siRNA but with a phase shift.

The advantage of the DICER reaction lies in the *amplification* of the signal because several siRNAs are generated from a single dsRNA molecule, each one ready to attack several new target RNAs. An even more efficient amplification of the signal for destruction would be obtained if target ssRNA, loaded with siRNA as a primer, was *complemented* by an RdRp to produce new dsRNA to be recognized by DICER again.

However, such a feedback cycle has yet to be shown *experimentally*. In any case, it would explain the functionality of host or viral RdRp genes in PTGS as inferred from genetic analysis. The *demonstrated* role of an inducible host RdRp in plant antiviral defense might be a further hint in the same direction.

Suppressors of PTGS

The PTGS process is thought to be a defense response against foreign genes, especially of viral origin. Therefore, it is not surprising that viruses have developed ways to combat such strategies. Consequently, certain viral genes were *discovered* to suppress PTGS.

Two of them, HC-Pro (helper component-proteinase) of potyviruses and ORF 2b of cucumoviruses, have been *intensively investigated* in this function. Although PVX was initially thought to lack such a capability, its p25 protein (part of the triple gene block with movement functions) inhibits PTGS under certain conditions.

These three examples, among several others, also represent *suppression* of PTGS at different steps in the course of the process. HC-Pro is able to switch off existing PTGS and leads to a decrease of siRNA levels. In contrast, CMV 2b has no influence on established PTGS but prevents its initiation, and PVX p25 abolishes the mobile signal of PTGS.

Whenever suppression of PTGS has occurred, it promotes not only parental but also unrelated viruses in *multiplication* and spread. Such synergistic effects were observed upon coinfection of two viruses as well as upon single-virus *inoculation* on transgenic plants harboring a viral PTGS-suppressor gene.

SUSTAINABILITY CONCERNS

Resistance breeding has always been a race between host response and viral evolution. Molecular techniques provide the breeder with new tools to accelerate transmission or selection of interesting host genes. Nevertheless, creating a new cultivar that is resistant to a particular virus and otherwise true to type for the market is still tedious work.

It is therefore necessary for *agriculture* and horticulture to choose sustainable strategies to be applied in practice. Most of the work discussed here has been performed with a few model plant species and laboratory strains of viruses.

The current challenge is to introduce resistance traits into *agronomically* relevant cultivars that have to encounter a variety of viral strains or viral species. For a growing number of virus problems, this aim has already been reached; for very important virus epidemics, e.g., geminiviruses, it is still a task.

To reduce the number of setbacks during this long-lasting process, a series of risk concerns have been evaluated by aimed experiments as well as field surveys. Most of them have been covered by a very *comprehensive* and detailed review, and therefore it is possible to summarize the most important topics here.

Tolerance

Contrary to real resistance, a tolerant variety, whether it is created by classical or molecular means, will accumulate virus populations that are as virulent as before on related plant species lacking a tolerance-inducing gene.

In geographically isolated field conditions such an approach might be helpful if no alternative is seen, but in the majority of *agronomically* relevant cases it might promote new epidemics of the same virus and/or accelerate the evolution of new virulent virus strains.

Resistance Breakage

In general, resistance based on multiple genes is less easily broken than a *monogenically* based resistance. Monogenic exceptions to this rule that were extremely durable (e.g., for the N gene) are obvious.

Again, the problem is similar irrespective of classical or molecular breeding. Pathogen-derived protein-mediated approaches tend to have a smaller spectrum of protective effects, whereas RNA-based strategies sometimes provide broader efficiency. In every case, there is no a priori indication of which trait will be broken soon and which will be long-lived. The probability has to be tested through case-by-case experiments and field trials.

Transcapsidation

Transcapsidation of two discrete but related viruses has been observed in classical field situations, where it may create an epidemic problem if changes in vector *transmissibility* are associated. Molecular studies have defined conditions for and frequencies of transcapsidation.

In the worst case, transcapsidation will create new virions that can be transmitted, e.g., from a transgenic crop plant to a next neighbor plant, but such a virion will not be harmful to a larger agricultural area because it is lost in the recipient plant. Nevertheless, a careful resistance strategy should aim to avoid any *pathogen-derived* sequence in the protective gene that contributes to vector transmission.

Recombination

Recombination between plant viruses is a well-established fact now. Some viruses use template switch as an obligatory step of replication (*pararetroviruses*) and are therefore prone to recombination. In other virus families, *recombination* is an accidental phenomenon.

Although it occurs at a low frequency, it is worth considering because of the huge numbers of viruses in plants. Mostly, recombinational effects are overlooked because wild-type viruses overgrow the recombinants. Consequently, evidence for recombination in field isolates of RNA plant viruses is limited.

In contrast to most RNA viruses, the DNA-containing *geminiviruses* show multiple footprints of recombination in their sequences, which has been associated with the evolution of resistancebreaking strains. Recently, a possible explanation for this tendency was found in that *geminiviruses* may replicate using a recombination-dependent pathway in addition to the classical rolling-circle replication. In summary, accepting that recombination occurs with different *frequencies* but always frequently enough to create new variants, the real critical question is whether new viral capabilities are selected that provide invasion of new plants or vectors.

This concern is equally relevant for natural coinfection of different viruses and for viruses infecting a cultivar containing viral transgenes because invading viruses have been shown to take up transgene sequences in different virus families.

In conclusion, viral sequences coding for vector *transmissibility*, tissue tropism, host range, or symptom expression should be identified and omitted from transgenic constructs.

Synergism

Suppression of silencing, as discussed earlier, is also a lesson for risk concerns using pathogen-derived resistance. It is necessary but not sufficient to analyze the manipulated trait by challenging with the target virus. In the field situation, unrelated viruses might be promoted rather than inhibited by the viral gene product.

The history of the discovery of PVX suppressor capabilities has shown that functions of these types are not always obvious but have to be elucidated by intelligent means. In conclusion, resistance traits to be released in the field have to be *challenged* in the respective crop plants by relevant unrelated viruses in addition to the usually tested cognate target virus. Moreover, because of the *uncertainties* of such tests, *surveillance* monitoring has to be carried out.

PERSPECTIVES

Pathogen-derived resistance (PDR) of the first generation had its merits as a step toward engineering virus resistance and, more important, in investigating the interaction of virus and host. However, it also has its limits and risks.

Now, the second generation of PDR in the form of gene silencing is superior in abandoning the necessity for functional viral genes, *providing* the *possibility* to silence the viral silencing suppressors, and extending the reservoir of effector molecules that might be directed against a broad spectrum of viruses. Possibly, this approach will gain the same role for plants as *immunization* for animals.

In addition to pathogen-derived resistance, the *overwhelming* progress in *deciphering* host responses and virus-specific recognition will change the main fields of research on resistance. Identifying receptor proteins and other components of the signal *transduction* pathway will lead to a profound understanding of host defense and open the *possibility* to *transfer* individual components of the resistance network to the crop plants of choice.

Chapter 13

GENETIC CONSEQUENCES

The gene transfer from crops into populations of wild *relatives* has become an important *scientific* and public issue since the *development* and *cultivation* of *genetically* engineered (GE) plants in the late 1980s.

The concerns related to the cultivation of GE crops, in *particular* those dealing with the possibility of *transgene* escape into the wild flora, have generated a multitude of studies on crop-to-wild gene flow.

While these studies have shown that such gene flow exists for almost all of the most *important* crops cultivated worldwide, only recently have new studies focused and are focusing on its *ecological* and genetic consequences.

Yet, in order to better assess the ecological and agronomic risks associated with the transgene flow to the wild flora, it is fundamental to understand the *mechanisms* and the *consequences* of such gene flow.

Studies on the existence of crop-to-wild gene flow have already been reviewed several times in the context of the *cultivation* of GE crops.

A general overview on the factors influencing gene flow, and containment measures is presented here. Risk of gene flow has a geographical component and we focus in Sect. 2 on the particular case of Switzerland.

While gene flow has been mostly *investigated* from crops to their closest wild *relatives*, further introgression may occur between wild species.

The importance of such "*bridge species*" is *explained* elsewhere in this chapter. Finally, the genetic and ecological consequence of transgene flow is evaluated elsewhere in this chapter.

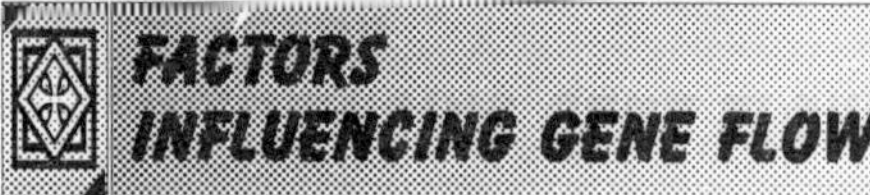

FACTORS INFLUENCING GENE FLOW

It is widely accepted that *hybridization* between two taxa depends on several key factors, such as their sympatry, the synchrony of their flowering periods, the existence of a common vector for the gametes, as well as their reproductive *compatibility* and the viability and fertility of the hybrids.

Generally speaking, gene flow between two taxa can thus be viewed as a two step process: (i) a first *hybridization* event, which leads to the production of first *generation* hybrids, followed by (ii) the introgression of part of the genome of one species into the other by successive *backcrosses*. Hybridization depends mainly on *straightforward* conditions, such as the need for the plants to grow close to each other and the potential for the exchange of pollen.

While the most obvious situation where both *conditions* are met is represented by *cultivated* fields where the wild relatives grow in close proximity, it is worth noting that crop plants growing as volunteers within fields of other crops or in other habitats represent *additional* contact zones between crops and wild relatives. In the case of GE crop, such a *situation* may lead to transgene escape to the wild flora. A notable example of this latter *situation* is that of rapeseed, which is *extremely* common to see in any kind of disturbed habitats even relatively distant from cultivated areas.

More generally, the *establishment* of feral crop populations in the *agroecosystems*, as well as outside the *cultivated* areas depends mainly on the crop features, such as seed dispersal by wind, water or animals, absence of dormancy, ripening period, persistence of seeds in the soil.

Agricultural *practices* (*harvesting period*, crop *rotation*, *till* vs. *no-till*) as well as post-harvesting procedures (*transportation*), can also greatly influence the emergence of volunteer plants. Finally, an *additional* potential source of transgenes is represented by first and *subsequent* generations of *hybrids* between GE crops and wild relatives, which can act as "*genetic bridges*" between the parental species.

Factors Influencing Hybridization

Hybridization is *influenced quantitatively* by numerous factors, some of them depending on the characteristics of the plants, while others are more related to the *environment*. Hybridization is frequent in *perennial* species and especially for outcrossing and clonal plants, as the produced hybrids can subsist clonally even in the case of reduced fertility. Pollen vectors play a major role, at least on the distance at which hybridization can take place.

For instance, maize pollen is known to be particularly heavy and *intraspecific* gene flow at distances greater than 50 meters is unlikely. In contrast, other *wind-pollinated* species can show large distance pollen dispersal events.

Watrud et al. discovered intraspecific hybrids of *Agrostis stolonifera* 21 km from the pollen source. While it is obvious that topography influences winds, a flat land favoring the pollen flow over long distances, it is worth *mentioning* that *microtopography* seems to have also an impact on the behavior of pollinator insects, by hiding or making more visible *potential* pollen sources and sinks.

However, predictions on the pollen *movements* seem more complicated in the case of insect pollinated species. Different *experimental* and modeling studies on the distance at which rapeseed pollen could produce hybrids, generated indeed *inconsistent* results, because these results depend *indirectly* on the factors *influencing* the activity of bees. Repeated contacts with crop *populations* are known to accelerate the *introgression* process.

However, *hybridization* as well is positively correlated with the *frequency* and the extent of the contact zones between crops and their wild relatives. Indeed, feral *populations* or *individual* volunteer crop plants will not only increase the area of contact, but also increase the potential for the overlap of flowering periods.

For instance, while in central Europe fields of *rapeseed* usually flower *simultaneously* in May, it is common to observe volunteers flowering from June till late October.

FACTORS INFLUENCING INTROGRESSION

Most factors influence both *hybridization* and *introgression*. While successful introgression is achieved when genes from one taxon are fixed in another one, several hybrid *generations* and parental individuals can be involved in the process.

All of these individuals and generations can coexist and exchange genes *simultaneously* for many years. Fitness of hybrids is essential to successful *introgression*. Moreover, *independent* of the pollen vector, the intensity and symmetry of pollen flow will determine both the direction of *hybridization* and the speed of *introgression* in a sink population.

Fixation of genes is known to occur more rapidly in small populations, which are also more prone to act as a pollen sink. Both *hybridization* and introgression are *facilitated* in *genetically* close species, such as crop and prickly lettuce (D'Andrea et al., *unpublished*) or crop and wild *sunflower*, rather than between more distantly related species like rapeseed and wild radish.

The actual *introgression* of crop genes into the genome will depend greatly on the existence of pre- and postzygotic barriers, which strongly depend on factors linked to the *evolutionary* divergence between the crop and its wild relative, the *incompatibilities* being *generally* higher between *genetically* distant taxa and lower between closely related taxa. Genetic barriers acting against *hybridization* between species are considered by several authors as "semi-permeable".

Individual genes or specific genome regions may be transferred during introgression processes, rather than entire genomes. Moreover, genes from one species may not be uniformly transmitted to another via *introgressed* generations, as selection does not act homogeneously within genomes. A factor that influences specifically *introgression*, rather than *hybridization*, is the observation that beneficial or neutral traits will be preferentially introgressed, compared to detrimental genes.

For example, silenced genes can be kept in recipient genomes, until they are *eliminated* by genetic drift. Additionally, several linked genes may be *transferred* together, especially if such complexes carry *positively* selected genes. The situation is more complex in polyploids where multiple copies of genes make genetic *interactions* even more complicated.

Moreover, related polyploid species often share only part of the genome *(e.g Triticum aestivum* and *Aegilops cylindrica, Brassica napus* and *B. campestris)* and introgression from one species to the other is easier for genes located on the homologous chromosomes, than for genes located in the homeologous ones.

CONTAINMENT OF TRANSGENES

One clue which arises from the existing studies on crop-to-wild gene flow is that *hybridization* between most crops and their wild relatives cannot be avoided. Therefore, if the goal is to impede the transfer of *transgenes* to the wild flora, gene flow has to be stopped at its source.

For this purpose, several strategies, each *possessing* advantages and drawbacks, have been proposed, which are mostly linked to the mechanisms and factors influencing *introgression* presented above. Since physical barriers, such as isolation by distance or hedge rows *bordering* fields appeared rapidly to be inefficient, genetic barriers based on the breeding systems of the crops were investigated.

One of the first ideas was to decrease or completely block gene flow via pollen, by *favoring* apomixis. However, many apomictic species preserve low to *moderate* sexual seed production, and moderate or high levels of pollen. It was thus *suggested* to induce male-sterility in GE crops. This system was applied to commercialized *Brassica napus* varieties.

In this rapeseed variety, the transgenic construct is induced by a *tapetum-specific* promoter, and produces a cytotoxin *(barnase)*. Only anthers express the lethal transgene, which leads to the destruction of the mother cells of pollen. However, male sterility does not prevent the formation of hybrids when wild relatives act as paternal parent, like in the case of bolting beets in south Europe.

Moreover, these two *strategies* can only prevent gene flow by pollen, while they have no effect on gene flow by seeds. It was *subsequently* suggested to insert transgenes in genomic regions, which have no or reduced mobility.

As mentioned previously, genomes are not *uniformly* transmitted, and some regions are more "*mobile*" than others. Targeting gene *insertion* in regions poorly transmitted should decrease the probability of gene escape.

However, in order to be efficient, this strategy has to be developed on a case-by-case basis, and introgressive patterns on all possible wild relatives of each crop should be known. A similar idea was *proposed* for polyploid species, where genomes non-shared by wild relatives could be chosen as insertion sites of transgenes. However, *recombination* events *between non-homeologous* genomes were observed in wild x crop hybrids involving *Brassica napus*, and *Triticum aestivum*.

Another proposition was to insert transgenes in the DNA of *mitochondria* or chloroplast, as organellar DNA is usually maternally transmitted, and should not be carried by pollen grains in Angiosperms. However, paternal inheritance of chloroplasts has already been observed.

For instance, transfer of genes from organelles to nucleus occurs at a low frequency in tobacco, as one pollen grain out of 16000 carries cytoplasmic genome elements in its nucleus. As for the strategies *presented* above, gene flow via seeds is not *prevented*. Therefore, so-called "seed suicide" techniques were proposed.

In these plants, the transgenic construct induces the *production* of lethal protein or blocks *physiological* functions during seed maturation, which makes it impossible for the seeds to *germinate*, but without *disturbing* albumen differentiation.

However, producing non-germinating seeds would impede farmers from sowing part of their harvest, which is a highly *controversial* issue from an ethical point of view. Another recent *technique* consists of the *chemically* induced removal of transgene from pollen cells during the gametogenesis.

The transgene is flanked by specific sites *(lox),* which allows its removal by a site-specific recombinase (Cre). The recombinase is coded by the transgene and expressed after induction. Recombinase-based *techniques* present currently two major drawbacks: the controlling system has to be activated by an external signal, that is the application of tetracycline, and *basically* every single cell involved in the sexual *reproduction* of the crop should be treated.

Finally, *post-hybridization* and fitness-based strategies were also suggested to avoid the spread of hybrid derivates in the environment. The idea is to lower the fitness of these plants by linking the transgene with traits which are neutral or *beneficial* in an *agricultural* context, but detrimental in the wild.

The genes responsible for traits such as dwarfing, loss of dormancy or non-shattering of seeds were proposed as suitable loci to place transgenes. However, there are at least two serious drawbacks in this strategy. First, the current *technology* does not allow placing of the *transgenic* construct in a precise location.

Second and probably more *important,* most of these socalled deleterious traits are recessive loss-of-function alleles related to the *domestication* of crops. These alleles would thus not be expressed in first *generation* hybrids with a wild plant, because of the presence of the *dominant*

Table 13.1: Characteristics collected for the crops and its wild relatives.

Common for the crops and its wild relatives	***Specific*** to the cultivated plant	***Specific*** to the wild relatives
Latin name	Extent of cultivation	Ecology
Vernacular names	Feral populations	Hybridization with the crop
Chromosome number	Frequent transformations which have led to a request for a field trial	Hybridization with other wild relatives
Pollen dispersal to the Swiss Red List	Recent transformation	Category of threat according
Breeding system Commercialization	GE field cultivation	Stability of the distribution Longevity
Levels of vegetation		

wild allele in their genome. In further *generations*, the deleterious allele would only be expressed in *homozygous* individuals, which would strongly reduce its capability to lower the fitness of these plants.

Moreover, if the hybrids are fertile, this strategy would not prevent them acting as a genetic bridge and *pollinating* the wild parent. Alternatively, this strategy could have a good efficacy when the transgene is coupled within the transgenic construct itself with one or two mutant genes *conferring* an ecological *disadvantage* (transgenetic mitigation), such as dwarfing, as demonstrated in tobacco introgressants.

GENE FLOW BETWEEN CULTIVATED PLANTS AND WILD RELATIVES: THE CASE OF SWITZERLAND

Risks related to transgenic plants are often investigated on a worldwide scale and several reviews have focused on this topic. Nevertheless, a regional perspective is necessary because crops vary among countries, wild species have often a limited *geographical* range and floras *composition* changes *geographically*.

Consequently, the distribution of crops and their ability to cross with their wild relatives vary regionally. Moreover, the genetic characteristics of a wild species, as for example its ploidy level, may vary according to their *geographical* range and can influence largely their ability to hybridize.

This is illustrated for example by tetraploid alfalf, *Medicago sativa* ($2n = 32$ chromosomes). In *Switzerland*, its wild relative, *Medicago falcata*, is tetraploid and has the same chromosome number ($2n = 32$) except in Unterengadin, where it is diploid ($2n = 16$).

Hybrids between the two species, *M. x varia*, are found frequently where both species are tetraploid, but are, on the contrary, very rare in the range of the diploid *M. falcata*. Risks of gene flow are *consequently* much lower in Unterengadin than in the other areas of Switzerland. Consequently, the results of one country cannot be *necessarily generalized* to another country without further investigations.

This is particularly true for *Switzerland*, where *topography* strongly influences the distribution of wild species and constrains agriculture. Its landscape typically illustrates that risks may vary from one area to the other. Distribution of wild relatives may also vary in time.

For example, global change, including both the global warming and the increase in disturbance as a *consequence* of human activity, has led to the northern expansion of several Mediterranean species. Similarly, change in agricultural practices may influence the contact zones between crops and their wild relatives, and consequently influence greatly the risks.

Therefore, *monitoring* over a long term the wild flora and the *agricultural* areas is necessary in order to evaluate the risks on a regional perspective. Switzerland has voted on November 27, 2005 a moratorium of 5 years on the outdoor cultivation of GE organisms for commercial purposes.

Probabilities of large-scale cultivation of *transgenic* plants are therefore low. Nevertheless, political changes may occur rapidly and therefore, *assessment* of potential risk of gene flow from crops to wild relative is necessary with a Swiss perspective.

The Swiss Federal Office for the Environment (FOEN) granted a study on risk assessment which

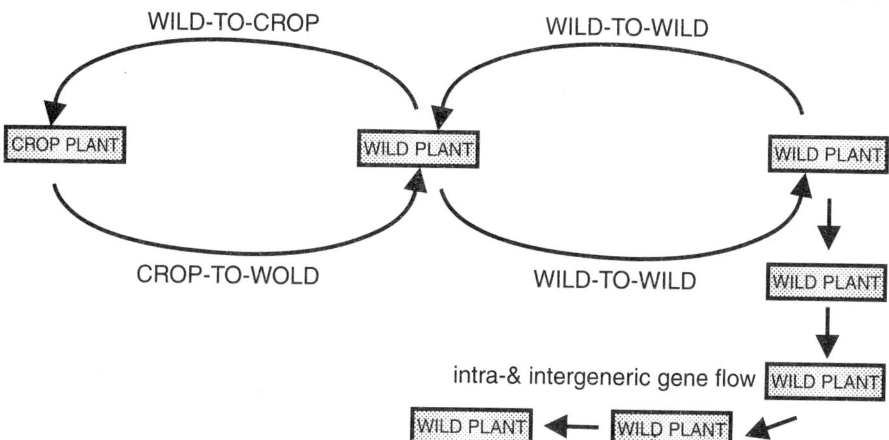

Figure 13.1: Bridge species and directions of gene flow in crop-wild hybrid complexes. The potential spread of transgenes into wild populations via wild-to-wild bridges and further introgression has been poorly investigated

focused on the main cultivated plants of Switzerland. For each of them, *bibliographical* data were collected on the crop and on most of the wild relatives.

From this, the risks of transfer of transgene to conventional varieties and to the wild or naturalized flora were evaluated. Risks of gene flow were never null between cultivars, as all crops *reproduce sexually*. Risks were evaluated as null for the wild flora when the crop *produces* no feral *populations* and no wild relative exists in Switzerland. It was low to medium in the case of autogamy, or of harvest before flowering (as for lettuce, out of the seed production areas).

Risk was *considered* as high for all allogamous species, those forming spontaneous or subspontaneous populations, or possessing wild relatives that hybridize readily with the crop. Risks may be examined in different perspectives.

For a monitoring program, the priority is to examine *commercialized* transgenic crops. Prior to the *authorization* of outdoor cultivation, it is important to evaluate on one hand the risks of *contamination* of non-transgenic cultivation, and on the other hand those of gene flow to the wild flora.

Priority Species for a Monitoring Program

Eleven cultivated species in *Switzerland* possess *commercialized* transgenic varieties elsewhere in the world. Six of them present a high risk of gene flow with other cultivars (alfalfa, carnation, chicory, maize, rapeseed and squash).

Others represent a lower risk as they are harvested before flowering, such as beet, or because seed do not mature in the regions, such as potato for example. Moreover, crops with an *autogamous* breeding system such as soybean, tobacco or tomato also present a lower risk of gene flow.

Potential Risks for the Contamination of Non-Transgenic Crops

Only crops which have *commercialized* GE varieties are mentioned below. The higher risks originate from the six allogamous species mentioned above. Medium risks are characteristics

Table 13.2: Summary of risks for the main crops cultivated in Switzerland.

Name		Crop to crop gene flow	Gene flow with spontaneous and naturalized flora*		Commercialization**	Main transformation
			Suisse	Europe		
Poaceae						
Agrostis stolon ifera L.	Creeping bentgrass	++	++	++	pending	Herbicide tolerance, agronomical properties
Avena sativa L.	Oats	+	++	++	FT	Virus Resistance (virus BYDV)
Cynodon dactylon (L.) Persoon	Bermuda grass	++	+	+	FT	Agronomical properties, herbicide tolerance
Festuca arundinacea Schreber s.l., *F. pratensis Hudson s.l.*	Fescue	++	++	++	FT	Product quality, fungal resistance
Hordeum vulgare L.	Barley	+	0	+	FT	Product quality, fungal resistance
Lolium perenne Hudson s.l., *L. multiflorum* Lamarck	Ryegrass	++	++	++	FT	Product quality
Poa pratensis L.	Smooth meadow-grass	++	++	++	FT	Herbicide tolerance
Triticum aestivum L., *Triticum spelta L.*	Wheat	+	+	++	FT	Herbicide tolerance, fungal resistance
Zea mays L.	Maize	++	0	0	Com	Insect resistance, herbicide tolerance
Fragaria x ananassa	Strawberry	+	+	+	FT	Fungal resistance, herbicide tolerance
Malus domestica Borkh.	Apple	++	++	++	FT	Product quality (fruit quality),

(Table Contd.)

						insect and bacterial resistance
Prunus avium L.	Cherry	++	++	++	FT	Modification of metabolism
Prunus domestica L.	European plum	++	++	++	pending	Virus resistance
Pyrus communis L.	Pear	++	++	++	FT	Product quality (fruit maturation)
Rubus idaeus L.	Raspberry	++	++	++	FR	Virus resistance, product quality
Asteraceae						
Cichorium intybus L.	Chicory	++	++	++	Com	Agronomical properties (male sterility), herbicide tolerance
Helianthus annuus L.	Sunflower	++	+	+	FT	Fungal resistance, insect resistance
Lactuca sativa L.	Lettuce	+	+	+	FT	Herbicide tolerance, product quality
Glycine max L.	Soybean	+	0	0	Com	Herbicide tolerance, product quality
Medicago sativa L.	Alfalfa	++	++	++	Com	Herbicide tolerance, product quality
Pisum sativum L.	Pea	+	+	+	FT	Herbicide tolerance, virus resistance Solanaceae
Lycopersicon esculentum Miller	Tomato	+	0	0	Com	Product quality, insect
resistance *Nicotiana tabacum L.*	Tobacco	++	0	0	Com	Product quality, virus resistance
Solanum tuberosum L.	Potato	+	0	0	Com	Insect resistance (doryphore), product quality
Other families						
Beta vulgaris L.	Beet	+	0	++	Com	Herbicide tolerance, virus resistance
Brassica napus L.	Rapeseed	++	++	++	Com	Product quality (oil quality), herbicide tolerance

(Table Contd.)

Brassica rapa L.	Rape	++	++	++	FT	Insect resistance (lepidopters), herbicide tolerance
Cucumis melo L.	Melon	++	0	0	FT	Virus resistance, product quality (fruit ripening)
Cucumis sativus L.	Cucumber	++	0	0	FT	Virus resistance, agronomic properties (salt tolerance)
Cucurbita pepo L.	Squash	++	0	0	Com	Virus resistance
Daucus carota L. tolerance)	Carrot	++	++	++	FT	Fungal resistance *(Alternaria* product quality
Dianthus caryophyllus L.	Carnation	++	0	0	Com	Product quality (colors modification)
Osteospermum ecklonis (DC) Norl	Cape Daisy	++	0	0	FT	Metabolism modification
Picea abies (L.) Karsten	Norway Spruce	++	++	++	FT	Gene marker
Pinus sylvestris L.	Scots pine	++	++	++	FT	Gene marker, forestry performance
Populus alba x tremula, Populus sp.	Poplar	++	+	+	FT	Herbicide tolerance, forestry performance
Vitis vinifera L., resistance *Vitis labrusca L.*	Grape	++	+	+	FT	Fungal resistance, virus

from either autogamous species with partial allogamy, or those which are not producing fruits in traditional practices (beet, potato).

Low risks exist for plants that do not flower, when vegetative parts are collected. Such *cultivation necessitates* a good management and strict control, in order to avoid any loss of seeds or unintended flowering. Some of the species *mentioned* above belong to that category, depending on their use.

Potential Risks for Gene Flow to the Wild or Naturalized Flora

High risk characterizes crops and wild relatives with no or low reproductive barriers, as for oilseed rape and creeping bentgrass. For example, escape of *transgenic* creeping bentgrass *(Agrostis stolonifera L.)* in non-agronomic areas was observed in the USA.

Medium risk occurs if the hybrid is partially fertile and *introgression* is possible. No *commercialized* transgenic crops belong to that category: pea, poplar, strawberry, sunflower and wheat. Some cultivated species have no wild relative in *Switzerland*; this is for example the case for beet, carnation, maize, melon, potato, soybean, tobacco, tomato and squashes.

Consequently, they do not represent a genetic threat for the natural flora, even if *containment* measures are needed to avoid crop to crop gene flow

Particularity of the Swiss Flora

Table elsewhere in this chapter reveals that, for some species, different risks were assessed between *Switzerland* and Europe. Barley present no risk for *Switzerland*, as no ancestor grows in this country, while in the eastern Mediterranean to Iran and West Central Asia, hybridization occurs readily with *Hordeum spontaneum*.

Wheat presents also a lower risk in Switzerland, where only *Ae. cylindrica* forms durable *populations, contrasting* with the Mediterranean area where several wild relatives of *Aegilops* are frequent. Finally, beet presents no risk of *outcrossing* with the wild flora because its wild relative *Beta vulgaris* subsp.

maritima is absent in Switzerland, while it is present close to the Atlantic coast and along the *Mediterranean* boarder.

THE IMPORTANCE OF BRIDGE SPECIES

Historically, the term "*bridge species*" has been used to designate wild plant species which could act, through artificial or natural *hybridization*, as a genetic bridge between wild *relatives* and closely related *cultivated* plants.

Figure elsewhere in this chapter shows that there are potentially three possible directions of the gene flow through bridge species: (1) wild-to-crop bridges, (2) crop-to-wild bridges and (3) wild-to-wild bridges.

The wild-to-crop bridges have been used by humans since millennia and are still used by breeders for the introduction of desirable traits from wild *relatives* into crops. As discussed above, the development of GE crops has brought much more attention to the gene flow the other way

Table 13.3: Number of wild relatives in European flora of the most important crop plants used for genetic transformation (only genera with GE members commercialized or used for field trials are listed) and estimation of their potential for wild-to-wild bridge formation. Symbols: – hybridization not observed, + hybridization observed but rare, ++ hybridization frequent, +++ hybridization extremely frequent.

Genus	Nb. of wild species in Europe*	Potential for wild-to-wild bridge formation in Europe (naturalized)		
		intrageneric	intergeneric	hybridizing with
Poaceae:				
Agrostis	24 (1)	+++	++	Polypogon, Calamagrostis
Avena	10 (2)	++	–	–
Cynodon	1	–	–	–
Festuca	165	+++	++	Lolium, Vulpia
Hordeum	8 (1)	++	++	Agropyron, Elymus
Lolium	5	+++	++	Festuca
Poa	43 (1)	+++	–	–
Triticum	3	+++	+++	Aegilops, Elymus, Secale
Zea	0	–	–	–
Rosaceae:				
Fragaria	4 (1)	+	–	–
Malus	6	++	++	Pyrus, Sorbus
Prunus	19 (2)	++	–	–
Pyrus	11	++	++	Malus, Sorbus
Rubus	c. 75 (c. 3)	+++	–	–
Asteraceae:				
Cichorium	3	–	–	–
Helianthus	3 (7)	+	–	–
Lactuca	15	++	–	–
Fabaceae:				
Glycine	0		–	–
Medicago	35 (2)	+	–	–
Pisum	1	–	–	–
Solanaceae:				
Lycopersicon	0	–	–	–

Nicotiana	3(4)	–	–	–
Solanum	3 (9)	+	–	–
Other families:				
Beta	5	+	–	–
Brassica	20	+++	+++	Raphanus, Sinapis, Diplotaxis, Hirschfeldia, Eruca, Erucastrum
Cucumis	(1)	–	–	–
Cucurbita	0	–	–	–
Daucus	10	+	–	–
Picea	2 (c. 8)	–	–	–
Pinus	13 (c. 13)	–	–	–
Populus	4 (c. 6)	+++	–	–
Vitis	1 (c. 9)	+	–	–

around, that is between *cultivars/crops* and their wild relatives. Surprisingly, the potential further spread of transgenes to other wild relatives via wild-to-wild bridges and so-called stepping-stones introgression has been rarely if ever studied in details in the GE plants context.

Thus, after a short *description* of the first well studied and described gene flow direction, more attention will be devoted to the still weakly explored subject of wild-to-wild bridges.

Wild-to-Crop Bridges

The term "*bridge species*" designates here wild relatives of cultivated plants which are used *during artificial* and/or natural *hybridization* procedures for crop improvement to circumvent some experimental or environmental constrains.

The ability to transfer genes between related plant species has been a great benefit in the *improvement* of cultivars for disease resistance, insect resistance, and/or end-use quality. This has been *especially* true in *allopolyploid* crops where there are multiple species that can act as donors.

The best documented examples come from studies of gene transfer from wild species to wheat *(Triticum aestivum)*. Romero et al. obtained for example the transfer of a cereal cyst nematode resistance gene from *Aegilops triuncalis* (donor) to hexaploid wheat using bridge species *T. turgidum*.

Fernandes et al. transferred to wheat stem and leaf rust as well as powdery mildew *resistance* from *Ae. squarrosa* (donor) through *hybridization* with *T. durum* (bridge species). Such methods imitate in fact the ancient *hybridization* events, which *happened* during *evolution* and *domestication* of some crop plants, e.g. the hexaploid wheat.

This bridge species method with development of intermediate natural or *artificially* synthesized

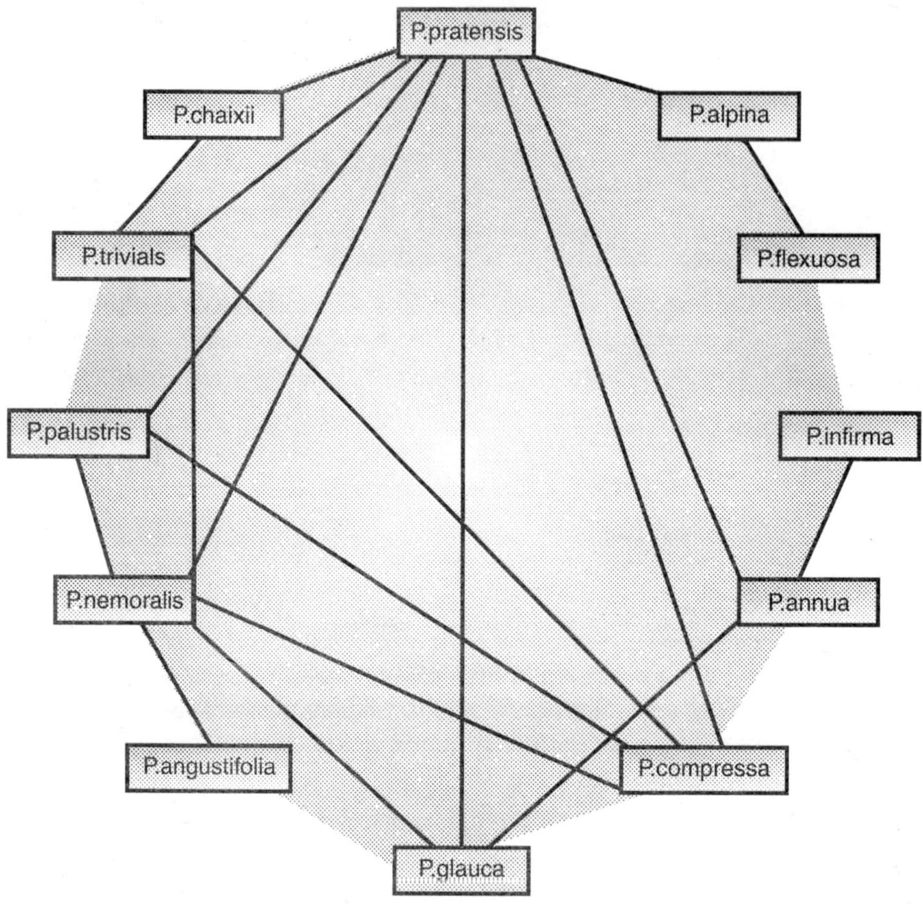

Figure 13.2: Wild-to-wild bridges: possible intrageneric hybridization in the grass genus Poa.

amphiploid hybrids is one of the *available* procedures to facilitate gene flow between wild relatives and crop. It has been used for many decades not only for wheat *cultivars* but also for many other crops (e.g. *Brassicaceae, Gossypium* sp., *Cucumis* sp.).

However, for numerous plant groups such *approaches* are very laborious and/or have low or no success (e.g. for some *Solanum* sp.).

"New Old Issue": Wild-to-Wild Bridges and Stepping-Stones Introgression

The *hybridization* and introgression between wild plants is a very well known *phenomenon.* Ellstrand et al. estimated that there are more than 1000 well studied and published examples of *spontaneous* plant hybridization.

Although at generally low frequencies and over long periods of time, genes (and thus also transgenes) can be *spontaneously introgressed* between different wild species. It is therefore surprising that there are practically no detailed studies and exhaustive reviews on the importance of wild-to-wild *hybridizations* and wild-to-wild bridges in the context of the transgene flow and GE

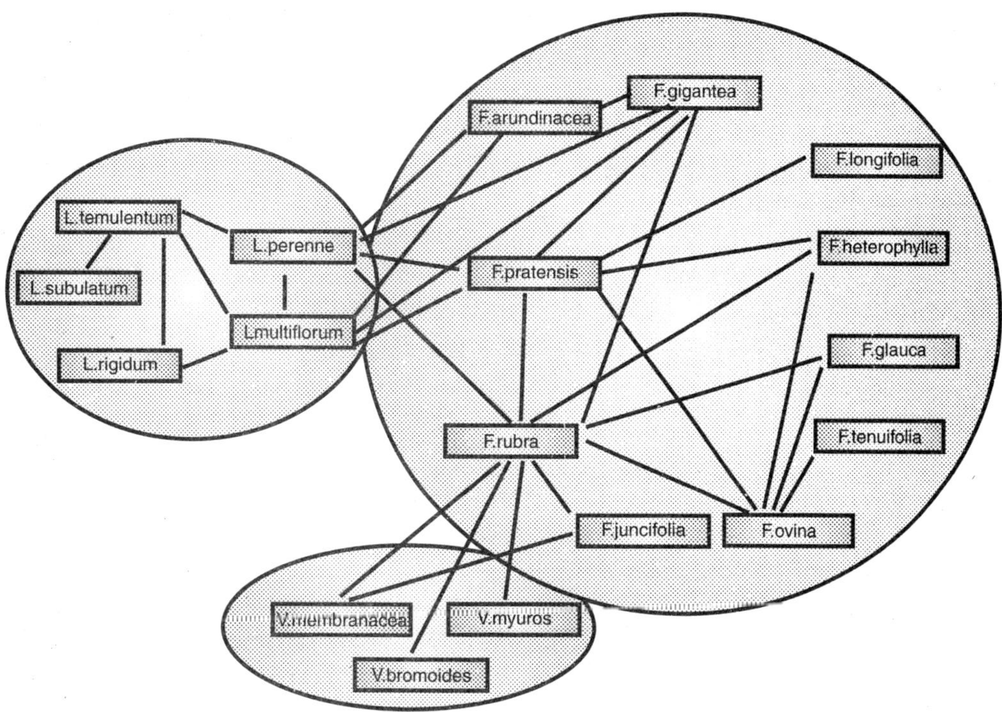

Figure 13.3: Wild-to-wild bridges: possible intra- and intergeneric hybridization between selected grass genera: Lolium, Festuca and Vulpia.

crops. How common are the natural hybridization processes between wild plant taxa? To answer this question we have to remember that there are two possible outcomes of *hybridization*. The first outcome is the present ongoing introgression. Mallet based on fundamental work on hybrid flora of the British Isles by Stace estimated that at least 25% of all wild plant species are able to hybridize *spontaneously* and/or are involved in ongoing *introgression processes* with other wild species.

Ellstrand et al. using the same data set concluded that up to 34% of families and 16% of all genera in Great Britain have at least one reported hybrid. Additionally, there are many very well-studied genera with numerous closely related species *producing* hybrid swarms, such as *Salix, Quercus or Eucalyptus.*

Rieseberg, based on the calculations of Ellstrand et al., concluded that we could expect a worldwide total of 27500 hybrid combinations among all Angiosperms. He added however, that it could be strongly *underestimated* since many regions, especially the tropics, are weakly explored and *documented* as far as their hybrid flora is concerned. The second result of *hybridization* is the ancient and present speciation.

Indeed, in many families and genera, polyploidization and hybridization were the main mode of speciation and diversification. Ellstrand et al. based on the *summarizing* works of Grant and Arnold concluded that more than 70% of plant species originated from hybrids.

As a consequence of these two well-documented hybridization outcomes, it has been often stated that the natural interspecific and even *intergeneric* hybrid formation is *ubiquitous* and uniform among higher plants or even the rule rather than the *exception.*

However, Ellstrand et al. demonstrated clearly that the *spontaneous* hybridization is non-randomly distributed among *systematic* plant groups. By analyzing five biosystematic floras from Europe, North *America* and the *Hawaiian Islands* they showed that certain phylogenetic groups are predisposed for hybridization.

To the most important hybrid families in practically all analyzed regions belong such crop-plant families as Poaceae, Asteraceae, Rosaceae and Fabaceae. Ellstrand et al. *enumerated* 13 of the most *important* food crops grown for human consumption.

Among them seven belong to Poaceae *(Eleusine, Hordeum, Oryza, Saccharum, Sorghum, Triticum, Zea),* and three to Fabaceae *(Arachis, Glycine, Phaseolus).* Hybridization seems therefore to be concentrated in a relatively restricted fraction of families and/or genera.

Moreover, many members of these highly *hybridizing* families have been genetically *modified* and mainly possess numerous wild relatives. Table elsewhere in this chapter lists all major plant genera and families of *European* flora *containing* crop plants with reported genetic transformation and/or with GE species used for field trials.

It shows how many wild relatives of transformed crops could be found in Europe and which of those taxa possess the highest ability for complex hybridization. Here again the family of Poaceae has the most important potential for wild-to-wild bridge formation.

Numerous of its mem-bers form easily both intra- and intergeneric hybrids. The only groups which could be compared with *Poaceae* are some genera of the family *Rosaceae* (*mainly fruit trees*) and the very well-known *Brassica* coenospecies complex.

It is worth mentioning that *detailed* studies and surveys on natural hybridization in wild taxa are *extremely* difficult. Abbott and Ellstrand et al. pointed out that the main *limitation* is the scarcity of modern biosystematic floras *containing* complete ecological, evolutionary and genetic information needed for such surveys.

Additionally, the documentation of *hybridization* and *introgression* faces several methodological and theoretical difficulties. There are many methods used in identifying hybrids ranging from *relatively* simple *morphological* measurements to complex *molecular* and *phylogenetic* analyses.

However, the majority of them, if not all, suffer from the fact that there are multiple explanations for the *morphological* and/or molecular *intermediacy* of a given hybrid candidate taxon. The morphological similarity for example could be simply a result of convergent evolution.

Martinsen et al. concluded that the hybrid detection based on morphological characteristics is additionally constrained by backcrosses, since it is known that a backcrossed hybrid often resembles the parental species. The development of molecular genetic markers has facilitated studies of hybridization and allowed one to detect even very low levels of introgression.

Additionally, it is possible with the *molecular* markers to track both the nuclear and *cytoplasmic* gene flow. However, the presence in one individual of molecular markers from two different species could be explained not only through recent *hybridization* but also due to shared ancestral characters (symplesiomorphy).

The differentiation between contemporary versus ancient introgression is difficult and has been studied in only a few taxa. *Poaceae:* Example of a Biologically Predisposed Family for Wild-to-Wild Bridge Formation Table elsewhere in this chapter and *detailed comparative* studies *mentioned* above demonstrate clearly the enormous potential of the family *Poaceae* for the wild-wild *hybridization* processes.

The importance of the *Poaceae* as an object of research reflects their *ecological* and *biogeographical* success as well as their enormous economic value. They occupy almost every habitat around the world, often being the *dominating* organisms.

The *Poaceae* comprises about 10000 species and between 600 and 900 genera. In addition to that, the family contains a very high percentage of species and cytotypes of polyploidy origin. More than 80% of grass species have undergone polyploidy which represents the highest percentage in Angiosperms.

Such a high level can be *explained* by successive regressions and *extensions* of the ranges which would favour *secondary* contact zones between related taxa, their *hybridization* and their subsequent polyploidization.

According to Wipff one of the most important grass groups being currently used in genetic transformations are the forage grasses as well as grass species used for turf and erosion control. Furthermore, Wipff gives four main reasons why this group is particularly at risk of spreading *transgenes*: they have undergone relatively little domestication; they have usually *numerous* wild relatives; they grow often in sympatry with these; they can grow as weeds outside cultivated areas or in other crop cultures.

To this grass group belong such common and species-rich European and North American genera as *Lolium, Festuca, Poa* and *Agrostis.* In the United States not less than 187 field tests were carried out between 1993 and 2006 with transgenic *Agrostis stolonifera,* 36 with *Poa pratensis,* 26 with *Festuca arundinacea,* 17 with *Cynodon dactylon* and 6 with *Lolium perenne.*

All mentioned species possess numerous wild relatives in Europe and are capable of hybridizing easily with them (e.g. *Festuca* with ca. 165 species, numerous *subspecies* and swarms of hybrids in Europe). Figure elsewhere in this chapter gives an example of intrageneric wild-to-wild hybrid complexes in *Poa.*

Genus *Poa* contains approximately 43 species in Europe and 300 species worldwide. *Intergeneric* hybridization is *extremely* common and results in serious classification *difficulties.* In *Poa pratensis,* which absorbed genomes from many different taxa, it is even impossible to trace its ancestors.

It was shown additionally that F1 hybrids between different *Poa* species can be completely fertile. Figure elsewhere in this chapter shows that almost 1/3 of all European *Poa* species are able to hybridize. They have mainly sympatric *distribution* even at a local level and have similar phenology.

It is additionally very probable that more detailed studies would reveal much higher levels of *intrageneric* hybridization between members of the genus *Poa.* Figure elsewhere in this chapter gives some further examples of wild-to-wild inter- and *intrageneric* hybrid complexes in three common European genera of *Poaceae.*

Table 13.4: Comparisons of fitness of F1 and BCs fo some crops; data compiled partly from [1]

	NT (non Type of Hybrid			Fitness (E=equivalent,	
		transgenic), *T (transgenic)*	*transgene*	*generation*	*H=higher, I=inter mediary, L= Lower)*
Oilseed rape					
Brassica napus	*Brassica rapa*	NT		F1	I
B. napus	*B. rapa*	NT		F2 and BC1	L
B. napus	*B. rapa*	T	glufosinate tolerance	F1	female fitness L to H: frequency and density dependent, male fitness L
B. napus herbivores;	*B. rapa*	T	Bt	F1	H, in presence of L in absence
B. napus	*B. rapa*	T	Bt	BC2	E (low herbivory)
B. napus	*B. rapa*	T	high laurate	F1	E
B. napus	*B. rapa*	T	high laurate	F1	E
B. napus	*B. rapa*	T	glufosinate tolerance	BC3	E
B. napus	*B. rapa*	T	glufosinate tolerance	BC1	E
Sunflowers					
Helianthus annuus	*H. annuus*(wild type)	NT		F1	L
H. annuus	*H. annuus* (wild type)	T	Bt transgene	BC1	H (natural herbivory)
H. annuus	*H. annuus* (wild type)	T	white mould resistance	BC3	H to E

(Table Contd.)

Sugar beet					
Beta vulgaris ssp. *vulgaris*	*B. vulgaris* ssp. *maritima*	NT		Fl, F2	E
B. vulgaris ssp. *vulgaris*	*B. vulgaris* ssp. *maritima*	T	viral resis ance	Fl, F2	E
Squash					
Cucurbita pepo	*Cucurbita pepo* (wild type)		NT	Fl, F2	L (Fl) to E (F2 and BC1)
C. pepo	*C. pepo* (wild type)	T	viral resistance	and BC1	L (Fl) to H (BC1 and BC2)
				Fl, BC1	in case of high disease
				and BC2	pressure. L for all in case of low disease pressure
C. pepo	*C. pepo* (wild type)	T	resistant to two	Fl	L (survival and seed
			pathogenic viruses	production)	
Maize					
Zea mays	*Z. mays* ssp. *mexicana*	NT		Fl	H then wild species
Zea mays	*Z. mays* ssp. *mexicana*	T	glyphosate tolerance	Fl	H then wild species

The reproductive *compatibility* and hybrid viability (even at intrageneric level) between *Lolium, Festuca* and *Vulpia* are very well documented. Intrageneric *spontaneous* hybrids between *Festuca* and *Lolium (= x Festulolium)* are not rare, they can be fertile and have an ability to backcross with either of the parents.

The *commonest x Festulolium* in Europe is the hybrid between *F. pratensis x L. perenne (= x Festulolium loliaceum)* which can be found in different types of pastures and *meadows* from Norway to Italy. Figure elsewhere in this chapter shows additionally that there are certain species *complexes* where hybrid *combinations* are possible in all directions.

This is the case for example in the following five species: *Festuca pratensis, F. arundinacea, F.gigantea, Lolium perenne* and *L. multiflorum.* The close relation of these species could be also demonstrated experimentally. Several authors proposed even to join both genera or to move some *Festuca* species into genus *Lolium.*

Additionally, some studies on the chromosome structure of *F. pratensis, L. perenne* and *L. multiflorum,* concluded that there are practically no barriers for gene exchange between these species. The majority of species represented in Figures elsewhere in this chapter fit very well the general characteristic of taxa predisposed for hybridization.

They are outcrossing with *incomplete* reproductive isolation between species, they are mainly perennials with well-developed vegetative spread. Further, they are wind-pollinated and the pollen dispersal up to 21 km has been shown (e.g. for *Agrostis).*

Thus, the geographic *proximity* as well as pollination does not represent any constrains. Additionally, they flower over a very long time period from May till August, thus even at a local scale the phenological overlapping is very common. The examples described above illustrate clearly that in selected vascular plant families and genera we could *potentially* expect a stepping-stone spread and exchange of genes with *unpredictable* effect.

Absolute containment of transgenes will be in such taxa practically impossible. Therefore, more experimental and descriptive work has to be done in order to evaluate the existence and importance of wild-to-wild bridges among a spectrum of taxonomic plant groups as broad as possible.

GENETIC AND ECOLOGICAL CONSEQUENCES ON WILD RELATIVES

Genetic and Ecological Consequences of Outcrossing

Outcrossing in plants may have different impacts, depending on the relatedness of the taxa. When a single species is involved, *chromosomes* are *homologous* and pair regularly. On the contrary, when related taxa hybridize, recombinations occur between homeologous chromosomes with the possible consequence of irregular pairing, leading to unbalanced gametes with reduced fertility.

Hybridization between crops and wild relatives is a very ancient phenomenon which has been *investigated* for a long period from an agronomist point of view, as gene flow from the wild species to the crop might lead to reduced yield and loss of the genetic purity of the cultivated varieties. More recently, while GE plants have been developed, *agronomists* and ecologists have been concerned by the consequences of transgene escape into non-transgenic crop fields or in wild relatives. Hybridization has genetic and ecological *consequences.*

Genetic consequences may be defined as the effects of the insertion of the genes in the target species itself and on the expression of genes. On the other hand, ecological *consequences* are considered here as direct or indirect effects on fitness. We discuss below the two types of *consequences* separately.

Consequences of the Transgene

The transgene itself may have genetic consequences for the recipient plants by interacting with other genes and leading to untargeted effects. In order to investigate this aspect, among many others, *Arabidopsis thaliana* has been used as a model species.

Metzdorff et al. analyzed, using cDNA *microarrays,* six independently transformed *A. thaliana* lines characterized by modified flavonoid biosynthesis. Although these transgenic lines possessed different types of *integration* events, no unintended effects were *identified.* Genetic *transformation* could also affect fitness, and may be in this case associated with a physiological cost.

For example, significant reduction of fitness was observed repeatedly associated with resistance to herbicide. Bergelson et al. observed for *A. thaliana* a 34% reduction in seed production for a mutant acetolactase synthetase gene that confers *resistance* to the herbicide *chlorsulfuron,* in comparison to the non-transgenic lines.

This cost in fitness was caused by pleiotropic effects due to the presence of the resistance genes itself, while no cost was associated with the expression of kanamycin resistance. Purrington and Bergelson obtained similar results by comparing mutant and transgenic herbicide resistant lines in two different *environmental* conditions: with or without fertilizer treatments.

The cost of resistance appeared in both treatments for the transgenic line, while no cost was associated with the mutant line in the high *fertilizer* treatment. Other *untargeted* effects may appear, such as the change in outcrossing rate observed in an outdoor *experiment* involving transgenic *A. thaliana,* without the proof that it was caused by the transgene itself.

Transgenesis may have also *unexpected* effects on crops. For example, the lignin content of Bt corn was significantly higher than that of non-Bt corn. A change in lignin content might affect the action of *herbivores* and have ecological consequences. Moreover, Prescott et al. *demonstrated* that post-translational modification of a plant protein (a-amylase inhibitor-1 from the common bean *(Phaseolus vulgaris))* led to the synthesis of a *structurally* modified form of the protein in pea *(Pisum sativum).*

This protein showed altered antigenic properties. While this example concerns human health, it shows that untargeted effects of transgenic plants on protein *expressions* occur. *Consequently,* we can infer that similar effects could lead to changes in ecological properties.

Consequences for Wild Relatives

Introgression involves chromosome segments *containing* possibly several genes. Therefore, the consequences of introgression will depend on the genes included in the *introgressed* segment, and on the site of *introgression* in the recipient species (linkage to other crop genes, pleiotropy).

Similarly, *introgression* from a transgenic crop to a wild relative will also depend on the insertion site of the transgenic line. Genetic *consequences* are expected to be those of *conventional* lines, except for the effect of the transgene itself.

Inference from Natural Observations

Natural *hybridization* is frequent in nature and the fitness of hybrids may be lower, equal or higher than that of their parents. Hybrid inferiority has been *recognized* as a rule for a long time. More recently, the importance of hybridization for *evolution* and speciation has emerged.

Hybrids may be at the origin to new *lineages*, which may lead to new species. Speciation might be either progressive or abrupt, when *polyploids* are formed by chromosome doubling. Because of their different *chromosome* number, allopolyploids are reproductively isolated, at least partly, from their parents.

According to Burke and Arnold, different genetic *mechanisms* operate behind low and high fitness of the hybrids. Hybrid inferiority would be caused in most cases by negative epistasis, while heterosis would be mostly the *consequences* of the *segregation* of additive genetic factors.

Inference from Conventional (Non-Transgenic) Wild x Crop Hybrids

Hybridization followed by repetitive backcrosses lead to *introgression*, the transfer of a part of the genome of one species to another. Depending on the *introgressed* genes and on their expression, *introgression* may lead to new characteristics which could affect the *ecological* properties of the target species.

Experimental data produced a broad spectrum of results on the relative fitness between hybrids and their parents. The *effectiveness* of gene flow will depend on the viability and the fertility of hybrids and of *subsequent backcrosses*. Several studies have involved hybrids between a *conventional* crop and their wild relatives.

For example, Hauser et al. have investigated the fitness of F1 hybrids, as well as F2 hybrids and *backcrosses* between *Brassica rapa* and oilseed rape *(B. napus)* in *experimental* crosses. Hybrids were as viable as their parents, produced more pods, but these later contained fewer seeds, with an overall fitness that was *intermediary* to their parents.

The fitness of F2 and backcrosses were on average lower, compared to that of their parents, and varied considerably, including individuals as fit as *B. rapa*. In another study, interspecific F1 hybrids between wild and cultivated radishes *(Raphanus raphanistrum x R. sativus)* had a lower fitness than the wild plant.

Nevertheless, a field experiment was set up with one half containing F1 wild-crop hybrids and the other half wild. After three years, the dominant white color of the flower of the crop persisted at a frequency ranging from 8% to 22%.

A similar study on carrot *(Daucus carota)* showed that hybrids between cultivated and wild carrots were more *sensitive* to frost than the wild parents, which limited their *survival*. Weed x crop hybrids between *Sorghum halepense* (Johnsongrass) and *S. bicolor* (cultivated sorghum) did not show any *difference* in fitness, suggesting that in this case, no barriers to gene flow exist.

Contrasting with that, a second generation of hybrids (S1 and BC1) between *Lactuca serriola* (prickly lettuce) and *L. sativa* (cultivated lettuce) germinated and survived better than their wild relative. Seed output of both classes of *hybrids* was greater with *L. sativa* but no *significant* difference was found with *L. serriola.*

Inference from Transgenic Wild x Crop Hybrids

Table 4 summarizes the results of fitness measurements comparing the hybrids of different generations for five crops, partly derived from Hails and Morley. Non-transgenic hybrids have usually lower, equivalent or intermediary fitness then their parents. A notable exception is the *experiment* of Guadagnuolo et al. which demonstrated *heterosis* of hybrids between glyphosate-tolerant maize *(Zea mays)* and teosinte *(Z. mays ssp. mexicana),* when *compared* to the wild parent.

Nevertheless, in the absence of selection pressure with herbicide, no difference was detected between transgenic and *non-transgenic* hybrids. Sunflowers have been *extensively* studied. Burke and Rieseberg investigated *transgenic* sunflower with an inserted gene of oxalate oxidase (OxOx) conferring *enhanced* white mold resistance in *cultivated* sunflower.

They *backcrossed* it with wild sunflower. No cost of the transgene was observed in the absence of the pathogen. When the plants were infected, the transgene *decreased* the *probability* of infection, this later having a *negative* effect on seed output.

Moreover, the disease effect varied among locations and no generalization was possible. The authors *insisted* on the necessity of replicating the *experiment* over space and time, as well as on the importance of genetic background and of *environmental* conditions.

Snow et al. *demonstrated* that, in the field, male sterile wild sunflowers *introgressed* with a Bt transgene produced more *inflorescences* than those without the transgene. These advantages were related to a decrease in insect damage.

Greenhouse *experiments* did not reveal any fitness cost of the transgene. In hybrids with *transgenic* rapeseed, relative fitness varied considerably, depending on the transgene and on the presence of *associated* selective pressure by insect herbivores.

Transgenic hybrids between wild *Brassica rapa* and rapeseed possessing a Bt transgene performed better than non-transgenic hybrids in the presence of *herbivores,* while their fitness was lower when *herbivores* were absent, showing a physiological cost of the transgene.

On the contrary, performances were equivalent in hybrids with or without a transgene coding for high laurate content. The same was true for glufosinate tolerance, in the absence of *herbicide* treatment. For practical reasons, only one transgenic line was used in most of the cited *experiments,* instead of using so-called *"sister lines",* possessing the same transgenic *construct* but in different insertion sites.

It is then delicate to assess the effect of the transgenes themselves on the fitness of hybrids and subsequent backcrosses, because the consequences on fitness may not be due necessarily to the transgene, but could depend on its insertion site.

Moreover, environmental conditions and the density of plants may also influence relative fitness. *Summarizing,* costs of the transgene have been observed in some cases but not in all. On the other hand, it is worth noting that in the mentioned studies, positive effects on fitness of transgenic hybrids has been interpreted as the direct effect of the transgene itself.

CONCLUSION

To date, a considerable amount of data has been gathered on potential and actual gene flow between crops and wild relatives. Such knowledge is *extremely* useful for the risk *assessment* associated with GE crops, especially when considering the regional component of the floristic composition.

The investigation of the case of Switzerland reveals differences with Europe, which modulate the evaluation of risk for several crops. It reveals also that not only the presence of wild relatives differ *geographically*, but that their genetic composition may vary and strongly influence gene flow, as was illustrated for alfalfa.

Other issues merit further investigation. Indeed, *transgenes* can be transmitted from crops to the closest wild relatives, but can also migrate further to other species, by successive crosses. A *bibliographical* survey of Poaceae illustrate that *hybridization* is widespread in some taxonomical groups. Genetic and ecological consequences of the transgene in a wild species have also been poorly investigated up to now.

The few *existing* studies show different pictures according to the species and the inserted trait. More *investigations* are needed to dissociate the *importance* of the insertion site and of the *transgenes* themselves. Moreover, the fitness of hybrids may vary according to *environmental* conditions and these interactions merit evaluation in nature.

It is interesting to note that several examples demonstrate that transgene *expression* give advantages to the wild species in cases of selective pressure, as for the Bt gene in the presence of herbivores. While generalization is difficult, any type of transgene which would influence fitness positively, such as for example the resistance to diseases could confer to the wild species a real ecological advantage.

Finally, given the diversity of the results observed in the various studies on gene flow, and on its consequences, it seems almost impossible to address all the questions *experimentally*. On the contrary, it is probably necessary to produce enough empirical data, in order to build realistic and reliable predictive models.

TRANSGENIC PLANTS WITH INCREASED TOLERANCE AGAINST MICROBIAL PATHOGENS

Disease resistance in crop plants is a major challenge in plant breeding. Within *industrialized* agriculture, the need for efficient self-protection of *cultivated* plants is likely to increase in the future. To achieve this goal, diverse *strategies* will be necessary and compete.

Conventional breeding has made great progress in *incorporating* natural defense genes, but the limitations of this method are also obvious. The progress in plant molecular biology now allows the generation of transgenic plants, thereby *exploiting* the mechanisms nature has *developed* to control and to limit the infection of microbial *pathogens* on plants.

An additional benefit of transgenic plants is the possibility to validate the usefulness of *endogenous* plant genes in defense strategies. Changes in the expression or composition of a desired gene may still be achieved by *conventional* breeding assisted by the results from transgenic plants. The possibility to transform all major crop plants-although sometimes tedious and labor *intensive-opens* a new opportunity for novel *enhanced* plant tolerance toward microbial pathogens.

Over the last few decades many of the natural plant defense strategies were thoroughly investigated, and as a result numerous mechanisms are known by now. For example, the concept of *pathogenesis-related* proteins (PR-proteins) has *revealed* an inducible defense system that is thought to have antimicrobial properties. The constitutive expression of a single or a few genes of this group of defense genes was started in the late 1980s but with limited success.

This will be covered in the first section of this chapter. On the other hand, new strategies for enhanced pathogen *tolerance* try to use the plants' signaling network for defense activation. As a consequence, a whole battery of diverse defense *reactions* is triggered (variable in different plant species), which seems to be more powerful than the overexpression of single *antimicrobial* proteins. These approaches acting on complex defense networks will be *described* in the second part..

SINGLE-GENE DEFENSE MECHANISMS

Pathogenesis-Related Proteins

About 40 years ago Ross performed *experiments* with tobacco Xanthi nc plants, which after viral inoculation exhibit a hypersensitive reaction in which a *limited* number of cells die and form a lesion. Plants that were inoculated with the tobacco mosaic virus showed much smaller lesions after a challenge infection 7 days later than newly *inoculated* leaves.

This phenomenon is now well known as systemic acquired resistance (SAR). Searching for the mechanisms underlying SAR, PR-proteins were discovered. Subsequently some of them were *biochemically identified* as hydrolases of fungal cell walls, namely β-1,3-glucanase and chitinase.

However, the biochemical properties and enzymatic function of other PR-proteins such as the well-characterized PR-1 remain puzzling. Transgenic tobacco plants *overexpressing* a chitinase gene from tobacco showed enhanced tolerance against fungal infection by *Cercospora nicotianae* indicating that high levels of plant hydrolyzing enzymes are a suitable strategy to increase *pathogen* tolerance.

By using a combination of a 8-1,3-glucanase and a chitinase gene, Broglie et al. demonstrated the *synergistic* effect of both enzymes, yielding a higher degree of resistance compared with the expression of each gene alone. A similar conclusion was drawn from a study in tobacco, in which a gene for a basic chitinase from rice and a gene for an acidic glucanase from alfalfa were *coexpressed* after appropriate crossing of individual transgenic plants.

The different gene *combinations* were compared, as was the level of expression of these hydrolytic enzymes in homozygous versus heterozygous plants. Based on the reduction of lesion size after *C. nicotianae* infection, it was shown that the combination of *glucanase* and chitinase *expression* even at a moderate level is more beneficial than the *expression* of either gene alone at a much higher level.

The concept of the constitutive expression of hydrolytic enzymes was later extended from tobacco to crop plants. The expression of chitinase in oilseed rape (*Brassica napus*) to obtain enhanced tolerance was tested in field trials after inoculation with three different fungal pathogens.

Although the overall protection of the transgenic plants in the field trials seems to be smaller than *previously* shown in experiments in a greenhouse, the *enhanced* tolerance in chitinase-expressing rape was effective against several fungi under natural field conditions.

Many other plant species were *transformed* with plant glucanases or chitinases, and most research groups were able to find at least one fungus that is sensitive to these hydrolytic enzymes. The reports on transgenic plants *overexpressiong* hydrolytic enzymes imply that this strategy might already be sufficient to combat most fungal pathogens.

However, this is obviously not the case. Quite often fungi were chosen for pathogenicity assays that are known to be sensitive to chitinases and/or glucanases, *Rhizoctonia solani* and *Trichoderma viride* being examples. In contrast, well-recognized plant pathogens are often not *significantly* inhibited in their pathogenicity. Thus, plant *hydrolases* are useful to limit the spread of some fungal *pathogens* and are likely to increase the basal tolerance of plants against fungal infections.

Whether the increased tolerance of transgenic plants with elevated levels of hydrolytic enzymes is the result of the direct inhibition of the fungal (tip) growth needs to be carefully analyzed in future work. Enzymatic cleavage of fungal cell walls liberating chitin or glucan oligomers will also activate diverse plant defense responses as these carbohydrate oligomers are potent elicitors in almost every plant.

The transcriptional activation of genes involved in lignin precursor *formation* or antimicrobial phytoalexins by elicitors is well known. The genes for PR-proteins of unknown biochemical function such as PR1 or PR5 were also *constitutively* expressed in tobacco plants. The PRla-overexpressing plants have a higher degree of resistance against a limited number of fungal *pathogens* from oomycetes.

However, no enhanced tolerance against other pathogenic fungi of tobacco or tobacco mosaic virus was achieved. It was later shown that PR1-proteins from *tobacco* and tomato inhibit the spore germination of *Phytophthora infestans* and reduce the lesion size of diseased tomato leafs.

Notably, the PRla isoform, used in the transgenic lines, was very inefficient and showed only 10% of the *biological* activity of the most potent antifungal isoform PRlg. The overexpression of a rice thaumatin-like gene of the PR5 family in rice plants gave *enhanced* tolerance against *Rhizoctonia solani*, the agent causing sheath blight disease.

The infected leaf area was reduced to one fifth in the best lines, *indicating* that the thaumatin-like gene is highly effective against *R. solani* infection. Expression of a similar osmotin-like gene in potato also enhanced tolerance against the late blight disease caused by *Phytophthora infestans*. One interesting point about PR-proteins in cereals is worth mentioning.

Wheat, for instance, expresses *hydrolytic* enzymes (β-1,3-glucance, chitinase) after pathogen infection. In contrast to this situation in *Arabidopsis* and tobacco, the status of a systemic acquired resistance in wheat is not correlated with the *constitutive* expression of these PR-genes. This raises the question of whether hydrolytic enzymes are an important part of the plant defense system at all.

Alternatively, other as yet unidentified genes (or mechanisms) are important players in plant tolerance to pathogens. Support for the latter view comes from experiments with *Arabidopsis* DNA microarrays in which many genes are *transcriptionally* induced in resistant plants.

The fact that 413 genes (out of -7000 genes *representing* 25% of the genome) were reported to show a consistently higher expression level in SAR or plant resistance indicates that there will be more than a thousand genes that are *significantly* induced in local resistance or SAR. This incredibly high number draws a far more complex picture of plant resistance than previously thought.

As well as being *frustrating* for researchers trying to dissect single-gene function in SAR, the high number of SAR-related genes is a huge challenge and opportunity for the plant molecular biologist to create novel transgenic lines with enhanced tolerance against a variety of microbial pathogens.

Defense Peptides

Plant and animals have developed an efficient mechanism to combat pathogens by using small antimicrobial peptides collectively termed defensins. These peptides are now divided into several families on the basis of sequence homology and structural properties.

They are usually relatively small (<60 amino acids) and in the case of plant defensins contain several cysteine residues that form one or more stable disulfide bridges. Defense peptides exhibit a broad spectrum of *antimicrobial* activity against bacteria, fungi, and even enveloped viruses.

In animal cells even parasites and tumor cells are inhibited. Most of the known defensin genes are from insects showing mainly antibacterial activity. The large diversity of these peptides (more than 500 varieties are known) provides a huge reservoir of genes that can be expressed in plants to enhance tolerance against pathogens, an approach that has just started to be exploited by plant molecular biologists. A plant defensin from radish (RsAFLP2) was *expressed* at high levels in tobacco plants.

Subsequent infection with the fungal pathogen *Alternaria longipes* revealed efficient protection of the transgenic plants resulting in more than 80% reduction of lesion sizes. Lipid transfer proteins were initially described as shuttle proteins, involved in the transfer of lipids between organelles.

Later, the antimicrobial activity of these peptides was discovered. Transgenic *Arabidopsis* plants overexpressing the lipid transfer protein LTP2 from barley showed a strong reduction in disease symptoms after infection with *Pseudomonas* syringae pv. tomato. Thionins are often found in quite high amounts in the endosperm of cereals and other plants.

They are toxic to plant pathogenic fungi but only at relatively high concentrations. Bohlmann et al. showed inhibition of the barley pathogen *Drechslera teres* at *concentrations* of 500 μM. Nevertheless, transgenic *Arabidopsis* plants expressing high thionin levels were shown to be more resistant to *Fusarium oxysporum* and *Plasmodiophora* brassicae. The *overexpression* of plant defense peptide genes to achieve higher tolerance against a broad range of pathogens was only partly successful.

A few pathogens (mainly bacteria) were restricted in their growth, but many other *pathogens* were not. This problem was overcome by the expression of chimeric defense peptides in potato plants. The synthetic peptides consist of two domains derived from cecropin (from the giant silk moth *Hyalaphora cecropia*) and melittin (the major component of bee venom). The Nterminus of the chimeric peptide had to be modified in order to be tolerated as *nontoxic* by the plant cells.

The transgenic potato plants were almost totally resistant against *Erwinia carotovora* even over a very long period of time (e.g., 6 months of tuber storage). This high degree of resistance was also observed after infection of potato plants with different fungi including *Phytophthora cactorum* and *Fusarium solani.*

As mentioned before, some defense peptides are also toxic to animals, implying the need for great care in the use of these defense molecules in edible plants. The transgenic potatoes containing the chimeric cecropin-melittin peptide were fed to mice for several weeks without any notable change in animal behaviour or body weight.

The large number of known potent defense peptides from insects combined with molecular biology tools will make it possible to exploit these natural defense *mechanisms* on a broad basis.

Ribosome-Inactivating Proteins

Ribosome-inactivating proteins (RIPs) are widely found in plants. They exhibit a specific RNA-N-glycosidase activity that selectively cleaves off an adenine residue from a conserved site of the 28S rRNA.

This prevents binding of the *elongation* factor 2 and consequently leads to an arrest in protein biosynthesis. RIPs do not inactivate the *ribosomes* of their own species but inactivate those of distantly related species.

Expression of the barley seed RIP in tobacco under the control of a wound-inducible promoter resulted in enhanced tolerance against fungal infections with *Rhizoctonia solani.*

However, attempts to express the barley RIP in wheat plants were *unsuccessful,* indicating that the constitutive *expression* of this protein is toxic for wheat to allow regeneration of transgenic lines.

RIPs are primarily antiviral proteins, and overexpression of RIPs often leads to resistance of the transgenic plant against a broad spectrum of plant viruses. However, an additional antifungal activity of RIP was observed when *overexpressing* pokeweed *antiviral* protein and mutant forms, which exhibit no N-glycosidase activity typical of the RIP function. The *advantage* of the mutant RIPs is their low toxicity compared with the original protein.

Plants with Elevated Levels of Antimicrobial Secondary Compounds

The efficient protection of many wild-type plants against microbial *pathogens* is thought to be mediated at least in part by toxic secondary metabolites from plants. Often these compounds require very complex *biosynthesis,* and many of the genes involved in their formation are not known or *characterized.*

These limitations usually make the formation of secondary metabolites with complex biosynthesis in transgenic plants very difficult. Therefore, today's strategies are based on the expression of a single gene (or a few genes) to equip a plant with a novel secondary metabolite.

A successful example is the expression of a stilbene synthase gene from grapevine (*Vitis vinifera*) in tobacco and crop plants under the control of its native pathogen-inducible promoter.

The enzyme requires only one *pcoumaroyl-coenzyme* A (CoA) (a lignin precursor) and three malonyl-CoA to form one molecule of the stilbene resveratrol, which has *antimicrobial* properties in plants. The novel phytoalexin accumulated after *Botrytis cinerea* infection to low millimolar levels within a few days, resulting in a reduction of diseased leaf area of roughly two thirds.

The same gene was later expressed in tomato, rice, and other crop plants. Again, a strong increase in basal pathogen tolerance was obtained. One drawback, however, is the *observation* that tomato plants producing *resveratrol* showed an increase in resistance against *Phytophthora infestans* (-50% reduction in diseased leaf area) but not against *Botrytis cinerea,* which was *efficiently* restricted on resveratrol-producing tobacco plants.

In retrospect, it is amazing to see that the grapevine stilbene synthase promoter is pathogen inducible in so many plants and that this inducibility is essential as the *constitutive* expression of the stilbene synthase gene results in detrimental effects such as male sterility in tobacco.

MULTIGENE DEFENSE MECHANISMS

Elevation of Endogenous Levels of Salicylic Acid

In the first section, strategies were applied that are based on the expression of a single gene (or a few genes) and a single target mechanism. From *epidemiological* studies it is evident that such strategies have a high chance of being overcome by pathogens, similar to resistance against chemical pesticides.

From this point of view, more complex defense strategies should be beneficial for enhanced long-term pathogen tolerance. One obvious strategy is to make use of the plant's own defense system, for instance, by lowering the *threshold* level above which a plant mounts an efficient set of defense reactions to combat microbial pathogens.

Verbene et al. described the *expression* of two bacterial genes in plant *chloroplasts* that lead to salicylic acid biosynthesis from chorismate. Transgenic tobacco plants have high levels (-100 μM) of salicylic acid glucoside (the plant's vacuolar storage form) and are resistant against the fungus *Oidium lycopersicon.*

Similarly, lesions after infection with tobacco mosaic virus were much smaller than those in wild-type plants, resembling the *establishment* of systemic acquired resistance (SAR). The constant production of salicylic acid in the transgenic plants turns on the immune system of plants. Although this strategy was so far tested only in tobacco, it seems to be very promising for many other plants.

Constitutive Systemic Acquired Resistance

Many laboratories have developed mutagenesis-based screens to look for plants with a defect in the plant immune system, simplified set equivalent to SAR. A single mutant was isolated independently by three groups. Thc gene is *synonymously* called *npr* (nonexpresser of PR-genes), *nim* (nonimmunity), or *sai* (salicylic acid insensitive).

Although the biochemical function of the NPR protein is not well understood, it seems to interact with transcription factors required for PR-gene expression in a salicylic aciddependent manner. One obvious experiment after the isolation of the *NPR* gene was to increase the expression level of this gene in transgenic plants. Luckily, the transgenic *Arabidopsis* lines showed strongly enhanced tolerance against infection by the biotrophic fungus *Peronospora parasitica.*

This was achieved by a threefold increase in the protein level of NPR, which turned out to be sufficient to activate the complex plant defense system constitutively, resulting in SAR and resistance against *P. parasitica.*

Hydrogen Peroxide

A surprisingly small and reactive molecule plays a key role in plant defense: hydrogen peroxide (H_2O_2). Previously, H_2O_2 was regarded as an unavoidable by-product of respiration and photosynthesis for which the plant cell has no use, and thus it is rapidly detoxified by means of, for instance, catalase or ascorbate *peroxidase.*

Over the past decade a totally different picture of the function of H_2O_2 and other reactive oxygen species has emerged from many studies. For instance, H_2O_2 drives the cross-linking o plant cell wall structural proteins. The local *toughening* of the cell wall is a barrier for *penetrating* fungi and is beneficial for the plant to mount a local defense to stop the ingression of the fungu Cross-linked cell walls were shown to be much more resistant towards microbial cell wall cleaving hydrolyses.

Along the same line, the expression of a wheat germin protein in wheat leaves results ir enhanced resistance against *Blumeria graminis* f.sp. *tritici*, the causal agent of wheat powdery mildew. It was shown that germin is oxidatively cross-linked in wheat cell walls at sites of attemptec fungal penetration. From a biochemical point of view, it is also clear that other compounds can be polymerized in H_2O_2-dependent processes.

Many other phenolic secondary *compounds* are candidates for mixed *polyphenols* beside the lignin precursors. Thus, it is conceivable that part of the enhanced pathogen tolerance of stilbene-producing plants is mediated by the supply of the phenolic compound resveratrol for *polyphenol formation* rather than the direct antimicrobial activity of this phytoalexin alone. The plant-pathogen interaction that results in *programmed* cell death of the hypersensitive reaction (HR) exhibits an extra *oxidative* burst several hours after contact between plant and microbe.

This phenomenon is widespread and therefore seems to be important in plant resistance. The H_2O_2 from the oxidative burst was shown to be a signal that diffuses locally around the site of the infection and thereby transcriptionally induces genes in neighboring cells. Furthermore, H_2O_2 pulses (<10 minutes) induce cell death in soybean cell cultures several hours later.

Although the concentrations used for the H_2O_2 pulses were relatively high (2-5 mM), a similar result can be obtained by supplying a constant H_2O_2 concentration of 1050 µM for several hours using the *enzyme* glucose oxidase. Following these ideas, *transgenic* plants were generated in which a catalase gene was largely suppressed by an antisense strategy.

As a consequence, the steady-state levels of H_2O_2 are higher and these plants are more sensitive to microbial pathogen attack, resulting in enhanced tolerance. These observations resemble findings in transgenic potato plants that express a glucose *oxidase* gene from *Aspergillus* in their cell wall.

The slightly elevated levels of H_2O_2 in the potato plants have a strong impact on pathogen resistance. Why and how a small increase in H_2O_2 causes the greatly increased pathogen tolerance remain a mystery waiting to be solved in future studies.

As a final remark, the catalase antisense plants are more resistant to pathogens but they are also more sensitive to oxidative stress caused by photosynthesis under high light conditions. One should be cautious about the likely reduction in cold tolerance and drought stress, two unfavourable environmental conditions that put oxidative stress on the plants.

It seems that the concentration of H_2O_2 has to remain within a certain margin in order to avoid detrimental side effects on the plant's tolerance to unusual *environmental* conditions.

Cell Death as a Trigger of Plant Resistance

Mutants with Spontaneous Cell Death

The most potent plant defense against microbial pathogens is the hypersensitive reaction, a form of programmed cell death in plants. The principle of the HR is based on the early recognition of a pathogen, which then actively triggers a particular cell death program in the attacked cell.

Although it is easily conceivable that an attack of a biotrophic fungus can be stopped efficiently by killing the plant cell in contact with the pathogen, the molecular basis for the general success of the HR to stop pathogen ingression remains to be solved in detail.

The scientific problem comes down to the question of what else is turned on by the programmed cell death of the HR that is not activated by cell death per se (for instance, wounding). In general, an HR in one leaf will establish an immune response (SAR) in the whole plant that allows a more efficient HR in the next *infection* event, as mentioned before for the tobacco mosaic virus-inoculated tobacco plants.

A lesson from these and other studies is that the plant's endogenous cell death program is a valuable tool for plant resistance. Plant breeders have used programmed cell death in plants for decades to achieve resistance against pathogens. The barley *Mlo* gene is probably the best *understood* example. In rare cases, a mutation in *the Mlo locus* causes *programmed* cell death of single cells in leaves, a phenomenon termed lesion mimic. The important thing about lesion mimic is the discovery that this cell death causes plant *responses* very similar to those that HR of a few cells would cause after a primary infection.

Thus, lesion mimic is a physiological equivalent of an HR. The *Mlo* gene was identified by positional cloning and predicted to be a membrane protein that is a negative regulator (repressor) of cell death. About 10 years ago, several groups started to look for lesion mimic mutants in *Arabidopsis.*

Many mutants have been identified, and at least for some of them the molecular mechanism is known. In contrast to the hidden cell death in *Mlo* barley plants, the *Arabidopsis* lesion mimics often show drastic phenotypes *including* dwarfism.

Transgenic Plants with Induced Limited Cell Death

Meanwhile, several different approaches have been taken to induce cell death in plants. Often the cell death behaves like the cell death in the hypersensitive reaction after pathogen contact and subsequently triggers a whole battery of plant defenses, usually including elevated levels of salicylic acid (SA), *induction* of PR-genes, and *immunity* by the SAR process.

One example is the bacterial ribonuclease barnase, which is a very potent enzyme that kills eukaryotic cells when present at a few molecules per cell. This enzyme is effectively inhibited by the small protein barstar. Using a pathogen-inducible promoter of a glutathione-S-transferase gene from potato, *Strittmatter* et al. expressed the barnase gene in potato plants.

To avoid killing of the whole plant by the leaky promoter, it was necessary to coexpress the barstar inhibitor. Potato lines in which the strength of the pathogen-inducible promoter led to a surplus of free active barnase showed pathogen-dependent cell death after *Phytophthora infestans* inoculation.

Thus, a totally artificial cell death process was able to enhance plant tolerance toward fungal infection. The limited success of the study is most likely due to a *nonoptimal* choice of the promoters used, but nevertheless it demonstrates impressively the power of artificial cell death-inducing systems. Another cell death-inducing molecule is the fungal protein cryptogein, secreted by *Phytophthora cryptogea.*

It is one of many similar proteins of *Phytophthora* species, which are collectively termed elicitins. Expression of the gene encoding cryptogein under the control of the pathogen-inducible *hsr203J* promoter in tobacco resulted in enhanced tolerance of transgenic lines against *Phytophthora parasitica, Thielaviopsis basicola,* and *Erysiphe cichoracearum* infection.

The mode of action seems to be the induction of a cell death program by the cryptogein protein, which then activates the general plant defense machinery. It is, however, currently anticipated that elicitins cause cell death only in tobacco species, thus *limiting* the use of this system in crop plants. A third example of induced cell death was published by Tang et al..

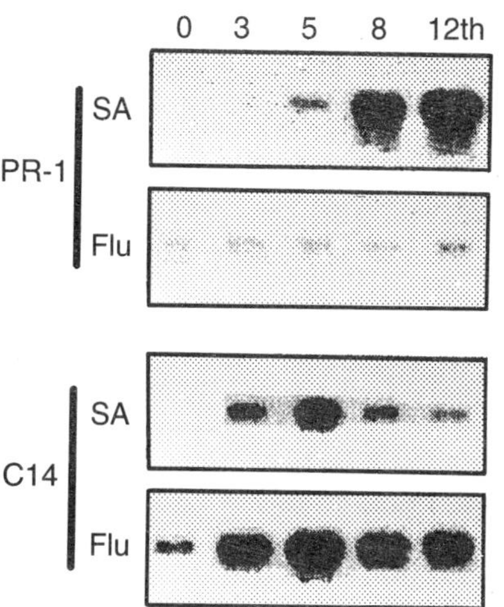

Figure 14.1: RNA blot with salicylic acid-regulated genes from tobacco. A BY- 2 tobacco cell culture was treated with 250 /uM salicylic acid (SA) or 25 /zM flufenamate (Flu) and samples were taken at designated time points. The upper set of samples was hybridized with a tobacco PR-la gene, showing the beginning of the induction of the PR-1 gene by salicylic acid whereas flufenamate is inactive in inducing the PR-1 gene. C14-1b is a tobacco gene of unknown function (88) that is only weakly induced by salicylic acid but strongly induced by flufenamate.

The researchers *constitutively* expressed the pto-kinase gene in tomato, which was identified some years ago and shown to be required for resistance against the bacterial pathogen *Pseudomonas syringae* pv. *tomato.* The constitutive expression of pto-kinase is already sufficient to induce programmed cell death in a limited number of cells in tomato leaves, subsequently activating the SAR response in tomato.

These transgenic plants exhibit broad spectrum pathogen tolerance as expected from the activated SAR response. Although the latter examples of engineered cell death are specific for particular plant species, a novel more generally *applicable* system for the induction of artificial cell death emerges from many studies of plant *resistance* and *microbial* avirulence genes.

As predicted from the early studies of Flor (1947), the interaction of a plant resistance gene product with a microbial avirulence gene product is the basis for the programmed cell death in the HR. Whereas the first *avr* genes were cloned from phytopathogenic bacteria in the early 1980s, the first plant resistance genes (*R* genes) were identified in 1994.

The rigorous test of whether the *avr* gene product by itself is sufficient to induce an HR was impressively answered and *confirmed* by studies in which the *avr* gene was *transiently* expressed in plant cells. Plant R genes seem to work functionally at least in closely related species.

For instance, the tomato *Cf-9* resistance gene was transformed into tobacco plants and the resulting transgenic lines still responded to the *corresponding* avr9 peptide from the tomato pathogenic fungus *Cladosporium fulvum.* When this tobacco line was crossed with a transgenic plant expressing the *avr9* avirulence gene, the siblings showed a whole-plant HR and died at the seedling stage, thus *confirming* the concept.

The expression of both *avr* and *R* genes in a strictly controlled pathogen-dependent manner

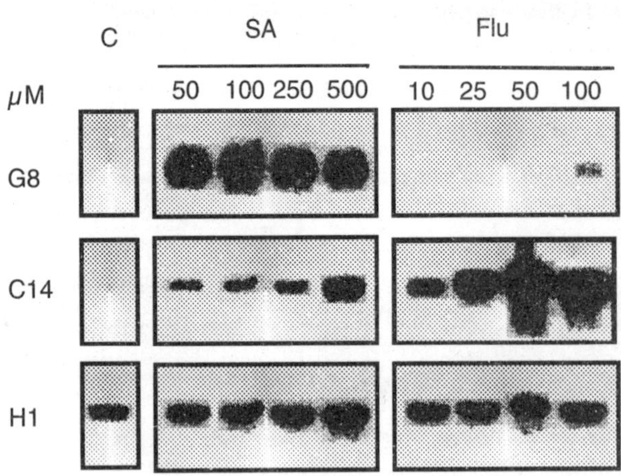

Figure 14.2: RNA blot with a dose-response experiment on salicylic acid-regulated genes in tobacco. A tobacco cell line (BY-2) was treated with different concentrations of salicylic acid (SA) or flufenamate (Flu) and collected for RNA isolation 5 hours later. The blot was hybridized with two tobacco genes (88) of unknown function, which exhibit different induction patterns. Whereas salicylic acid strongly induces the G8-1 gene, flufenamate is largely inactive in this response. In contrast, the C14-1b gene shows a reversed gene induction pattern with weak induction by salicylic acid and a strong increase in mRNA caused by flufenamate. The equal loading was verified by rehybridization of the blot with a gene for the tobacco histone 1 (H1).

is one of the most promising strategies for engineered cell death and subsequent activation of the plant's immune system. A great variety of suitable promoter elements for such experiments is currently under development.

The use of two different pathogen-inducible promoters for the resistance and the avirulence gene will help to minimize the detrimental effects of *unintentional* cell death. Thus, the regulation of cell death is an important issue and understanding it is necessary for further exploitation of *programmed* cell death as a novel mechanism for enhanced pathogen tolerance.

SALICYLIC ACID FUNCTION IN PROGRAMMED CELL DEATH

A central player in many but not all forms of programmed cell death in plants is salicylic acid. This was first demonstrated in transgenic tobacco and *Arabidopsis* plants expressing a salicylate hydroxylase gene from *Pseudomonas putida* called *nahG*.

These plants are still capable of synthesizing SA, but as soon as SA starts to accumulate it is converted into catechol by the enzyme salicylate hydroxylase. *Arabidopsis* plants of the Col-O ecotype, which as wild-type plants are genetically resistant to *Peronospora parasitica* infection, were totally *colonized* by the fungus in nahG-expressing plants.

This conversion of an incompatible to a compatible interaction could be reverted by spraying with high concentrations of salicylic acid or the synthetic analogue INA (2,6-dichloro-isonicotinic acid), indicating that SA is a key control molecule in plant resistance. Some of the dwarf lesion mimic mutants of *Arabidopsis* mentioned before could also be reverted to wild-type-like plants when crossed with *nahG* plants. Thus, the question arises of how SA controls *programmed* cell death in plants.

The discovery tour begins with a binding protein for SA, characterized from tobacco, that was shown to be a catalase, pointing to increased levels of H_2O, as the driving force of programmed cell death. This view was later extended by the finding that the other major H_2O_2-scavenging enzyme, ascorbate peroxidase, can also be *inhibited* in tobacco by SA. This model is attractive at first glance as H_2O_2 is an important signaling molecule in plant defense, as outlined earlier.

However, many other groups have tested the phenomenon in various plant species, and none of their studies has shown a significant inhibition of catalase or ascorbate peroxidase at *physiologically* relevant concentrations (<100 μM).

For example, in soybean SA (100 μM) neither inhibits both enzymes in vitro nor interferes with the capacity of soybean cell cultures to metabolize H_2O_2, which reflects the in vivo situation. In a model system for programmed cell death in plants, we investigate the HR in soybean cell cultures (cv. Williams 82) triggered by the avrA protein of the bacterial pathogen *Pseudomonas syringae pv. glycinea.*

The HR occurs according to the gene-for-gene hypothesis requiring the Rps2 resistance gene in soybean and the *avrA* avirulence gene in *Pseudoinonas.* The advantage of the cell culture system is its *flexibility* and the possibility to *manipulate* the system easily using inhibitors or activators.

The HR requires SA (~50 μM), which can be added to the cell culture medium to complete the cell death program. This phenotype in soybean resembles the studies with *nahG Arabidopsis* plants, in which the HR is also dependent on SA. The addition of SA to soybean cell cultures strongly *accelerates* the HR, finally leading to faster cell death.

By using the vital stain Evans Blue, we showed loss of *membrane* control as the final sign of cell death in the HR after about 8 hours in the SA-accelerated HR compared with about 14 hours in control inoculated cells without SA (similar to the time range of the HR in plants). Using this *acceleration* for a screenable test system, we identified several chemicals that can substitute for SA.

To our surprise, the chemicals were diverse in structure and thus made it initially difficult to come up with a model to explain their *biochemical* function. We have *collectively* termed these chemicals FASs (functional analogues of SA).

A rigorous check of the literature revealed an emerging function of FAS compounds in animal cells. Almost all of them are ligands of a transcription factor system in humans, the *peroxisome* proliferator-activated receptors (PPARs). The PPARs are a *subfamily* within the superfamily of nuclear hormone receptors, which are posttranslationally activated by binding their specific ligands.

One therapeutic aspect of PPARs in humans is their relevance in type II diabetes, which can be treated by the uptake of synthetic PPAR ligands (such as *troglitazone*) on a daily basis. This drug can also be used in soybean to complement and accelerate the HR, triggered by *Pseudomonas* bacteria, and by this criterion is an FAS compound.

The outlined model predicts that genes in plants are *transcriptionally* induced by SA or FAS compounds. We have described a novel putative lectin-encoding gene from soybean that is induced by both groups of compounds as predicted. Using *differential* display and subtractive suppression hybridization, we have identified a larger set of genes, which are transcriptionally induced by salicylic acid and FAS compounds (C Anstatt, N Auslander, A Ludwig, G Schwerdtfeger, M Hansen, R *Tenhaken, unpublished* results).

This set probably includes novel genes, which are required for the execution of programmed cell death in a salicylic acid-dependent manner. Chemicals such as INA or the *benzothiadiazole* Bion® are thought to mimic SA and are thus able to activate the *signaling* process leading to SAR.

This raises the question of whether FAS chemicals are similar to SAR inducers in their mode of action. *Arabidopsis* and tobacco treated with SA or Bion show a strong induction of the PR-1 messenger RNA (mRNA). In contrast, the FAS chemical *flufenamate* was unable to induce the same response in tobacco, pointing to different signal *transduction* pathways.

In the model plant tobacco, several SA-inducible genes were described besides the classical PR genes, for instance, in a study by Horvath and Chua. Whether theses genes are novel PR genes in the sense that they are induced in plant-pathogen interactions remains to be analyzed.

We have chosen the *C14-1b* gene as a probe to test whether FAS *compounds* will induce genes in tobacco as well as in soybean. The sensitive induction of the tobacco *C14-1b* gene by *flufenamate*, which occurs at a much lower *concentration* compared with SA, is an example. As also shown in Figure elsewhere in this chapter, another tobacco gene, *G8-1*, is strongly induced by salicylic acid but almost not induced by the FAS compound *flufenamate*.

These observations underline the different signal transduction pathways and mode of actions in which salicylic acid is involved in plants. The data can be *summarized* in a new model in which SA controls plant resistance by at least two independent processes. In the first place, high concentrations of SA are needed to execute the plant cell death program, and the predicted mode of action is the transcriptional activation of genes (which mostly remains to be identified in future studies).

This function of SA can be mimicked by FAS compounds as shown for soybean. The second major function of SA is the participation in the establishment of the plant immunity (SAR). This function of SA can be potently mimicked by INA or Bion. Our current goal is to identify an SA/FAS-regulated *transcription* factor that is involved in programmed cell death in plants.

By functional analysis of the promoter, we identified *a cis* element in an FAS-responsive gene that is also specifically bound by nuclear protein extracts in gel *retardation* assays. Controlled *activation* or repression of this factor will probably be a valuable tool to modify *programmed* cell death in plants.

We anticipate a novel mode of enhanced plant tolerance toward microbial pathogens by engineering the execution of a natural cell death program and making use of the powerful natural broadspectrum resistance that plants have developed during evolutionary history.

CONCLUSIONS AND FUTURE PERSPECTIVES

The dream of transgenic plants resistant to viruses, bacteria, fungi, and insects is still (and is likely to be forever) a fantasy. What has been achieved in the last 15 years in creating transgenic plants with *enhanced* tolerance against *pathogens* is, however, very remarkable.

The rapid success took advantage of decades of biochemical work of plant pathologists and has now opened a wide field of approaches for novel resistance principles in plants as a defense against *microbial* pathogens. Clearly, from today's point of view, the *approaches* that activate the host's defense machinery will be successful.

Artificial cell death triggered under the strict control of *pathogeninducible* promoters is my personal favourite. Although we can already use the plant's innate immune system, we basically understand very little of how it works. Detailed knowledge of single or network-like mechanisms will be a *prerequisite* for a next generation of *engineered* plants that specifically activate certain parts of the complex immune response required in particular for *individual* pathogens.

15

Chapter

CLONING FORESTRY SPECIES

Forest play a major role in *maintaining* climatic stability, conserving water and soil, housing biological diversity and serve as a valuable source of various timber and non-timber products. India with its wide geographical distribution is endowed with rich forest resource and has two of the eighteen hotspots in biodiversity in the world.

Traditionally, *communities* have lived in close harmony with the forest and their dependence on this important resource has taught them to be caring for sustenance. In the recent past, however, this situation has changed *tremendously* and the forests are being heavily over-exploited leading to reduction in forest cover, lowering of plant density, and eroding of floral and faunal diversity.

On account of intense population pressures (both human and cattle) and heavy reliance of inhabitants on forests to cater their daily needs, the forests are under severe strain. This problem is quite *complicated* and has no easy solutions given by the fact that forests belong to the State Governments and thus conservation is viewed as the Government's responsibility while harvesting in many of these areas is the privilege of the local *communities*.

There are many industries, which are dependent on forest resource, and at the time of independence many concessions were given to them, which includes making timber available at *subsidized* rate. Many such actions have caused heavy damage to our forests. Much of this loss is yet to be made up.

This problem is further *aggravated* by the fact that there is no incentive for industries to get themselves involved into growing of raw material *required* by them. Further, due to fewer job options in the rural parts, cattle rearing and collection of non-timber forest produce remain the *favourite* revenue-earning *activities.* Since cattle are left in open for *grazing,* natural *regeneration* of the forests has become very difficult.

This has resulted in denudation of several areas and spread of *wastelands* in the country. To repair the damage already caused to our forests and to restrict their future abuse, the Government of India has formulated *several* plans and policies directed *towards* large-scale *afforestation* and using *improved* planting material for higher yields.

Due to *increasing* human needs, it is not *possible* to divert *agricultural* land for *forestry* purposes and the only option *therefore,* is to improve the productivity of existing forests.

This involves *selection* of suitable species (matching species with sites), using *superior* quality *planting* material, managing the *plantations* properly, and developing a *programme* for sustainable harvesting. While the importance of *conventional* breeding in improving the *productivity* cannot be *undermined,* breeding of trees is *technically difficult* and time consuming.

Since the generation time in most tree species is very long, in many cases one may not even see the results of the *experiments* in lifetime. It may take *several* decades to release an improved variety/clone.

Fortunately, most trees species are *cross-pollinated* and *consequently* lot of genetic *variability* exists in nature today. For immediate gains, it would be *worthwhile* to exploit this genetic variability *existing* in nature by selecting and cloning superior genotypes/individuals from their natural population.

CLONING OF TREE SPECIES BY CONVENTIONAL METHODS

Compared to *horticultural* plants, research in tree species has lagged behind. There has been very little interest shown by the private sector in this field and that too mainly in short rotation crops and softwoods. General *interest* in cloning of hardwood species started with *eucalyptus.* Aracruz (Brazil) took the lead in raising *commercial plantations* of *eucalyptus* through rooting of cuttings.

The concept of raising plantations by pulp and paper *companies* is not new and many *countries* including United States, Australia and New *Zealand* are involved in *similar* kind of *activities* but largely with pines.

Commendable work has also been done in Thailand and Indonesia on hardwood species such as acacia, casuarina, eucalyptus, teak etc. and increase in productivity has been reported. Of late, in India too, foresters who are the custodians of our forests have realized the importance of planting clonal material.

Massive projects have been launched by several state forest departments for raising clonal nurseries. Some initiatives have also been taken by private companies such as ITC Bhadrachalam, JK industries, West Coast Paper Mills and Andhra Pradesh Forest Cooperation.

However, the total plantlet production through *conventional techniques* is far from adequate. This is largely because till date *methods* largely of rootings of *cuttings* have been developed only for a few species and that too are *effective* only when the mother tree is in a juvenile phase.

MAJOR CONSTRAINTS IN VEGETATIVE PROPAGATION

- Because of large size of the propagules only few functional *cuttings* can be derived from the desired clone/genotype.
- In many tree species the cuttings lose their ability to root by the time a particular clone is evaluated for its useful traits.
- The cutting-raised-plants tend to form adventitious roots which unlike the tap root of seedlings do not penetrate very deep inside the ground, thereby, making the plant highly prone to felling by strong winds.
- Propagation through cuttings also poses a potential risk for spread of various systemic diseases.
- Propagation through cuttings is extremely slow and season specific
- Depending on the species and the efficiency of asexual methods of propagation, the production cost of cutting raised plants is marginally to significantly higher in comparison to seed-raised plants. This is quite a crucial factor for the foresters as they are often given large target of afforestation and have limited funds at their disposal.

MICROPROPAGATION

Tissue culture *perhaps* is the most *commercially* exploited field of plant *biotechnology*. It overcomes many of the constraints that the *conventional* methods of *propagation* are inflicted with. Cloning of plants under aseptic *conditions, commonly* called *micropropagation* results in mirror images of selected mother plants on a large-scale within a short period of time.

Micropropagation assumes greater *significance* in those species which cannot be regenerated or are difficult to regenerate by *conventional* methods such as seeds and *vegetative* propagation, where conventional methods are *inadequate* to meet the demand of planting material, and vast *variability* exists in seed-raised progenies.

ADVANTAGES OF MICROPROPAGATION

Rapid multiplication

By using an efficient protocol one may produce over a million plants *starting* from a single bud.

Saving of space

Unlike conventional cuttings, that measure 8–12 inches in length and occupy lot of space, large number of cultures can be *accumulated* within a small area.

Production of disease free plants

The plants produced by tissue culture are free of almost all bacterial and fungal diseases. In those species where virus *infestation* is known to affect the quality of the plant as well as the productivity, virus *elimination* can be achieved by tissue culture. Since virus *elimination* is a time *consuming* and expensive process, it can only be applied if one *produces* a large number of plants from a single explant, which is free of known viruses.

Clonal uniformity

Unlike seedlings which *represent* only the half siblings, the tissue culture raised plants are true-to-the-mother type and there is no *segregation* of genes or change in genetic character/ traits in the progeny during the *regeneration* process.

Independent of seasonal constraint

Since plants are produced in controlled conditions of light, temperature and humidity, there is no effect of the outside *environment* on the regeneration process. While the plants can be produced independent of season inside the lab, the transplantation process remains dependent on the season.

TISSUE CULTURE OF TREES

Tissue culture of woody species was first reported by Gautheret way back in 1933. However, the progress made with trees has been rather slow as compared to *herbaceous* species. This is largely because tree species have a distinct juvenile and an adult phase and trees, especially in their *adulthood*, are more recalcitrant to tissue culture technology.

Further, they have a long gestation period and thus, field evaluation and *commercial* exploitation takes much longer vis-a-vis *agricultural* and horticultural species.

Although *micropropagation* process has been in use in the developed world for several decades, in India the *commercial* importance of this *technique* was realized only in late 1980s and early 1990s when several tissue culture *companies* were set-up.

However, most of these companies were export-oriented units with focus on *ornamentals*. By

Table 15.1: Area covered under tissue cultured plants of various forest species till March 31, 2002

S. No.	Species dispatched	No. of plants area covered (ha)	Spacing	Approximate
1.	*Anogeissus pendula*	447144	3 m × 3 m	402.46
2.	*Anogeissus latifolia*	127532	3 m × 3 m	114.79
3.	*Eucalyptus spp.*	1600481	3 m × 2 m	960.67
4.	*Populus deltoides*	1235410	3 m × 5 m	1854.96
5.	*Dendrocalamus strictus*	95385	5 m × 5 m	238.46
6.	*Paulownia fortunei*	220981	4 m × 5 m	441.96
7.	Miscellaneous	11094	3 m × 5 m	16.65
	Total	3738027		4029.95

Table 15.2: Number of tissue cultured plants of various forest species dispatched to different states for field trials and routine plantations till March 31, 2002.

State	Total number of plants dispatched
Assam	17163
Bihar	20517
Delhi	85113
Gujarat	20905
Haryana	1704507
Himachal Pradesh	1400
Jammu & Kashmir	29700
Madhya Pradesh	45106
Maharashtra	2735
Orissa	4321
Punjab	30075
Rajasthan	616580
Uttar Pradesh	1034635
Tamil Nadu	8404
West Bengal	10779
Kerala	1300
Karnataka	4835
Miscellaneous	99952
Total	3738027

and large these companies had a general *reluctance* to venture into tissue culture of forest trees on account of following reasons:

Policy matter

Being export-oriented units with a buy-back *arrangement* with their collaborators, these *companies* have largely been catering to the demand of their *collaborators.*

Technical problems

There are several technical problems *associated* with tissue culture of forest species and there are very few groups in the country who have the *technical* capability to deal with them.

Commercial factors

As compared to *ornamentals* (most of which are seasonal and demand frequent replacement), the market of forest species is *relatively* small on account of their *perennial* nature and *selective* users. The paucity of funds with most of the State Forest Departments who are expected to be the main users also deterred these *companies* to take up tissue culture of forest species.

Tissue Culture Pilot Plant

To meet this challenge, the Department of *Biotechnology* (DBT), Government of India in 1989 decided to set-up a Tissue Culture Pilot Plant (TCPP) at TERI for mass propagation of forest species using tissue culture *technique* to augment the biomass *production* in the country.

Located within TERI's 36-hectare campus at Gual Pahari, Gurgaon, Haryana, here all the infrastructural facilities ranging from modern *laboratories* and *greenhouses* to nurseries *required* for mass production of tissue *cultured* plants, are available.

In 1997, this Tissue Culture Pilot Plant was upgraded into a *Micropropagation Technology* Park (MTP) to provide an effective platform for transfer of the proven tissue culture related *technologies* to the *entrepreneurs*. Thus MTP has an annual capacity of over two million plants.

Objectives of Micropropagation Technology Park

- Propagate superior clones of various plant species on a large-scale using tissue culture technology
- Multiply those species on a mass-scale which are difficult to regenerate by conventional methods of propagation
- Multiply species *in vitro* where conventional methods of propagation are inadequate to meet the demand of planting material
- Enhance further the productivity of *in vitro* raised plants using symbionts such as *rhizobia and mycorrhizae*
- Impart training in the field of plant tissue culture
- Technology transfer to new entrepreneurs or industry for commercialization
- Function as a think-tank for the tissue culture industry

Achievements of TCPP/MTP

- *Established* a modern, *indigenously* designed tissue culture *laboratory* with an annual production capacity of two million plants at Gurgaon (Haryana).
- Developed *micropropagation* protocols for a large number of species and refined procedures for several others so as to make them suitable for large-scale propagation.
- Supplied over 12 million plants of various species to different state forest departments, *non-governmental organization*, agro-based companies, private growers etc.
- Successfully *demonstrated* the application of tissue culture *technology* at the farmers' field.
- Established high survival, plant *uniformity*, and better growth rates of tissue culture plants as compared to *conventional* propagules.
- Successful *technology* transfer to industry.

- Contractual research/plant production for clients.
- Created awareness about MTP and the tissue culture *technology* through lectures, demonstrations, seminars/workshops and exhibitions.
- Conducted several training programmes.

Criteria for the Selection of Hardwood Species

For the species that can be *conventionally* propagated through seeds and exhibit wide variability, tissue culture is of immense value if the plus trees are mass multiplied. To achieve this, the selection of the mother tree must be done very carefully. Also it is necessary to select newer and newer clones to avoid *monoculture* and *degeneration* of clone. Some of the criteria followed for selections are:

General Criteria

- A tree can be evaluated earliest at half its rotation age. For eucalyptus and populus this age could vary from 4 to 5 years while for species like teak this may be as long as 30 years.
- Superior growth in height and diameter of the bole is judged in relation to neighboring trees of the same or similar age. Isolated trees cannot be marked as plus trees.
- The marked tree should be free of all diseases.

Criteria for Stem Form

- Straight bole.
- Leading shoot must be showing active growth.
- No spiral grain.

Criteria for Crown and Branching Habit

- It should provide dense mass of healthy foliage.
- Good natural pruning and well-healed knot scars.
- Branches should be small in relation to the stem at the point of origin.

Multiplication of Tree Species at TERI

Following tree species have been/are being multiplied at TERI's production facility:

- *Anogeissus spp. (A. pendula* and *A. latifolia)*
- Bamboos *(Bambusa tulda, Bambusa arundinacea and Dendrocalamus strictus)*
- Eucalyptus *(E. tereticornis, E. camaldulensis* and *E. citriodora)*
- Paulownia fortunei
- Poplars *(P. deltoides and P. euphratica)*
- *Leucaena* hybrids

Till March 31, 2002 nearly 3.7 million plants of various forest species alone had been dispatched to various State Forest Departments, NGOs and private growers for field trials and routine *plantations*. These plants would cover an area of over 4000 hectares.

Field Trials

Although TERI has been into production of forest species by tissue culture since 1991, the *evaluation* of the tissue cultured plants started much later because it is *recommended* that the performance of a forest species should be *evaluated* only after it had completed half its *rotation* age. The field trial data of various species available thus suggest the following:

- High survival rate of tissue cultured plants in the field at times even when the soil and other growth conditions are not favourable and life saving irrigation facilities are lacking.
- The plants showed high degree of clonal *uniformity*.
- Most of clones (CPTs) selected and multiplied at TERI outperformed the local clones or seedling raised plants in biomass production. Depending on the nature of the clone and its suitability at a particular location, the gains varied from marginal to significant (upto 200%).
- In the initial trials of *Populus deltoides* some problem of formation of 'kinks' was observed which was later rectified by modifying the regeneration procedures and management practices.

Anogeissus spp.

Anogeissus pendula

A. pendula is a very slow growing tree that grows 9 to 15 m in height and 1 m in girth. The tree is *essentially* an inhabitant of dry and hot regions of Haryana, Madhya Pradesh, Rajasthan and southern Uttar Pradesh, where the annual rainfall ranges between 400 and 800 mm.

It can also withstand a *temperature* regime of 3°C to 47°C. While the leaves are used as fodder, the timber is valued for its strength and working qualities. It is used extensively for making various items of domestic and agricultural use. The wood is also *consumed* for making *charcoal* of high calorific value.

The utility of this species makes it highly vulnerable to felling by rural *communities* and *grazing* by their livestock. Regeneration through seeds is extremely difficult and is not much in practice as the *viability* of seeds is very low (0.2–0.4%). Methods of vegetative *propagation* by *cuttings* are not yet available.

In the absence of *identified* plus trees and recalcitrant nature of adult tissues, cultures were *established* from seeds. For tissue culture work, the mother trees were carefully selected on the basis of their *phenotype* and the seeds were collected only from tall and healthy looking trees.

The shoots obtained from aseptically raised seedlings served as the explant. The shoots were multiplied by axillary branching method and rooted individually on a suitable rooting media. After 4 weeks of hardening inside the greenhouse and *polyhouse*, the plants were hardened further in the nursery for at least 3 months before transfer to the field. Till March 31, 2002, over 4.4 lakh plants of *A. pendula* had been lifted from TERI's *facilities* by various forest *departments* and other agencies for field trials and routine plantations.

Most of these plants were lifted by *Haryana* Forest Department and planted in Aravalli Hills. The feedback received from the concerned forest *departments* suggests a *transplantation* success of ovèr 85%. Since *A. pendula* is a very slow growing species other growth *parameters* such as height, girth, etc. do not hold much relevance in early years of plantation. Hence, the *emphasis* has been accorded only to the survival success.

In the absence of conventional seedlings no controls were possible. Generally, the tissue cultured plants of a particular *genotype exhibited* similar growth pattern. However, as expected, there was some variation in the *performance* of the plants of different genotypes. In a 36-month-old trial conducted at National Research Centre for Agro-forestry, Jhansi, AP-28 has proved to be the most *promising* genotype. The tallest plant of this particular *genotype* attained a height of 365 cm.

Since these plants were grown under routine *plantations, performance* of individual *genotypes* could not be monitored. Furthermore, in the absence of conventional propagules, the comparison of tissue cultured plants with *seedlings* was not possible. The *available* data clearly suggest that by and large tissue cultured plants of *Anogeissus pendula* have survived well in the field.

This is despite the fact that most of these plants were planted in *extremely* hostile conditions (*poor soil and no irrigation*) prevailing in the barren hills of Aravalli. Low survival in few trials was mainly due to *unsuitability* of the site or biotic interference. The plants are *constantly* being monitored for their growth *performance* and in coming years more data would be available on the subject.

Production of over 4.4 lakh plants and high survival of tissue cultured plants in the field fully testify the utility of *in vitro technology* in mass propagation of a forest species which was almost impossible *regenerate* by *conventional* methods.

Anogeissus latifolia

Commonly referred to as 'dhaura', *A. latifolia* is a large tree that grows upto 33 m in height and 2.4 m in girth. It is commonly found in the forests of the sub-Himalayan tract and Shivalik hills. The tree is found at its best in Madurai, Coimbatore, and Salem districts of Tamil Nadu and some parts of Maharashtra, Karnataka and UP. Like *A. pendula, A. latifolia* is also a good fodder and timber tree.

The timber is fairly durable and is deployed for making furniture, cart-axles, shafts, poles, tool handles etc. The regeneration problems in conventional methods are similar to that described for *A. pendula and,* therefore, justify the need of *in vitro* techniques for plant propagation.

To initiate cultures, seeds were collected from healthy looking trees growing in Udaipur (Rajasthan). After *removing* the seed coat, the seeds were put for *germination* and the shoots derived from 3-week-old seedlings were used for further *multiplication.* Till date, nearly 1.2 lakh tissue cultured plants have been lifted from TCPP/MTP. Almost 80% of these have been planted in Haryana.

Since a majority of plants were transferred to the field only during the last couple of years, it is premature to comment upon the specifics of various growth parameters. However, initial feedback received on the *performance* of tissue cultured plants suggest high survival rate and *vigorous* growth. A large *percentage* of plants were grown as routine *plantation* for which the forest departments do not maintain any record.

In some cases the trials were laid initially but were *abandoned* later due to heavy biotic pressure or various *administrative* reasons. Nevertheless, repeated requests for the plants made by the *endusers* suggest that in *vitro* plants are doing well in the field.

Bamboos

Bamboos are one of the fastest growing *perennial* grasses belonging to the family Poaceae. On account of their *versatility* and immense utility, bamboos have been used for a variety of purposes since times immemorial. Being *straight, light, hard* and *strong,* bamboos are extensively used for *construction* of houses, scaffoldings, ladders, bridges, fences, furniture, sticks, tool handles, pipes, basket mats and a large number of items of domestic and agricultural use.

Bamboo leaves are used for thatching and are also valued as fodder. However, the most *important* use of *bamboo* is in the paper and pulp industry to which it serves as the basic raw *material. Over-exploitation* of bamboo resources by paper and pulp industry, bad *management* practices and *interference* by biotic factors such as *grazing* and forest fires are some of the major factors that have resulted in scarcity of bamboos.

Although *propagation* of bamboos take place both by seeds as well as vegetatively, however, both the methods of *propagation* are beset with many problems that restrict their large-scale use. In view of the constant increase in demand, the scarcity of *planting* material and the problems associated with *conventional* methods of *propagation*, development of effective *in vitro* methods of propagation are highly desirable.

TERI scientists have developed *in vitro regeneration* protocol for four bamboo species viz., *Bambusa tulda, Bambusa arundinacea, Dendrocalamus longispathus and D. strictus.* However, keeping in view the demand of various species and area of distribution, the *emphasis* was laid only on mass propagation of *D. strictus.*

Commonly known as '*lathi bamboo*', *D. strictus* is a densely tufted bamboo with strong culms that grow 20 to 50 ft in height and 1 to 3 inches in diameter. It is the most widely grown bamboo species in India. *D. strictus* is found in almost all parts of the country except northern parts of West Bengal, Assam and other very moist areas.

It grows well on dry, properly drained soil up to a height of 2,000 m. Unlike most other bamboos, culms of *D. strictus* are either solid or have a very narrow lumen. Because of this property, *D. strictus* is relatively harder and stronger than other bamboo species.

For *initiation* of cultures, seeds were dehusked and after surface *sterilization* cultured on 2,4D containing medium for induction of callus and somatic embryos. The somatic embryos were multiplied for several passages on a suitable *multiplication* medium. On being transferred to a *germination* medium the somatic embryos formed plantlets. Till March 31, 2002 over 95,000 plants had been *dispatched* to various states.

Eucalyptus spp.

Commonly known as '*safedd*', *eucalyptus* is a versatile tree that grows in almost all parts of the country, from coastal areas to an elevation of 200 m. It can attain a height of 40–50 m and a girth of 1 to 1.4 m. The tree is valued for its fast growth, high adaptability to grow in *different* kind of soil and climatic *conditions,* and multiple uses.

The wood is heavy, hard and mostly straight grained. In India, the *plantation*-grown wood is mainly used for *scaffolding, construction* of houses, making rayon-grade pulp and paper pulp, agricultural *implements*, furniture, boxes, carts, etc. Eucalyptus is one of the fastest growing tree species producing large amount of biomass. Because of its rapid and straight growth that casts very little shadow, eucalyptus is extremely popular as an agro-forestry species.

It is easy to cultivate and can even be grown in *nutritionally* deficient soils. One of the major *advantages* of growing *eucalyptus* is that the animals do not browse it and therefore, its protection does not pose any problem. Also, after planting once, one can have three harvests without going for re-planting. *Conventionally*, eucalyptus is *propagated* through seeds.

However, due to segregation of genes, the seed-raised population is highly heterogeneous. Clonal propagation of *eucalyptus* by rooting of cuttings has met with limited success. Not only it is difficult to obtain large number of plants of a particular clone by *conventional vegetative* methods, but also there is a potential risk of spread of various diseases along with the propagules.

In contrast, using tissue culture *technology*, a large number of healthy and disease-free plants of selected clones can be produced within a short span of time. At TERI, we have been successful in *multiplying* three species of *eucalyptus* i.e., *E. tereticornis, E. camaldulensis* and *E. citriodora*. However, most of the *production* has been of *E. tereticornis* only.

Disease-free trees in possession of various *desirable* traits, such as faster growth, higher biomass, straight bole etc. were selected from the natural population or field *plantations* of different state forest *departments*. Referred to as 'Candidate Plus Trees (CPTs)', such superior clones served as the source material for tissue culture work.

The CPTs were coppiced in a particular season to obtain juvenile shoots. Single node *segments* (explants) derived from such coppiced shoots were then used to initiate cultures. Under the influence of the media, the axillary bud present at the node sprouted and formed shoot(s). *In vitro* shoots were then *multiplied* and rooted *separately* on well defined media.

The *tissue-cultured* plants were hardened inside the *greenhouse* before their transfer to the field. Till March 31, 2002, 1.6 million tissue-cultured plants of eucalyptus had been supplied to various state forest *departments*, NGOs and private growers for field trials and routine plantations.

Field data confirms high *transplantation* success (more than 90%), *uniform* and faster growth, higher yields and better timber qualities. In some of the clones selected and *multiplied* at TERI, the yield is more than twice as compared to *conventional* (seed raised) plants. Whereas seedraised *plantations* have yielded a maximum mean annual *increment* (MAI) of 20 m^3/ha/year, TERI clones have shown growth with MAI up to 40 m^3/ha/year.

Under natural (non-irrigated) *conditions*, the average yield of TERI clones after 6 years of *planting* is estimated to be around 120 tons/ha as against only 80 tons/ha in case of seed-raised plants. Higher yields can be expected if the *plantations* are raised under irrigated conditions.

Paulownia Fortunei

Paulownia is receiving *increasing* attention as a short rotation woody species. A species of Chinese origin, it is characterized by fast growth, *attractive* growth habit and flowers, and biomass production. Besides timber, *Paulownia* leaves are used for fodder and flowers for honey production.

The value of *Paulownia* for *afforestation,* mine site reclamation and inter-cropping systems has also been demonstrated. Despite all its potential uses, the species could not be *evaluated* at the commercial level in India because of lack of *planting* material. Although *conventionally Paulownia* can be propagated through seeds as well as *vegetatively* from root or shoot cuttings, yet these methods are not adequate to meet the demand of planting material that is required for carrying out extensive field trials.

At TERI, success has been achieved in developing a complete *micropropagation* protocol of *P. fortunei* using adult tissue. Till March 31, 2002, over 2.2 lakh tissue-cultured plants had been dispatched from TERI's MTP. Since *P. fortunei* is an exotic species and its planting material is not so easily available, the ideal edapho-climatic conditions required for its growth in India are not yet known.

With the availability of planting material it will now be possible to carry out extensive field trials in different geographical conditions. Based on the performance suitable *Paulownia* growing areas may be identified and industrial *plantations* be raised.

Populus spp.

Populus deltoides

P. deltoides, which was first introduced in eastern UP, has now become a common tree in Tarai region and states of Punjab and Haryana. It thrives well in tropical and sub-tropical regions of India. It is an excellent source of biomass, and as a raw material its wood accounts for 50–60% for plywood and nearly 90% for match stick industry.

The wood being light and of low density is an excellent source of *packaging* material. To *maintain* its clonal nature, the species is always propagated through *vegetative* means and the seeds are mainly used for breeding purposes. For vegetative propagation, stem cuttings derived from superior trees are used. It is *recommended* that only the leader shoot are used to derive cuttings because cuttings obtained from the side branches are not successful and the plant tends to die within 2–3 years of raising.

However, the number of cuttings that can be obtained from the leader shoot of a *particular* tree is rather small. Therefore, in order to meet the ever-increasing demand of industry, it would be useful to carry out *micropropagation* of *P. deltoides.* Mass *propagation* of several superior clones of *P. deltoides* such as G-3, G-48, D-121, L-34 and S7C15 using tissue culture technology has been undertaken at TERI and over 1.2 million plants have been dispatched.

In the initial lots of tissue cultured plants that were transferred to the field, many of the plants showed kinks/bends in the stem. Sometimes the *percentage* of such plants was as high as 40%. However, cuttings derived from such kink-bearing plants in the following year produced almost normal plants. More than 95% of the plants were straight and the remaining plants showed *decreased* degree of bends.

Disappearance of bends confirms the fact that this problem was not due to any change in the genetic make-up of the plants during the course of *in vitro* process. The clonal fidelity of the tissue cultured plants was further confirmed by DNA fingerprinting.

In order to overcome the problem of kink formation in tissue cultured plants, the *regeneration* protocol as well as the management practices adopted in the field were modified. Following the same, the frequency of shoots bearing kinks became *negligible*.

Populus euphratica

P. euphratica is a unique species that can tolerate drought as well as water logging. Besides *P. deltoides*, TERI has also worked out efficient protocol for *in vitro* regeneration of *P. euphratica*. However, due to restricted *geographical* distribution and limited demand, the emphasis *continues* to be on the mass propagation of *P. deltoides*.

CONCLUSIONS

TERI is one of those few organizations not only in India but in the world that are involved in large-scale production of superior quality planting material of various tree species using tissue culture technology. The dispatch of over 3.7 million tissue *cultured* plants of tree species clearly *demonstrates* the technical feasibility of using tissue culture technology for large-scale production of forest species.

The clonal *uniformity*, and thereby increase in *productivity*, signifies enormous potential the *technology* has to offer for increasing land *productivity* and thus face the *challenge* of meeting *biomass* needs of the country.

16

Chapter

GENETIC TRANSFORMATION

Somatic embryogenesis (SE) depicts an asexual process that leads to the *formation* of an embryo from somatic cells either *in planta* through apomixis or in vitro through tissue culture. Somatic embryos are capable of *germinating* and producing plants in a manner very similar to their zygotic counterparts.

Since its discovery in Norway spruce in 1985, SE has become a method of choice for clonal propagation of conifers because of its high and sustained *productivity* and the amenability of *embryogenic* cultures to cryogenic storage.

Production of conifer somatic seedlings involves several steps: (a) induction of *embryonal* tissue (rapidly *proliferating* cultures of early-stage somatic embryos); (b) establishment and *proliferation* of embryonal lines in culture via periodic *subculturing*, from which large amounts of embryonal tissue can be produced; (c) maturation of somatic embryos via transfer of embryonal tissue onto medium containing abscisic acid (ABA); and (d) *germination* of mature somatic embryos and transfer of the resulting somatic seedlings into soil.

Conifer SE has become a primary enabling technology for genetic *engineering* because embryonal tissue is amenable to genetic *transformation* via cocultivation with A. *tumefaciens.*

Combined with rapid selection of transgenic embryonal tissues and highly efficient seedling *regeneration* via somatic embryo maturation, the production of transgenic spruce has now become routine.

To illustrate this process, we will describe first the initiation and maintenance of embryonal tissues from three spruce species *(Picea mariana, P. glauca,* and *P. abies),* followed by the production of *transgenic* embryonal tissues, regeneration of the transgenic trees and molecular *characterization* of transgenic tissues.

MATERIALS

Plant Material

1. Immature cones or mature seeds of spruce spp.
2. Spruce embryogenic cultures.

Tissue Culture

Stock Solutions

1. 1OX MLV stock (modified Litvay's medium [1]): 8.21 g/L of NH_4NO_3, 9.5 g/L of $KN0_3$, 9.25 g/L of $MgS0_4 . 7H_20$, 1.7 g/L of KH_2PO_4 (monobasic), 0.11 g/L of $CaC1_2 . 2H_20$, 100 mL MLV micronutrient stock (100X), 100 mL of MLV vitamin stock (100X), 1 g/L of myo-inositol, 0.4 g/L of iron-ethylenediaminetetraacetic acid (Fe EDTA). Store frozen in 100-mL aliquots for further use.
2. 100X MLV micronutrient stock: 0.415 g/L of KI, 3.1 g/L of 1·131303, 2.1 g/L of $MnSO_4 . H_2O$, 4.3 g/L of $ZnSO_4 .7H_20$, 0.125 g/L of $Na_2MoO_4 .2H_2O$, 0.05 g/L of $CuS0_4 .5H_2O$, 0.013 g/ of $COC1_2 .6H_2O$. Store frozen in 100-mL aliquots for further use.
3. 100X MLV vitamin stock: 0.05 g/L of nicotinic acid, 0.01 g/L of pyridoxine HCl, 0.01 g/L of thiamine-HCl. Store frozen in 100-mL aliquots for further use.
4. 6-Benzylaminopurine (BA), 0.5 mg/mL stock solution.
5. 2,4-Dichlorophenoxyacetic acid (2,4-D), 1 mg/mL stock solution.
6. Glutamine, 25 mg/mL stock solution.
7. 10 *mM (±)-cis, trans-ABA,* 2.64 mg/mL stock solution.

Media

1. MLV: 1X MLV salts with vitamins, 1 g/L of casein hydrolysate (casamino acids), 20 g/L of sucrose, 2.2 mL/L of 2,4-D (1 mg/mL stock solution), 2.2 mL/L of BA (0.5 mg/mL stock solution), pH 5.7. Autoclave and add 20 mL of filter sterilized glutamine (25 mg/mL stock solution) to cooled medium. If semisolid medium is required, add 4 g/L of gellan gum (Phytagel, Sigma, St. Louis, MO) before adjusting pH and before autoclaving.
2. MLV maturation medium (MLVM): identical to MLV but replace 2,4-D and BA with ABA at 60 μM and add 60 g/L of sucrose and 6 g/L of gellan gum.
3. MLV germination medium MLVG: identical to MLV but without plant growth regulators and with 6 g/L gellan gum.
4. *Agrobacterium* growth medium (YEP): 10 g/L of Bacto yeast extract, 10 g/L of Bacto-peptone, 5 g/L of NaCl, pH 7.2. After autoclaving, add 2 mL of filtersterilized 1 M $MgSO_4$ sterilized 1 M $MgSO_4$.

Other Chemicals

1. Standard reagents for molecular biology work are described Russell.
2. Acetosyringone: 200 mM stock solution, prepare by dissolving the powder in dimethyl sulfoxide (DMSO, Sigma). Aliquot and store at –20°C.
3. Kanamycin sulfate: 25 mg/mL of stock solution, prepare by dissolving the powder in water and sterilize by filtration (22 μm pore size). Aliquot and store at -20°C.
4. Rifampicin: 25 or 50 mg/mL stock solution, prepare by dissolving the powder in DMSO. Aliquot and store at –20°C.
5. Gentamicin sulfate: 20 mg/mL stock solution, prepare by dissolving the powder in water and sterilize by filtration. Aliquot and store at –20°C.
6. Timentin: 250 mg/mL stock solution; prepare by dissolving the powder in water and sterilize by filtration. Aliquot and store at –20°C.
7. Cefotaxime sodium: 250 mg/mL stock solution; prepare by dissolving the powder in water and sterilize by filtration. Aliquot and store at –20°C.
8. All the above cited chemicals are unstable at high temperatures. Thus, they should be added to the autoclaved medium once it has cooled to approx 60°C. Swirl to mix thoroughly before pouring the medium in Petri dishes.
9. (β-glucuronidase (GUS) histochemical buffer: 0.5 mg/mL of X (5-bromo-4-chloro-3-indolyl glucuronide), 100 mM sodium phosphate, pH 7.0, 0.5 mM ferrocyanide, 0.5 mM ferricyanide, 0.5% (v/v) Triton X-100, 1 mM ethylenediamine tetraacetic acid (EDTA).
10. 4-Methyl umbelliferyl glucuronide (MUG) base buffer: 150 mM phosphate, 0.1 % Triton X-100, 0.1% Na sarcosine, 10 mM EDTA, 50 μg/mL of RNaseA, 25 mM sodium metabisulfite, pH 7.0.

Culture Conditions

Embryonal tissues are maintained at approx 23°C in the dark in an environmentally controlled growth chamber. Maturation of somatic embryos is done under indirect light (20–30 μmol m^2s) and germination of plantlets is conducted at approx 23°C under a 16-h photoperiod (90–110 μmol m^2s, TRUE-LITE®).

Transformation Vectors and A. tumefaciens Strain

Agrobacterium tumefaciens strain C58/pMP90 is used in our laboratory for all the genetic transformation experiments in conifers. The *Agrobacterium* strain also contains a binary vector with a selectable marker (kanamycin or hygromycin).

We have used successfully two types of binary vectors, pBINPLUS (4) and the pCAMBIA series. For a detailed list of *Agrobacterium* binary vectors and technical details about these vectors, the reader should consult Hellens et al..

METHODS

The methods described in the subheadings that follow outline (a) the initiation of somatic embryogenesis (somatic embryonal tissue), (b) consideration about the plasmid vectors and the transformation of *A. tumefaciens, (c)* the transformation of embryonal cultures, (d) the characterization of transgenic cell colonies, and (e) plant regeneration and establishment of transgenic trees in a greenhouse.

Somatic Embryogenesis:

Initiation and Proliferation of Embryonal Tissues

1. Immature or mature seeds of *P. glauca, P. mariana,* and *P. abies* are surface disinfected according to the published protocols and the whole megagametophytes (containing the zygotic embryo) or isolated mature zygotic embryos are excised from the seeds. The explants are placed onto MLV medium.
2. Once the embryonal tissue appears either directly from the zygotic embryo or from the micropylar end of a *megagametophyte* (usually after 6-10 wk of culture) it is separated from the explant and placed onto fresh medium of the same *composition* for *proliferation.* The embryogenic cell line is considered established if it grows in a consistent and vigorous manner following multiple *subcultures,* conducted every two weeks.
3. The same medium is used for *proliferation* of embryonal tissue, *cocultivation* with A. *tumefaciens* and selection of transformed tissue cocultivation medium Is supplemented with 50 µM acetosyringone. Unless stated otherwise, all cultures are kept in the dark at 23°C.

Introduction of Binary Vectors into Agrobacterium

Agrobacterium strains are distinguished by their antibiotic resistance, carried either chromosomally or by a tumor-inducing (Ti) plasmid. For genetic transformation, the *Agrobacterium* strain generally contains a binary vector that will confer another antibiotic resistance for bacterial propagation of the binary vector, as well as antibiotic selection of transgenic tissues.

1. This procedure was adapted from An et al.. A single Agro*bacterium* colony is grown in 2 mL of YEP media at 28°C overnight.
2. Then, 50 mL of YEP is inoculated with 2.0 mL of the overnight culture and grown to OD600 nm of 0.5.
3. Following centrifugation for 5 min at 2700g, the cell pellet is resuspended into 10 mL of 0.15 M NaCl, followed by centrifugation for 5 min at 2700g, and the cells are resuspended into 1.0 mL of ice-cold 20 mM $CaCl_2$.
4. Then, 1 µg of DNA is mixed with 200 µL of cells in a 1.5-mL Eppendorf tube and incubated for 30 min on ice. This mixture is then frozen for 1 min in liquid nitrogen and the tube is placed into a 37°C water bath until the cell mixture has thawed.
5. Then, 1 mL of YEP medium is added and the cells are incubated at 28°C for 2-4 h with slow shaking.
6. Following centrifugation for 1 min the cells are resuspended in 100 tL of YEP medium, followed by plating onto semisolid YEP medium containing 100 µg/ mL of rifampicin, 50 µg/mL of kanamycin sulfate, and 20 µg/mL of gentamicin sulfate and the plate is incubated at 28°C. Transformed colonies appear within 2–3 d.

Agrobacterium Transformation of Embryonal Tissue

Cocultivation of Embryonal Tissues With A. tumefaciens

1. Day 1. A single colony of *A. tumefaciens* containing the desired binary plasmid is inoculated into YEP medium containing 50 or 100 mg/mL of rifampicin, 50 mg/mL of kanamycin sulfate, and 20 mg/mL of gentamicin sulfate, and incubated overnight at 28°C with shaking (250 rpm).
2. Day 2. Fifty microliters of bacterial suspension is transferred into 50 mL of YEP medium containing the same antibiotics and grown overnight under the conditions described elsewhere in this chaptrer.
3. Day 3. The bacterial cells are pelleted by centrifugation and resuspended in the MLV medium to an optical density of OD600 nm 0.6.
4. Embryonal tissue is collected in a sterile test tube, and suspended in a liquid MLV medium at a ratio of 100 mg in 1.0 mL of medium to which an equal volume of bacterial suspension is added. This results in a final ratio of 50 mg of embryonal tissue per milliliter of *Agrobacterium* suspension (OD 0.3).
5. Finally, a sterile solution of acetosyringone is added to a final concentration of 50 μM.
6. For the first hour the cocultivation is carried out in the liquid medium in the dark at 23°C on a shaker (110 rpm). Subsequently, 1.5 mL of suspension containing 75 mg of embryonal tissue is poured over a 70-mm filter paper disk that is placed in a Bichner funnel and a short low-pressure pulse is applied to drain excess liquid medium.
7. Each filter paper, all covered with a layer of embryonal tissue, is then placed onto a 90 × 15-mm Petri dish containing semisolid MLV medium containing 50 μM acetosyringone and incubated at 23°C in the dark for 2 d.

Inhibition of A. tumefaciens Growth

1. Day 5. Filter papers are either transferred onto fresh semisolid medium of the same composition but supplemented with 400 mg/L of timentin, or the cells are collected and washed in a liquid MLV medium.
2. The washing step is often necessary to reduce the density of *A. tumefaciens* cells that multiply during the cocultivation and that may overgrow the plant cell culture. Usually, this has an adverse effect on the embryonal culture viability.

   To collect embryonal tissues for washing, the filter paper is placed adjacent to the inner wall of the Erlenmeyer flask and 10 mL of the liquid from a pipet over the surface of the filter paper until all or most of the cells are dislodged and collected in the flask. Tissues from more than one filter paper representing the same experimental treatment may be collected in one flask for washing.
3. An additional 10 mL of the medium may be added to reduce further the density of bacterial cells. The cells are then collected on a fresh filter paper using a Biichner funnel, and the filter paper is placed onto a fresh medium of the same composition and cultured as described above.

Selection of Transformed Cell Colonies, Proliferation of Transgenic Lines

1. Day 8. The filter papers are examined under the stereomicroscope and tissue colonies showing signs of growth are picked and subcultured individually onto fresh medium containing 400 mg/L of timentin and 25 mg/L of kanamycin for *P. abies,* or 35 mg/L of kanamycin for *P. mariana* and *P. glauca.* Note that each cluster of growing embryonal tissue has been produced by an individual transformation event and thus each represents a distinct transgenic line or "transline".
2. Day 15. Subculture each clump of embryonal tissue onto fresh medium containing the same concentration of kanamycin, but with 300 mg/L of cefotaxime instead of timentin.
3. Continue subculturing every 2 wk. Transformed tissues should show vigorous growth, whereas the nontransformed tissues initially show dramatic reductions in growth rate, and eventually die, usually by the third subculture (after 6-8 wk on kanamycin-containing medium).
4. The translines are considered established after 16 wk of continuous growth on a medium with kanamycin (and cefotaxime); thereafter, the subcultures are performed on medium without kanamycin and cefotaxime.

Molecular Characterization of Spruce Translines

Following antibiotic selection and once sufficient embryonal tissue has grown, various techniques can be used for molecular characterization of each putative transline. A primary objective is to provide support each *embryonal* transline is truly transgenic, *although* growth in the presence of antibiotics has in our hands proven to be a reliable indicator that *embryonal* tissues are transgenic.

Second, the level of transgene expression can be an important *consideration* for the selection of those *translines* from which somatic embryos will be matured and somatic seedlings produced. Finally, the same techniques can be used to follow both spatial and the *expressions* in somatic embryos and seedlings. Protein and nucleic acids extraction procedures for plants usually start with the grinding of the material in liquid nitrogen.

For all the methods described in the following subheadings, traditional *grinding* using a mortar and pestle in liquid nitrogen works fine. However, specific grinding tools are available *commercially* and we have successfully used the FastPrep® System from Q-BIOgene.

This system is a benchtop homogenizer that works at high speed and is very efficient for rapid lysis of various samples (*from tissue culture material to needles*). The samples to analyze are placed in 2.0-mL resistant tubes *containing* lysing matrix particles (ceramic beads) and the *extraction* buffer.

A short pulse (30-40 s) of vigorous shaking of the tubes will cause the particles to impact the sample from many directions in the extraction buffer. This operation will result in the release of nucleic acids and proteins into the *homogenization* buffer and the sample can then be *recovered* from the lysate after centrifugation.

Under the next subheadings we will provide some of the *techniques* used for the molecular *characterization* of the translines. Unless otherwise stated, all molecular methods are carried out according to Sambrook and Russell.

Histochemical Staining for GUS Activity

1. Assuming that the *transformation* vector expresses the *gus* gene, *histological* staining with X-Gluc is an effective and rapid method for *visualizing gus* transgene activity. We use a procedure based on that described by Jefferson in which tissues are completely submerged into GUS histochemical buffer and incubated in the dark at 37°C for 24 h, although room temperature can also produce equivalent results and allows microscopic *visualization* of staining over time.
2. The speed of color development and staining intensity can provide a qualitative indication of the level of *gus* transgene expression. In addition, the pattern of staining can be used to evaluate tissue specificity of the promoter used to drive *gus* gene *expression*. Embryonal tissue, somatic embryos, developing buds, and needles have all been found to produce very low levels of endogenous GUS activity, levels that are well below the detection level of X-Gluc histochemical staining. Caution must be exercised, however, for tissues taken from plants in soil, as artifactual staining can be produced by infecting fungi and bacteria.

Quantitative Fluorescent Assay for GUS Activity

1. A fluorescence-based assay using MUG is commonly used to provide a quantitative measurement of *gus* transgene activity, which, although it requires some effort to set up, is still significantly easier to conduct than transgene messenger RNA (mRNA) *accumulation* assays. The approach involves preparation of a tissue extract followed by a GUS *enzymatic* assay in which a small amount of tissue extract is mixed with the MUG substrate that produces a fluorescent molecule, methyl umbelliferone (MU), on cleavage by GUS. The amount of GUS activity present in the sample is thus determined by taking samples of the reaction mixture over time, and determining the *concentration* of MU via *fluorescence* using a fluorometer. GUS activity (generally expressed as picomoles of MU produced per minute) is then *normalized* against the concentration of total protein in the sample.
2. However, we have found that normalization to DNA *concentration* can be more *effective*, in that the determination of DNA concentration via SYBR Green I fluorescent is much easier to conduct and more accurate than that of protein *determination*. In addition, this allows GUS activity to be expressed upon a "per cell" basis, as opposed to protein content of the tissue, which better reflects *gus* transgene activity.
3. The following procedures were developed for large-scale processing and analysis of transgenic tissues, in which samples are processed at room temperature and enzymatic protein and DNA assays are conducted in microtiter plates. For additional details and *illustration* of this protocol, the reader is referred to Rutledge and C6te, in which the difficulties of assaying GUS activity from *transgenic* tissues of woody plants are also examined in detail.
4. Extracts are prepared by *macerating* tissues for 90 s at speed 6.0 using a FastPrep® System from Q-BIOgene in 2.0-mL screw-cap microfuge tubes containing 100 mg of glass beads (0.5 mm, Biospec Products, Bartlesville, OK), a single ceramic bead (5 mm, Bio101) and 1.0 mL of MUG base buffer. Base buffer can be supplemented further with 100 mg/

mL polyvinyl polypyrrolidone (PVPP) for tissues containing phenolics and/or tannins. However, addition of PVPP was found to be unnecessary for embryonal tissues and somatic embryos of spruce. Extracts are then clarified by centrifugation at room temperature and 150 µL aliquots placed into the wells of a 96-well microtiter plate also at room *temperature*, from which samples are taken for *enzymatic*, protein and DNA determinations, using a *multichannel* pipet.

5. Protein *concentrations* are determined using the Bio-Rad Bradford Protein Assay kit (Bio-Rad, Hercules, CA) by mixing 5 µL of extract with 200 µL of diluted reaction mix in a microtiter plate, which is read in a standard microtiter plate *spectrophotometer* along with diluted BSA protein standards according to the manufacturer's instructions. Care must be taken to ensure that protein concentrations are within the linear range of the assay.
6. DNA concentration *determinations* are conducted by mixing 5 µL of extract or DNA standard with 200 µL of a 1/3000 dilution of SYBR Green I (Molecular Probes, Eugene, OR) in Tris-ethylenediaminetetraacetic acid (TE) (10 MM Tris, 1 mM EDTA, pH 7.0). The DNA concentrations in the tissues extracts are then calculated by comparison to the fluorescence produced by a dilution series of a DNA standard (Lambda DNA, Roche Molecular Systems, Alameda, CA) prepared in extraction buffer. In our laboratory, *fluorescence* is measured using a Fluorolite1000 microtiter-plate reader (Dynatech Laboratories, Chantilly, VA; filter set: 485 nm excitation–BP22 and 530 nm emission–BP30).
7. Microtiter-plate MUG assays are conducted in duplicate for each extract, using a 200-µL reaction volume containing 5 tL of extract and 1.0 *MM* MUG (Sigma) in base buffer lacking RNaseA. The microtiter plate is covered and incubated at 37°C in an air-circulating oven. Then, 20-µL aliquots are taken from the reactions using a *multichannel* pipette every 10 min for a total of 60 min, and *immediately* mixed with 180 tL of stop buffer (0.2 M Na_2CO_3) in the wells of another microtiter plate. MU *concentrations* are determined based on a standard curve derived from six MU standards placed into this microtiter plate, and *fluorescence* is *determined* using a Fluorolite 1000 microtiter-plate reader (Dynatech Laboratories; filter set: 365 nm excitation-BP15 and 450 nm emission-BP65). GUS enzymatic rates are then calculated by averaging the slope of MU production from each of the duplicate *reactions* and *reported* as pmol MU/minute/milligram of protein or nmol MU/minute/microgram of DNA.

PCR Analysis of Genomic DNA

Confirming the *integration* of the transgene into genomic DNA is another method for molecular *characterization* of translines. In many cases, the presence of the gene used for antibiotic selection is the primary target, although other segments of the *transformation* vector (such as the transgene itself) are also used.

1. Genomic DNA is extracted from embryogenic tissue using Qiagen Genomic-tips (Qiagen, Valencia, CA) and the Qiagen protocol for plants. As mentioned previously, homogenization of plant tissues is done using the FastPrep® System.
2. Polymerase chain reaction (PCR) analysis is usually conducted on DNA samples from individual transgenic lines, non-transgenic lines, and from a negative control that contained

no DNA. PCR reaction mixtures (50 tL) contained 1.5 *MM* MgCl2, 100 μM of each dNTP, 1 tM of each primer, 1X of the supplied buffer, 2.5 U of *Taq* DNA polymerase and 100 ng of template DNA. Thermocycler parameters were as follows: 10 min preheat at 95°C; 25 cycles of 94°C for 1 min, 58°C for 1 min, and 72°C for 1 min. We have performed several PCR amplifications specific to the neomycin phosphotransferase *(nptll)* gene using genomic DNA from various transgenic spruce species. The use of those *nptll* gene specific primers (5' CTGGCCACGACGGGCG TTCCTTG 3' and 5' GAATCGGGAGCGGCGATACCGTAAA 3') resulted in the amplification of a 545-bp DNA fragment. The products of the PCR reactions were analyzed by electrophoresis on a 1% agarose gel and stained with ethidium bromide.

RNA Extraction and Transcript Accumulation Analysis

In many cases, in particular for transformation vectors lacking the *gus* gene, it is necessary to quantify transgene activity in terms of mRNA transcript *accumulation*. Standard molecular *techniques* are used for Northern or real-time PCR analysis.

The procedure of RNA extraction has been based on either the method described by Chang et al., or the RNAeasy Plant Mini kit (Qiagen). Tissue *homogenization* using the FastPrep® System as described for tissue extraction for GUS assay has also been found to be an effective alternative to grinding tissue in liquid nitrogen and has been found to be a very rapid and effective method for extracting RNA from embryonal tissue and somatic embryos of spruce.

Plant Regeneration and Growth in a Greenhouse

The maturation of *non-transformed* and transgenic somatic *embryos, germination*, and growth in a potting mix are performed according to the published protocol.

Somatic Embryo Maturation

1. The tissue pieces are first suspended in a liquid MLV medium without plant growth regulators in a centrifuge test tube and are vigorously shaken to dissociate the pieces into fine cell suspension.
2. Then, 3 mL (or less) of the cell suspension is transferred onto a filter paper disk in the Buchner funnel and a short, low-pressure pulse is applied to drain the liquid and anchor the cells to the filter paper.
3. Subsequently, the filter paper with the cells is placed on MLVM medium. The cultures are placed under low-intensity light, 16-h photoperiod, at 23°C for 78 wk.

Somatic Embryo Germination and Conversion to Plantlets

1. The cotyledonary and morphologically normal somatic embryos are collected individually under the stereomicroscope and placed horizontally on a MLVG medium in Petri dishes for germination and plantlet conversion.
2. The somatic embryos are kept for the first 7–10 d under low light intensity and then placed under higher light intensity until both a root and an epicotyl develop.

Potting and Acclimatization of Plantlets

1. Plantlets that show both a growing root and an epicotyl with several needles may be

planted in a substrate (1:1 peat–perlite mix) in small containers and kept in a mist chamber for 12–14 d under greenhouse conditions.

2. After this period, the humidity is gradually reduced and the plantlets can be grown outside the mist chamber.

NOTES

1. Alternatively, cells are collected *manually* with a spatula and washed in 15 mL of MLV. The cells are then collected on a filter paper by filtration using the Buchner funnel. Cefotaxime at 300 mg/L also can be used agent.
2. High density of cultured cells after cocultivation with *A. tumefaciens* can potentially create a problem with respect to the recovery of chimeric translines. If the transformed cells are proliferating in close proximity to each other then there is a possibility that two independently transformed cell colonies will "*fuse*" and create a chimeric transline. Thus, it is important to make frequent microscopic observations of postcocultivation cultures and separate rapidly growing colonies to prevent them from "fusing."
3. Our results (*unpublished data*) indicate that the selection period can be shorter, only 10-12 wk, without creating a problem of escapes or recurring *Agrobacterium* growth. However, the latter requires further research.
4. It should be noted, however, that although it has also been very successful for extracting RNA from flushing buds, we have not been successful in using the RNAeasy kit for extracting RNA from mature needles.

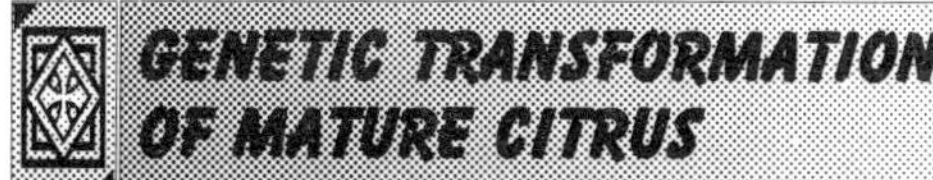

GENETIC TRANSFORMATION OF MATURE CITRUS

Plant development involves a juvenile phase *characterized* by the production of *vegetative* organs with a different size and shape than adult organs and by the inability to produce flowers and fruits, and a mature phase *characterized* for the *acquisition* of *meristematic* competence to initiate flowering and fruiting. In addition, in most tree species there is a transition phase between the juvenile and the adult periods that can last several years and that is characterized by scarce *flowering* and fruit production.

In woody fruit species, the juvenile phase and the transition period can last as long as decades, drastically *prolonging* the time required to analyze mature traits. In many woody fruit genus, most commercial varieties are *vegetatively* propagated and are hybrids of unknown origin or budsports that have been selected by growers based on a good *agronomic* behavior.

High heterozygosity, large size, genetic *incompatibility* limitations, and lack of knowledge on how the most important horticultural traits are inherited make conventional breeding a long-term effort. Even when traditional breeding may be effective, another major obstacle is the long period of time between generations.

Genetic *engineering* would allow the insertion of specific genes into the unknown genetic *background* of elite varieties, theoretically adding desirable traits without affecting existing horticultural characteristics. However, one limitation to improvement of woody fruit species through genetic *engineering* might be the necessity of *working* with juvenile tissues as source of material for transformation.

Maturation and aging seem to be *responsible* for the explant regenerative potential decline found in plant tissue culture of most woody species. Furthermore, juvenile tissues show higher sensitivity to *Agrobacterium-mediated* transformation than mature ones. For these reasons, juvenile material has been extensively used for genetic transformation of woody species.

There are two options: (a) Material derived from seeds or seedling organs, such as zygotic embryos, hypocotyls, or cotyledons can be used; however, this implies a passage through a sexual stage and therefore a drastic reshuffling of the genome and a *subsequent* alteration of cultivar properties; and (b) embryogenic cells of somatic origin, somatic embryos, or even in vitro *micropropagated* tissues can be used, which would result in *regeneration* of transgenic plants with cultivar properties; however, they would be juvenile, and therefore would require several years of cultivation before horticultural and commercial traits of the transgenic plants could be evaluated.

As a careful evaluation of the horticultural characteristics of mature plants bearing fruits is a standard procedure for releasing any new fruit variety to the market, genetic engineering would have limited applications unless tissue from mature plants can be readily transformed.

Development of transformation procedures that allow bypassing the juvenile phase could greatly reduce the time and costs involved in improving and evaluating transgenic woody fruit trees species. This is the case of important citrus genotypes, as sweet orange trees, for which up to 20 yr may be needed to lose these juvenile characters.

We describe here a method to transform mature material of citrus plants based on: (a) *grafting* adult buds onto juvenile rootstocks for invigorating the mature tissues; (b) *optimizing* tissue culture conditions and media to shift citrus cells at the explants to a competent state for *Agrobacterium-mediated* transformation and *regeneration*; and (c) grafting in vitro of regenerating shoots onto decapitated seedling rootstocks as a high efficient alternative to shoot *elongation* and rooting.

This method has been proved successful for the transformation of adult sweet orange, sour orange, lime, and some mandarin genotypes. Moreover, this general *approach* could be applicable to *transformation* of mature tissues from other woody fruit plants.

In the case of sweet orange, species we will use as a reference in this chapter, it has led to the production of transgenic plants flowering and bearing fruits in 14 mo after transferring to the greenhouse. This is the standard period of time required for mature plants to achieve the adequate size and vigor to flower and set fruits.

MATERIALS

Plant Material

1. Source of plant material: plants propagated in the greenhouse (18-27°C) by grafting of buds from adult sweet orange (Citrus sinensis *L.* Osbeck cv. Pineapple) trees on a vigorous rootstock, such as C. volkameriana Ten & Pasq. From these propagated plants, only the

newly elongated first flushes will serve the objective.

2. Material for in vitro graft: seedlings of Troyer citrange *(C. sinensis L.* Osbeck × Poncirus trifoliata *L.* Raf.) germinated in vitro on seed germination medium (SGM) and grown in the dark for 2 wk.

3. Material for greenhouse graft: seedlings of rough lemon *(C. jambhiri* Lush) germinated in nursery and grown under greenhouse conditions (18-27°C) for approx

5. mo.

Tissue Culture Media and Components

1. Seed germination medium (SGM): 4.3 g/L of Murashige and Skoog (MS) salts, 10 g/L of agar (Bacto-agar, Difco, Detroit, MI), pH 5.7.
2. Inoculation medium (IM): 4.3 g/L of MS salts, 10 mL/L of vitamin stock solution, 30 g/L of sucrose, pH 5.7.
3. Cocultivation medium (CM): IM plus 2 mg/L of 2,4-dichlorophenoxyacetic acid (2,4-D), 2 mg/L of indole-3-acetic acid (IAA), 1 mg/L of 2-isopentenyl-adenine (2,i-P), 8 g/L of agar, pH 5.7.
4. Shoot regeneration medium (SRM): IM plus 3 mg/L of 6-(BAP). Medium is semisolidified using 10 g/L of agar at pH 5.7, supplemented with 100 mg/L of kanamycin sulfate, 500 mg/L of cefotaxime, and 250 mg/L of vancomycin.
5. Shoot-tip grafting medium: 4.3 g/L of MS salts, 10 mL/L of vitamin stock, 75 g/L of sucrose, pH 5.7.
6. Vitamin stock: 10 g/L of myo-inositol (Duchefa, Haarlem, The Netherlands), 20 µg/L of *thiamine-HCl* (Duchefa), 100 µg/L *pyridoxine-HCl* (Duchefa), 100 µg/L of nicotinic acid (Duchefa).
7. 2,4-D (Sigma, St. Louis, MO) stock solution: 5 mg/100 mL. Prepare by dissolving the powder in a few drops of dimethyl sulfoxide (DMSO). Adjust volume with double-distilled water. Store at 4°C.
8. IAA (Sigma) stock solution: 5 mg/100 mL. Prepare as for 2,4-D and store at 4°C.
9. 2,i-P (Sigma) stock solution: 5 mg/100 mL. Prepare as for 2,4-D and store at 4°C.
10. BAP (Sigma) stock solution: 5 mg/100 mL. Prepare by dissolving the powder in a few drops of 1 *N* NaOH. Complete final volume with double-distilled water. Store at 4°C.
11. Kanamycin sulfate (Duchefa) stock solution: 100 mg/mL. Prepare by dissolving 1 g of powder in 10 mL of double-distilled water. Sterilize by filtration through a 0.2-µm membrane (Minisart, Sartorius, Gottingen, Germany), make 1-mL aliquots in sterile Eppendorf tubes and store at -20°C.
12. Cefotaxime stock solution: 250 mg/mL. Prepare by dissolving 1 g of powder in 4 mL of double distilled water. Sterilize by filtration through a 0.2-µm membrane, make 1-mL aliquots in sterile Eppendorf tubes and store at-20°C.
13. Vancomycin stock solution: 250 mg/mL. Prepare as for cefotaxime, aliquote, and store at -20°C.

All media are sterilized by autoclaving at 121°C for 20 min. Antibiotics are added to the medium after autoclaving.

Bacterial Strain and Vector

1. Bacterial strain: *Agrobacterium tumefaciens* EHA105, which is a disarmed derivative of *A. tumefaciens* A281. This strain holds chromosomic resistance to nalidixic acid.
2. Binary vector: The T-DNA of the binary plasmid usually contains, apart from the expression cassette/s of interest, a selectable marker gene, such as neomycin phosphotransferose II *(nptII),* which confers resistance to kanamycin, and a reporter marker gene, such as (3-D-glucuronidase *(uidA)* or green fluorescent protein *(gfp),* under the control of constitutive promoter and terminator sequences. The binary plasmid is introduced into *Agrobacterium* by electroporation.

Culture Media for A. Tumefaciens

1. Luria broth (LB) medium: 10 g/L of tryptone, 5 g/L of yeast extract, 10 g/L of NaCl, pH 7.5.
2. Kanamycin sulfate stock solution: 100 mg/mL.
3. Nalidixic acid (Sigma) stock solution: 25 mg/mL. Prepare by dissolving 250 mg of powder in a few drops of 1 *N* NaOH and then add water to complete 10 mL. Sterilize by filtration, make 1-mL aliquots in sterile Eppendorf tubes and store at -20°C.
4. Liquid culture medium: LB medium containing 25 mg/L of kanamycin sulfate, and 25 mg/L of nalidixic acid.
5. Agar culture medium: LB medium, plus 10 g/L of agar (Difco), pH 7.5, with 25 mg/L of kanamycin sulfate, and 25 mg/L of nalidixic acid.

All media are sterilized by autoclaving at 121°C for 20 min. Antibiotics are added to the medium after autoclaving.

Other Solutions

Surface sterilant: 2% (v/v; stems) or 0.5% (v/v; seeds) sodium hypochlorite solution containing 0.1% (v/v) Tween-20 (Merck, Darmstadt, Germany).

Special Equipment

1. Culture chamber allowing temperature, humidity, and illumination control. Standard conditions are fixed at 26°C, 60% relative humidity, and a 16-h photoperiod at 45 $\mu E/m^2/s$ illumination.
2. Incubators allowing temperature control at 26–28°C.
3. Orbital shaker allowing temperature and speed control.
4. Spectrophotometer.

METHODS

1. Grow A. tumefaciens on LB agar culture medium (with antibiotics) at 28°C for 2 d. Take

one loopful of bacteria and transfer to 100 mL of LB liquid culture medium (with antibiotics) and grow overnight at 28°C on an orbital shaker at 200 rpm. Measure absorbance at 600 nm of a 1-mL aliquot of the bacterial overnight culture in a spectrophotometer to calculate bacterial concentration.

2. Centrifuge the bacterial culture at 2000g for 10 min in 40-mL sterile centrifuge tubes with cap (Beckman Instruments, Palo Alto, CA), discard the supernatant, resuspend and dilute the pellet with IM to a concentration of approx 4 x 10^7 cells/ mL. Pour 25-mL aliquots of the diluted culture into sterile glass 10cm diameter Petri platcm diameter Petri plates.

Explant Preparation

1. Select stem pieces from first flushes of propagated adult sweet orange plants. Strip stem pieces of their leaves and small thorns, brush carefully with soap and water, disinfect for 10 min in surface sterilant, and rinse three times with sterile distilled water.
2. Cut transversely 1-cm-long internodal stem segments with forceps and sterile scalpel (or small garden scissors) and keep in sterile humid plates until all stem pieces have been prepared.

Inoculation, Cocultivation and Selection

1. Immerse explants (approx 40 explants per plate) into the *A. tumefaciens* culture and incubate for 15 min with gentle shaking.
2. Blot dry on sterile filter paper, and place horizontally on plates containing CM (approx 20 explants per plate) for a 3-d cocult 26°C at a low light intensity (10 μE/m^2/s, 16-h photoperiod).
3. After cocultivation, transfer the explants to SRM (10 explants per plate). Maintain cultures in the dark for 2–4 wk at 26°C and then transfer to a 16-h photoperiod, 45 μE/m^2/s illumination at 26°C. Explants will be subcultured every 3–4 wk and any fungus- or bacteria-contaminated explant should be discarded.

Recovery of Whole Transgenic Plants

1. Shoots should develop from the cut ends of explants 3-5 wk after cocultivation. Check the transgenic nature of the regenerated shoots by performing a histochemical GUS assay or by testing GFP expression. GUS- or green fluorescent protein (GFP)-negative shoots are considered as nontransformed, and commonly called escape shoots.
2. Graft in vitro apical portions of the GUS- or GFP-positive shoots onto decapitated seedlings of Troyer citrange. Rootstock preparation is as follows: peel seeds, remove both seed coats, disinfect for 10 min in surface sterilant, and rinse three times with sterile distilled water. Sow individual seeds onto 25-mL aliquots of SGM contained in 25 × 150 mm glass tubes and incubate at 27°C in the dark for 2 wk. Decapitate seedlings leaving 1-1.5 cm of the epicotyls. Shorten the roots to 4-6 cm and remove the cotyledons and their axillary buds. Place the regenerated shoot onto the apical end of the cut surface of the decapitated epicotyl, so that contact is with the vascular ring.
3. Culture grafted plants in shoot-tip grafting medium and maintain at 25°C, 16 h of

photoperiod and 45 μE/m²/s of illumination. Scions develop two to four expanded leaves 3-4 wk after grafting.

4. Grafting of in vitro-grown plants onto vigorous rough lemon rootstocks in the glasshouse allows the rapid acclimatization and development of the plants.
5. Monitor plant growth and development. Putative mature transgenic sweet orange plants show morphology and growth habits of an adult plant, as compared to control mature plants. In fact, whereas juvenile plants show a pronounced thorniness, transgenic mature plants are almost thornless, similar to the mature plants from which the explants are taken for transformation. After fourteen months in the greenhouse, the transgenic and control plants usually start to flower and set fruit, confirming their mature nature.
6. Putative transgenic plants should be assayed by polymerase chain reaction (PCR) to detect the presence of the transgene(s). Southern blot analyses must be performed to confirm the stable integration of the transgene(s), and Northern blot and Western blot analyses would confirm their expression in the transgenic plants.

NOTES

1. In a preliminary study, the regenerative potentials of juvenile explants and explants coming from the first, second, and third flushes of mature sweet orange plants were compared. Explants from first and second flushes of mature plants showed a reduction of regeneration frequency of 50-70% compared to juvenile explants. The third flush showed a more pronounced regenerative decline that made it useless for our purpose.
2. We use to keep separate stock solutions of MS macroelements and microelements, but a good laboratory practice is required to prepare and keep clean and uncontaminated solutions. A comfortable method is using commercial MS salts, weighed and presented in individual bags for 1 L of medium.
3. Hormone solutions are not kept sterile in the refrigerator, so the possibility of *contamination* exists. If the stock solution is contaminated, discard and prepare a new one before mixing with the other components of the media.
4. We prefer to make 1-mL aliquots of antibiotic solutions to avoid possible *contaminations.* In the case of tissue culture media, one or two full aliquots will serve to reach the final desired concentration for 1 L of medium.
5. In a previous study performed in vivo by inoculating sweet orange *seedlings* with different nondisarmed *Agrobacterium* strains, strain A281 was shown to be the most virulent in the infection of this genotype and others of the genus *Citrus.* This is the reason of using a disarmed derivative of A281 for our *transformation* experiments.
6. Plasmids of reference, with a T-DNA only containing marker genes, could be p35SGUSINT or pBIN19-sGFP. Both have been used in our laboratory and work very efficiently for the genetic transformation of many plants. Bacterial resistance to kanamycin, present in both plasmids, together with the chromosomic resistance of EHA105 to nalidixic acid, is used to select the bacteria.

7. It is *convenient* to determine the growth curve (A_{600} vs bacterial cell *concentration*) for the bacterial strain used in the *transformation* experiment. Bacterial culture should grow to the *exponential* phase to play all its infectious potential (A_{600} between 0.1 and 1.0, in the case of strain EHA105). For sweet orange, calculate the volume of bacterial culture *necessary* to prepare 40 mL of 4 × 10^7 cells/mL suspension in the *centrifuge* tubes. If it is too small, prepare an intermediate 4 × 10' cells/mL suspension in IM. A higher bacterial *concentration* (approx 10^1) results in lower *transformation* frequency because plant cells become stressed; lower bacterial concentration (approx 10^6) results in a lower *transformation* frequency and in this case fewer cells at the cut end of the explant become transformed.
8. Flushes should be in a good ontological state, neither too tender (they would not bear *Agrobacterium* infection) nor too lignified (as to keep an acceptable *regenerative* potential).
9. We use sterile soft paper towels to help explants to dry. It is important to eliminate any bacterial liquid residue, as it can be a source of bacterial overgrowth during cocultivation.
10. Cocultivation in a medium rich in auxins provides to the wounded plant cells of explants an appropriate treatment to shift them to a competent state for *transformation*, involving *dedifferentiation*, induction of cell division, and callus proliferation. Prolonging cocultivation period does not increase transformation frequency, but it frequently results in *Agrobacterium* overgrowth and subsequent decrease in regeneration frequency of transformed shoots. Therefore, a 3-d cocultivation is routinely used.
11. If explants were carefully dried after inoculation, they will not show an excess of bacterial growth at this point. But if this is not the case, immerse them in sterile water with *cefotaxime* at 250 mg/L for several minutes and blot them dry again before *transferring* to SRM.
12. Culture of explants in the dark improves callus formation and the progress of transformation events to regenerate transgenic shoots and avoids the regeneration of escape shoots that could be stimulated by the exposure of explants directly to light. Two weeks in the dark is normally the most appropriate period to favor callus *formation* in the case of sweet orange. This may be different for other citrus genotypes. Indeed, the explants should be kept in darkness until they develop a prominent visible callus formed at the cambial ring.
13. Considering GUS- or GFP-negative shoots as escapes is convenient, but it should be noted that it can lead to errors in the actual number of *transformants*, because silencing or low expressing events or even partial T-DNA integrations are not accounted with this criterion.
14. After 2 wk in the dark at 27°C, Troyer citrange seedlings should be transferred to the refrigerator at 4–8°C to slow growth. They can be used within 15 d or 1 mo without appreciable loss in grafting efficiency.
15. For the in vitro grafting of long shoots (0.5–1 cm), cutting the basal end as a wedge and introducing it into a small *longitudinal* incision practiced on the upper part of the rootstock can also be helpful to facilitate vascular contact and success of the graft.

16. During development of the grafts, it is necessary to check them periodically and to remove, by using sterile small scissors, any shoot not coming from the grafted scion. The growth of other shoots could weaken the connection between rootstock and transgenic scion.
17. To ensure a rapid and successful acclimatization, it is important to follow good greenhouse practices. We recommend working with sterile potting substrate, vigorous seedlings, and keeping grafted plants in plastic bags that will be *progressively* opened over approx 1 mo. This will help to maintain an optimal degree of moisture and *temperature* and will facilitate a gradual process of acclimatization.
18. An alternative approach to shorten the juvenile period is the transformation of juvenile citrus plants with the APETALA1 gene from Arabi*dopsis thaliana.* Transgenic plants show a drastic reduction in the juvenile period, flowering and setting fruits within the first year after their transfer to the greenhouse. Genetic *retransformation* of plant material coming from these plants would allow the rapid evaluation of the expression of transgenes incorporated into the plant in a second *transformation* round.

17 Chapter

MARKER GENES

Recently, there has been dramatic progress in the field of *transgenic technology*. These advances have been applied to crop *improvement*, and many transgenic crops with novel *characteristics* have been produced.

Transgenic crops with novel traits have been widely used as breeding *materials* to produce *commercial* varieties. However, current *transformation* methods have four pitfalls regarding their *incorporation* into breeding programs:

(a) The negative effects of selection agents decrease the ability of transgenic cells to proliferate and *differentiate* into transgenic plants.

(b) Recent public concerns regarding the release of antibiotic-resistance genes limit their use for the *commercialization* of transgenic crops.

(c) The presence of marker genes in transgenic plants precludes the use of the same marker genes for gene stacking through *retransformation*.

(d) The stacking of highly expressed genes through sexual crossing enhances the possibility of homology-dependent gene silencing.

Therefore, it would be desirable to develop a selection system that uses positive markers to reduce these negative effects and a system for removing selectable marker genes so that the same *selectable* marker gene can be reused for *sequential transformation*.

We have developed removal systems combined with a positive marker, which are called Multi-Auto Transformation (MAT) vectors, to address these four pitfalls. Agrobacteria can infect a wide range of plant species and induce crown galls or hairy roots. Their amazing capability for in vivo *transformation* depends on functions of the oncogenes on the T-DNA of Ti- or Ri-plasmids.

The oncogenes manipulate the hormonal level and sensitivity of transgenic cells and induce their *proliferation* in vivo. The MAT vector system is designed to use oncogenes for cell *proliferation* and regeneration of transgenic plants.

The MAT vectors combine these genes with the site-specific *recombination* system (R/RS) to remove them from transgenic plants after *transformation* that recovers the normal phenotype. The oncogenes of Agrobacterium tumefaciens include the ipt and iaaM/H genes, which *catalyze* cytokinin and auxin synthesis, respectively.

Cytokinin and auxin are major plant growth *regulators* that control growth and development in plants. The R/RS system is derived from the plasmid pSR1 of Zygosaccharomyces rouxii, and consists of R *recombinase* and its recognition site (RS). R *recombinase* mediates *recombination* between RS recognition sites and excises the DNA *fragment* flanked by the two RS sites in the same orientation.

The oncogenes and the recombinase gene (R) are flanked by two directly oriented RS sites and placed on the T-DNA region of a binary vector plasmid. The gene of interest is inserted into the T-DNA region outside of the R/RS cassette.

These genes on the T-DNA region are transferred integrated into the genome by infection with Agrobacterium. The oncogenes of the R/RS cassette differentiate transgenic cells. The R gene is expressed in transgenic cells and R recombinase excises the R/RS cassette from the plant genome.

The resulting *transgenic* plants have only the gene of interest and one RS site in the genome. This chapter describes the *application* of MAT vector systems to tobacco and rice.

Cloning Method of the Gene of Interest into MAT Vectors

MAT vectors are derivatives of a disarmed binary vector plasmid pBI121 and have oncogenes and the *recombinase* gene *(R)* flanked by two directly oriented *RS* sites in the T-DNA region. The gene of interest is inserted into the T-DNA region outside of the *R/RS*. We have constructed different MAT vector plasmids and present here *procedures* for cloning the gene of interest.

Two-Step Transformation Method by ipt-Type Vectors

The *ipt-type* MAT vectors combine the *R/RS* system with the *ipt* gene, which catalyzes cytokinin synthesis. First, the *ipt* gene regenerates transgenic shoots, and then it is removed by the *R/RS* system to generate marker-free transgenic shoots.

Single-Step Transformation Method by ipt-Type Vectors

Most economically important crops, including rice, are *regenerated* through auxin-dependent *embryogenesis*. Single-step transformation methods were developed for the application of *ipt-type* MAT vectors to embryogenic plant species. First, the *ipt* gene induces *proliferation* of transgenic callus and embryogenesis, and then the *R/RS* system removes the *ipt* gene to *regenerate* marker-free transgenic plants directly, without the production of ipt-shooty intermediates.

Two-Step Transformation Method by rol -Type Vectors

The rol-type MAT vectors combine the *R/Rs* system with the *rol* genes, which increase auxin sensitivity. First, the *rol* genes induce transgenic roots, and the addition of cytokinin *regenerates* transgenic shoots. The *R/RS* system then removes *rol* genes to generate marker-free transgenic shoots.

MATERIALS

MAT Vector Plasmids

Component plasmids to construct MAT binary vectors:

1. pTL7 binary plasmid: The vector pTL7, a derivative of pBI121 (Clontech, Franklin Lakes, NJ), has LacZ' multicloning sites and an *Sse8387I* site between the left and right border sequences. The *PstI, Sse8387I* and *SphI* sites of LacZ' multicloning sites are deleted in the pTL7 plasmid.
2. pTSattp binary plasmid: The binary vector pTSattp, a derivative of p131121, has a *ccdB* gene flanked by the *attP1* and *attP2* sites and an *Sse8387I* site between the left and right border sequences.
3. MAT cassette plasmids: The MAT cassette plasmids, derivatives of pHSG398 (Takara Shuzo, Kyoto, Japan), have the oncogenes *(ipt, rol)* and recombinase genes (R) flanked by two directly oriented RS sites at the *Sse8387I* site.
4. MAT binary vector plasmids: The MAT binary plasmids, derivatives of pBI121, have LacZ' multicloning sites and a MAT cassette between the left and right border sequences. A list of MAT binary vector plasmids is shown in Table elsewhere in this chapter. Plasmid containing the gene of interest.

Table17.1: MAT Binary Vector Plasmids

Plasmid	Gene of interest	MAT cassette
pIPT5	*Nos-nptII,* 35S-gusA, *35S-ipt*	
pIPT10	*Nos-nptII,* 35S-gusA, Native-ipt	
pIPT20	*Nos-nptII,* 35S-gusA, rbcS-ipt	
pIPTIMH	*Nos-nptII,* 35S-gusA, Native-ipt, *iaaM/H pTL7 lacZ'*	
PTS attp	*ccdB*	
pNPI132	*NOS-nptII,* 35S-gusA	35S-R, *35S-ipt*
pMAT8	*lacZ'*	GSTII-R, Native-ipt
pMAT8 :GUS	35S-gusA	GSTII-R, Native-ipt
pMATIMH	Nos-gusA	GSTII-R, Native-ipt, *iaaM/H*
pRBI11	*NOS-nptII,* 35S-gusA	GSTII-R, rbcS-ipt
pNPIBOGFP	*NOS-nptII,* 35S-gusA, *35S-hpt*	35S-R, *35S-GFP, 35S-ipt*
pMAT130HmGUS	35S-gusA	35S-R, *35S-hpt, 35S-ipt*
pEXM120	35S-gusA	35S-R, rolABC

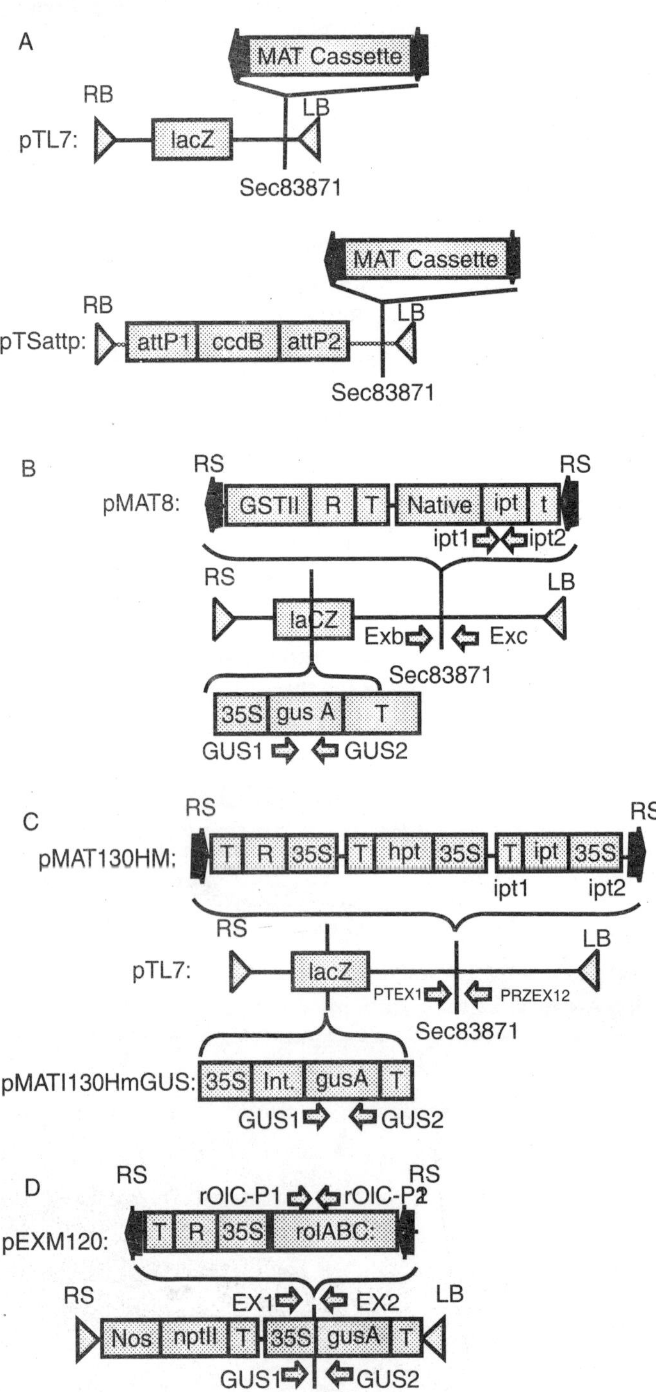

Fig. 17.1: (opposite page) Constructions of MAT vectors. (A) The pTL7 plasmid has LacZ multicloning sites for the gene of interests and an Sse8387I site for the MAT cassette. The pTSattp plasmid has the ccdB gene flanked by attB sites for the gene of interests and an Sse8387I site for the MAT cassette. (B) The pMAT8:35SGUS has a 35S-GUS gene and a MAT cassette that contains a native ipt gene and a GST-II-R gene. PCR primers (IPT1-2, GUS 1-2, Exb-c). (C) The pMATI30Hm plasmid has a 35S-GUS gene and a MAT cassette that contains a 35S-ipt gene, a 35S-R gene and a 35S-HPT gene. PCR primers (IPT1-2, GUS 1-2, PTEX1-PRZEX12). (D) The pEXM120 plasmid has a Nos-NPTII gene and a 35S-GUS gene. A MAT cassette, that contains ro1ABC genes and a 35S-R gene, is placed between a 35S promoter and a start codon of GUS gene. PCR primers (rolC-P1-2, GUS 1-2, EX1-2).

Culture Media, Plasmids, and Reagents (Two-Step ipt)

1. Plant materials: *Nicotiana tabacum* cv. Petite Havana SRI plants.
2. MS medium: Murashige and Skoog (MS) salts (Icn) and vitamins (Sigma Aldrich, St. Louis, MO), 20 g/L of sucrose, 0.8% agar (INA agar-BA30; Funakoshi), pH 5.6. 3. Acetosyringone (Sigma Aldrich).
4. α-Naphthalene acetamide (NAM) (Sigma Aldrich).
5. Kanamycin (Wako Chemical).
6. Carbenicillin (Wako Chemical).
7. Safener (R29148).
8. pMAT8:35SGUS: The pMAT8:35SGUS vector plasmid, a derivative of pBI121, has a 35S-GUS gene and a MAT cassette that contains a native *ipt* gene and a GST-II-R gene. A list of MAT binary vector plasmids is shown in Table elsewhere in this chapter.
9. YEB medium: 0.49 g/L $MgSO_4 \cdot 7H_2O$, 5 g/L of beef extract, 1 g/L of yeast extract, 5 g/L of peptone, 1.2% Bacto-agar, pH 7.2.
10. FastDNATm Kit (Q-Bio gene).
11. Nylon membranes (Hybond-N, Amersham Pharmacia Biotech).
12. DIG-dUTP, DIG Easy Hyb (hybridization solution), DIG Wash and Block Buffer Set (Roche Diagnostics GmbH).
13. Cooled-CCD LAS 1000 system (Fuji Photo Film).

Culture Media, Plasmids and Reagents (Single-Step ipt)

1. Plant materials: mature rice seeds *(Oryza sativa L.* cv. Nipponbare).
2. N6 liquid medium: N6 salts (N6 basal salt mixture, Sigma) and vitamins (Sigma), 30 g/L of sucrose, pH 5.8.
3. Co-N6CL2 medium: N6 salts and vitamins, 30 g/L of sucrose, 10 g/L of glucose, 0.4% Gelrite (Gellan Gum; Wako Chemical), 10 mg/L of acetosyringone, pH 5.2.
4. N6CL2 medium: N6 salts and vitamins, 30 g/L of sucrose, 10 g/L of glucose, 0.4% Gelrite, pH 5.8.
5. MSR medium: MS salts and vitamins, 30 g/L of sucrose, 30 g/L of sorbitol, 2 g/L of casamino acids, 0.4% Gelrite, pH 5.8.
6. Hygromycin solution (Roche Diagnostics).
7. 2,4-Dichlorophenoxyacetic acid (2,4-D) (Sigma).
8. pMAT13OHmGUS: The pMAT13OHmGUS vector plasmid, a derivative of pBI121, has a 35S-GUS gene and a MAT cassette that contains *a 35S-ipt* gene, a 35S-R gene, and a 35S-HPT gene.
9. YEB medium.
10. Kanamycin.

11. Acetosyringone.
12. Carbenicillin.
13. DNAeasy Plant System (Qiagen, Valencia, CA).
14. MS medium.

Culture Media, Plasmids, and Reagents (Two-Step rol)

1. Plant materials: *Nicotiana tabacum* cv. Petite Havana SRI plants.
2. Culture media, plasmids, and reagents are the same as those for the *ipt* type MAT vector, except that culture is done under continuous dark.
3. a-Naphthalene acetic acid (NAA) solution (Sigma).
4. 6-Benzylaminopurine (BA) solution (Sigma).
5. 3-Indolebutyric acid (IBA) (Sigma).
6. NAM.
7. pEXM120: The pEXM120 vector plasmid, a derivative of pBI121, has a Nos*NPTII* gene and a 35S-GUS gene. A MAT cassette, that contains *ro1ABC* genes and a 35S-R gene, is placed between a 35S promoter and a start codon of the *GUS* gene. Removal of the MAT cassette causes expression of the *GUS* gene. A list of MAT binary vector plasmids is shown in Table elsewhere in this chapter.
8. FastDNA™ Kit (Q-Bio gene).

METHODS

Cloning Procedures (MAT Vectors)

We present three procedures for cloning the gene of interest.

Two-Component Type (Standard)

1. When the gene of interest has no *Sse8387I* site, the pTL7 plasmid is used for cloning.
2. Both the plasmid containing the gene of interest and pTL7 plasmid are digested with appropriate restriction enzymes.
3. The gene of interest is ligated into the multicloning sites of pTL7 plasmid.
4. Recombinants are identified by blue/white colony selection.
5. Both the MAT cassette plasmid and pTL7 plasmid containing the gene of interest are digested with *Sse8387I*.
6. The MAT cassette is ligated into the *Sse8387I* site of recombinant pTL7 plasmid. 7. The recombinant pTL7 plasmid containing both the gene of interest and the MAT cassette is identified by digestion with appropriate restriction enzymes.

Two-Component Type (GATEWAY)

1. When the gene of interest has *Sse8387I* sites, the pTSattp plasmid is used for cloning.

2. Both the MAT cassette vector plasmid and pTSattp plasmid are digested with *Sse8387I*.
3. The MAT cassette is ligated into the *Sse8387I* site of the pTSattp plasmid.
4. The gene of interest flanked by *attB* sites is amplified by polymerase chain reaction (PCR).
5. The amplified gene of interest is incubated together with the recombinant pTS3 plasmid containing the MAT cassette and the recombinase BP clonase.
6. Recombinants are identified by negative selection.
7. The recombinant pTSattp plasmid containing both the gene of interest and MAT cassette is identified by digestion with appropriate restriction enzymes.

Binary Type

1. The MAT binary vector plasmids are digested at available multicloning sites.
2. The plasmid containing the gene of interest is digested with appropriate restriction enzymes.
3. The gene of interest is ligated into the multi-cloning sites of the MAT binary vector plasmid.
4. Recombinants are identified by blue/white colony selection.
5. The recombinant MAT binary vector plasmid containing the gene of interest is identified by digestion with appropriate restriction enzymes.

Two-Step Transformation Procedures (pt-Type)

Agrobacterium Suspension Culture

1. The pMAT8:35SGUS vector plasmid is introduced into the disarmed *A. tumefaciens* strain LBA4404 by electroporation.
2. Transformants are selected and maintained on YEB agar medium containing 50 mg/L of kanamycin.
3. A fresh colony is inoculated into 10 mL of YEB liquid medium without any antibiotics and cultured overnight at 27°C.
4. The suspension culture is diluted to A630 = 0.25 with sterilized water.

Explant Preparation

1. Leaves from greenhouse-grown tobacco plants are surface-sterilized by 1 % (v/v) sodium hypochlorite solution for 5 min, followed by three rinses with sterile distilled water.
2. Leaves are cut into approx 8-mm square pieces and immersed in sterilized water until infection is performed.

Infection

1. Leaf segments are immersed in diluted *Agrobacterium* suspension culture for approx 1 min.
2. They are blotted dry on sterilized filter paper to remove excess of suspension culture.
3. They are placed on hormone-free MS agar medium containing 40 mg/L of *acetosyringone* for 3 d of cocultivation at 25°C.

4. The inoculated leaf segments are transferred to hormone-free MS agar medium containing 500 mg/L of *carbenicillin* and cultured in a culture room or growth chamber at 25-28°C under *continuous* light.
5. They are transferred to fresh medium every 2 wk.

Selection of Transgenic Shoots

1. One month after *Agrobacterium* infection, the regenerated adventitious buds are separated from the leaf segments and transferred to the same medium.
2. After 1 mo of cultivation, developed shoots are classified into two groups according to their phenotype: (a) normal shoots and (b) abnormal shoots.
3. Genomic DNA is extracted from the leaves of both normal and abnormal shoots using a FastDNA™ Kit, and used for PCR analysis.
4. PCR is performed under standard conditions with 1 min of denaturation, 1 min of annealing, and 2 min of extension at 94°C, 60°C, and 72°C, respectively, for 30 cycles.
5. Reaction products are resolved by electrophoresis in a 1.8% (w/v) agarose gel.
6. About 10-40% of normal shoots are marker-free transgenic plants. These transgenic plants are maintained in a flask on hormone-free MS agar medium containing 500 mg/L of carbenicillin.

Induction of Marker-Free Transgenic Plants

1. About half of ipt-shooty lines are excision- and β-glucuronidase (GUS)-positive ones by PCR. These lines are subcultured monthly to hormone-free MS agar medium containing 500 mg/L of carbenicillin and 30 mg/L of Safener.
2. Normal shoots develop from these ipt-shooty lines within 3 mo of induction with Safener. These shoots are transferred to hormone free MS agar medium containing 500 mg/L of carbenicillin, grown normally and rooted.
3. Genomic DNA is extracted from leaves of these normal shoots using a FastDNA™ Kit, and used for PCR analysis.
4. About 80% of normal shoots that develop from ipt-shooty lines are marker-free transgenic plants.

Southern Analysis of Marker-Free Transgenic Plants

1. Genomic DNA is isolated from in vitro grown transgenic plants by a modified cetyltrimethyl-ammonium bromide (CTAB) method.
2. Ten to twenty microgram of DNA samples are digested by appropriate restriction enzymes, separated on 0.8% (w/v) agarose gel and blotted to nylon membranes.
3. The probe DNA fragment, part of the *GUS* gene, is labeled by PCR using DIGdUTP following the supplier's instructions.
4. Hybridization, washing, and detection are performed using DIG Easy Hyb (hybridization solution) and DIG Wash and Block Buffer Set following the supplier's instructions.

5. Hybridization signals are detected with a cooled charge-coupled device (CCD) system.
6. Most marker-free transgenic plants have only a low copy number of transgenes (one or two genes).

Single-Step Transformation Procedures (ipt-Type)

Agrobacterium Suspension Culture

1. The pMAT130HmGUS vector plasmid is introduced into the disarmed *A. tumefaciens* strain ERA 105 by electroporation.
2. Transformants are selected on YEB agar medium containing 50 mg/L of hygromycin and 50 mg/L of kanamycin.
3. A fresh colony is inoculated onto YEB agar medium containing 50 mg/L of hygromycin and 100 mg/L of kanamycin and cultured over two nights at 27°C.
4. Transformants are cultured on YEB liquid medium overnight at 27°C.
5. The collected bacteria are suspended with N6 liquid medium containing 10 mg/L of acetosyringone.

Explant Preparation

1. Mature rice seeds are sterilized in 75% (v/v) sodium hypochlorite solution for 30 min and washed thoroughly in sterilized water.
2. The sterilized seeds are germinated on N6CL2 medium for 5 d at 30°C under continuous light.

Infection

1. The germinated seeds are immersed in diluted bacterial suspension (OD_{630}= 0.15) for 1.5 min and blotted dry with sterilized filter paper to remove liquid excess.
2. The germinated seeds are cocultured with *Agrobacterium* for 3 d at 28°C on Co-N6CL2 medium.
3. After cocultivation, the germinated seeds are washed with sterilized water containing 500 mg/L of carbenicillin and blotted dry with sterilized filter paper to remove liquid excess.
4. The seedlings are transferred to N6CL2 medium containing 2 mg/L of 2,4-D, 25 mg/L of hygromycin, and 500 mg/L of carbenicillin.
5. After 1 wk of cultivation, the scutellum tissues are aseptically excised from germinated seeds. The excised scutellum tissues are cultured on N6CL2 medium containing 4 mg/L of 2,4-D, 25 mg/L of hygromycin, and 500 mg/L of carbenicillin for a week.
6. After 1 wk, scutellum tissues are transferred to MSR medium containing 500 mg/L of carbenicillin.

Selection of Transgenic Shoots

1. After 1 wk of cultivation, the proliferated calluses are separated from scutellum tissues and transferred to MSR medium containing 500 mg/L of carbenicillin.

2. After 1 wk, regenerated shoots from these calluses are transferred to the same medium.
3. Genomic DNA is extracted from leaves of regenerated shoots using a DNAeasy Plant System, and used for PCR analysis.
4. PCR is performed under standard conditions with 1 min of denaturation, 1 min of annealing, and 2 min of extension at 94°C, 60°C, and 72°C, respectively, for 30 cycles.
5. Reaction products are resolved by electrophoresis in a 1.8% (w/v) agarose gel.
6. About 5% of the regenerated shoots are marker-free transgenic plants and 40% are transgenic plants with marker genes (ipt).

Induction of Marker-Free Transgenic Plants

1. Marker-free transgenic lines and transgenic lines with marker genes are divided into sublines with a single shoot and subcultured for 1 wk on MS medium containing 500 mg/L of carbenicillin.
2. After rooting, genomic DNA is extracted from leaves of each separated shoot using a DNAeasy Plant System, and used for PCR analysis.
3. From transgenic lines with marker genes, about 2-3% of the sublines are marker free transgenic plants.
4. After 5-6 wk, these transgenic plants are transferred to a greenhouse at 25°C under an 11-h/13-h light/dark cycle.
5. After about 3 mo, seeds are obtained from both marker-free transgenic plants and transgenic plants with marker genes.
6. Seeds are germinated in water. DNA is isolated from seedlings and used for PCR analysis.
7. Marker-free transgenic plants are segregated from transgenic plants with marker genes in their progeny by crossing.

Two-Step Transformation Procedures (rol -Type)

Agrobacterium Suspension Culture

1. The pEXM120 vector plasmid is introduced into the disarmed *A. tumefaciens* strain EHA105 by electroporation.
2. Transformation procedures (*Agrobacterium* suspension culture, explant preparation, and infection) are the same as those described for the *ipt* type MAT vector, except that culture is done under continuous dark.

Selection of Transgenic Roots

1. Inoculated leaf segments are transferred to hormone-free MS agar medium containing 500 mg/L of carbenicillin every 2 wk under continuous dark.
2. One month after *Agrobacterium* infection, the regenerated roots are separated from the leaf segments and transferred to the same medium containing 1 mg/L of BA and 0.1 mg/L of NAA under continuous light.

Selection of Marker-Free Transgenic Shoots

1. After 2 mo, the regenerated buds are separated from roots and transferred to hormone-free MS medium *containing* 500 mg/L of carbenicillin.
2. After 1 mo of cultivation, the developed shoots are classified into two groups according to phenotype: (a) normal shoots and (b) abnormal shoots, and *maintained* in a flask on hormone-free MS agar medium *containing* 500 mg/L of carbenicillin.
3. Genomic DNA is extracted from leaves of both the normal and abnormal shoots using a FastDNA™ Kit, and used for PCR analysis.
4. PCR is *performed* under standard conditions with 30 s of *denaturation*, 1 min of annealing, and 1.5 min of extension at 94°C, 60°C, and 72°C, respectively, for 30 cycles.
5. Reaction products are resolved by electrophoresis in a 1.8% (w/v) agarose gel.
6. About 20-30% of normal shoots are marker-free transgenic plants and 10-20% are chimeric transgenic plants.
7. These *transgenic* plants are transferred to a greenhouse. After about 2 mo, seeds are obtained from both marker-free transgenic plants and *chimeric* transgenic plants.
8. Seeds are germinated in pots and DNA is isolated from seedlings for PCR analysis. 9. Chimeric transgenic plants are segregated into marker-free *transgenic* plants in their *progeny* by crossing.

Notes

1. The *ipt* gene that codes for isopentenyl transferase is used to induce shoot *formation*. Since the control of both *cytokinin* and auxin is needed to optimize the hormone levels in plant tissue and to *regenerate* transgenic shoots in many plant species, we also constructed MAT vector plasmids that combine *ipt* genes with the *iaaMIH* genes to *manipulate* both the auxin and cytokinin levels. The *iaaMIH* genes code for a tryptophan *monooxygenase* and an *indoleacetamide* hydrolase, which *catalyze* auxin synthesis.
2. The *rol* genes responsible for the proliferation of hairy roots are used to induce root formation. We also constructed MAT vector *plasmids* that combine the *rol* genes with the *iaaH* gene to manipulate the auxin level, as the auxin level in plant tissue must be increased to *regenerate* transgenic roots in many plant species.
3. We constructed MAT vector plasmids that combine the *rol* genes with the *ipt* gene to induce shoot formation from *transgenic* roots. The *rbcS* promoter is used to control the expression of the *ipt* gene. First, the *rol* genes induce transgenic roots under *continuous* dark, and then the *ipt* gene regenerates *transgenic* shoots under continuous light. Transgenic shoots with the *ipt* gene exhibit the ipt-shooty phenotype and marker-free *transgenic* plants are developed from these ipt-shooty lines.
4. PCR is performed using by PLATINUM™ *Taq* polymerase (Life Technologies) or KOD-Plus (Toyobo) according to the *manufacturer's* protocol. The pUC19 plasmid *containing* the gene of interest at LacZ' *multicloning* sites is used as a template. A forward primer (attB-P8) and a reverse primer (attB-P7) are used to amplify the gene of interest with terminal

attB1 and *attB2* sequences by PCR.

The primer sequences are as follows:

attB-P8: 5'-ggggacaagtttgtacaaaaaagcaggctgagcggataacaatttcacacagg-3';

attB-P7: 5'-ggggaccactttgtacaagaaagctgggtcgacgttgtaaaacgacggccagt-3'.

5. The recombinase BP clonase is used to replace the *ccdB* gene of pTSattp plasmid with the gene of interest according to the protocol of the Gateway Cloning System (Life Technologies).
6. The reaction mixture is transformed into an E. *coli* DH5a strain (Takara Shuzo). Because the *ccdB* gene of pTSattp plasmid is lethal to this strain, only recombinants with replaced pTSattp plasmids can survive.
7. The GST-II promoter is less active in A. *tumefaciens* than the 35S promoter. However, the preparation of fresh bacterial culture is highly recommended to protect MAT cassettes from removal events in A. *tumefaciens.*
8. In the case of using *ipt-type* MAT vectors containing *iaaMIH* genes, explants are also placed on hormone-free MS agar medium. The *ipt-type* MAT vectors carrying only the *iaaH* gene are used with culture medium containing 0.04-0.2 mg/ mL of NAM, as the *iaaH* gene codes for an indoleacetamide hydrolase, which can convert NAM into NAA.
9. Nontransgenic buds regenerate together with transgenic buds, as the overproduction of cytokinin by the *ipt* gene causes it to leak out from transgenic cells. We fused the *ipt* gene with several different promoters to optimize the cytokinin levels for the proliferation and differentiation of transgenic cells. The *ipt* gene with the *rbcS* promoter is especially useful for increasing the percentage of transgenic shoots in hybrid aspen.
10. These abnormal shoots exhibit the ipt-shooty phenotype and lose apical dominance and rooting ability because of the overproduction of cytokinins.
11. Two pairs of PCR primers are designed to verify the presence of the *ipt* and *GUS* genes, and removal of the R/RS cassette.

    The primer sequences in Figure elsewhere in this chapter are as follows:

    IPT 1: 5'-cttgcacaggaaagacgtcg-3';

    IPT2: 5'-aatgaagacaggtgtgacgc-3';

    GUS 1: 5'-gtggaattgatcagcgttgg-3';

    GUS2: 5'-gcaccgaagttcatgccagt-3';

    Exb: 5'-agcctgaatggcgaatgcct-3';

    Exc: 5'-cgattaagtgggtaacgcc-3'.
12. In marker-free transgenic plants, the predicted 0.5-kb excision fragment and 1.7-kb GUS fragment are amplified by the primers Exb-Exc and GUS 1-GUS2, respectively, and the predicted 0.8-kb ipt fragment is not amplified by IPT1-IPT2.
13. Owing to expression of the R gene in the callus, removal events occur early during

regeneration and marker-free plants appear. Analysis of normal plants is highly recommended to obtain marker-free plants.

14. These ipt-shooty lines are chimeric transgenic plants that contain transgenic cells in which excision events do and do not occur. The predicted 0.5-kb excision fragment, 1.7-kb *GUS* fragment and 0.8kb ipt fragment are amplified by the primers Exb-Exc, GUS 1-GUS2, and IPT1-IPT2, respectively.
15. The primer sequences are as follows:

    GUS 1: 5'-gtggaattgatcagcgttgg-3';

    GUS2: 5'-gcaccgaagttcatgccagt-3'.
16. If more than one expressed copy of the *ipt* gene is inserted into the plant genome of the transgenic shoots, the *elimination* of one copy would not cause a loss of *ipt* function (ipt-shooty). This inference leads to the expectation that marker-free transgenic plants will be derived from low-copy-number transgenic plants.
17. The preculture period and hormone content of the *preculture medium* greatly affect the *generation* efficiency of marker-free transgenic rice plants. These conditions should be *independently* evaluated for each rice species.
18. Two pairs of PCR primers are designed to verify the presence of the *ipt* and *GUS* genes, and removal of the R/RS cassette.

    The primer sequences in Figure elsewhere in this chapter are as follows:

    IPT 1: 5'-cttgcacaggaaagacgtcg-3';

    IPT2: 5'-aatgaagacaggtgtgacgc-3';

    GUS 1: 5'-gtggaattgatcagcgttgg-3';

    GUS2: 5'-gcaccgaagttcatgccagt-3';

    PTEX 1: 5'-cgtgccagctgcattaatgg-3';

    PRZEX12: 5'-ggagcccccgatttagagcttgac-3'.
19. In marker-free transgenic plants, the predicted 0.8-kb excision fragment and 1.7kb *GUS* fragment are amplified by the primers PTEX1-PRZEX12 and GUS1-

GUS2, respectively, whereas the predicted 0.8-kb *ipt* fragment is not amplified by IPT 1-IPT2.

20. Nontransgenic plants regenerate together with transgenic plants. About 40-50% of regenerated shoots (100-200 lines) from 1500 germinated seeds are transgenic plants.
21. These lines with marker genes are chimeric transgenic plants that contain transgenic cells in which excision events do and do not occur. The predicted 0.8-kb excision fragment, 1.7-kb *GUS* fragment and 0.8-kb *ipt* fragment are amplified by the primers PTEX1-PRZEX12, GUS1-GUS2, and IPT1-IPT2, respectively.
22. Transgenic shoots with marker genes *(ipt)* can root and produce seeds.
23. The *ipt* genes are removed from about half of chimeric transgenic plants by crossing.
24. Transgenic roots exhibit the hairy root phenotype that can grow rapidly and be maintained

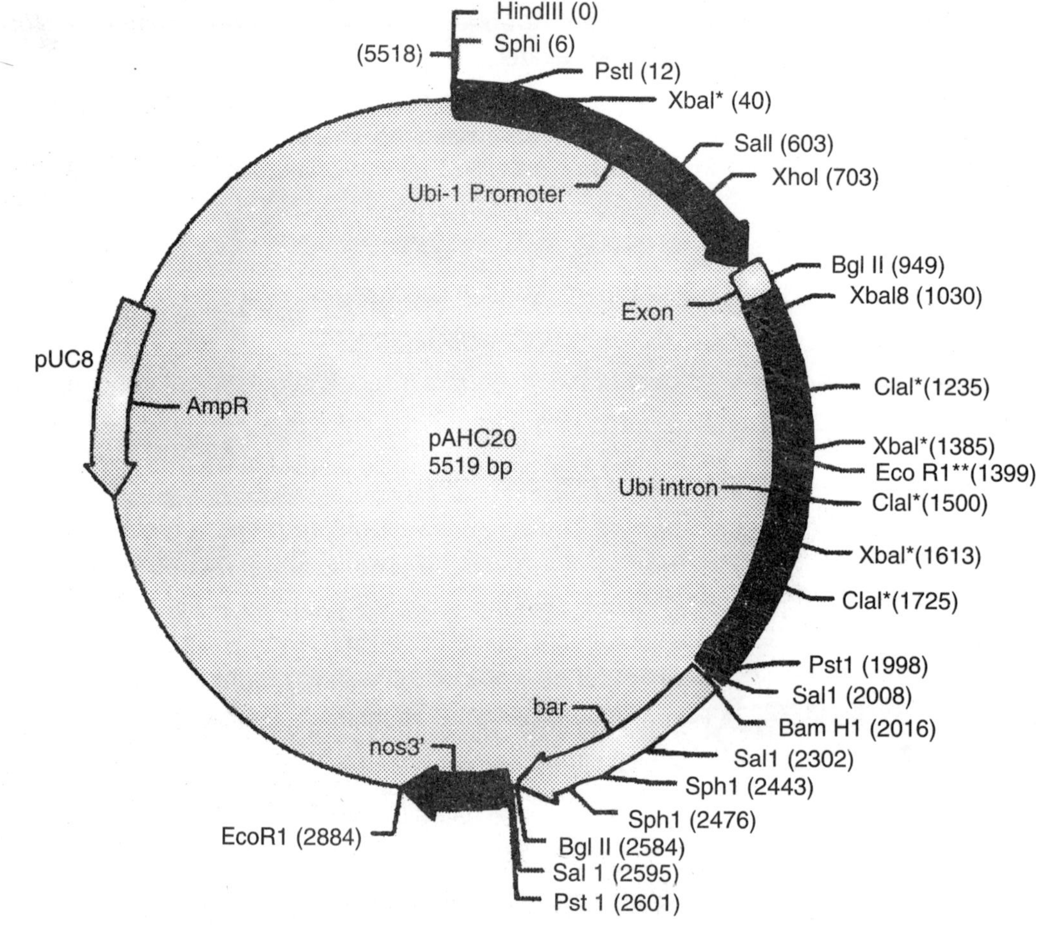

Figure 17.2: Schematic diagram of pAHC20.

in long-term cultures. About 70% of the regenerated roots are transgenic roots.

25. The addition of 0.1 mg/L of IBA to MS agar medium increases the number of transgenic roots. Instead of IBA, 0.1 mg/L of, NAM is used for rol-type MAT vectors combined with the *iaaH* gene.

26. These abnormal shoots exhibit wrinkled leaves and shortened internodes due to the expression of the *rol* genes. About 30% of the regenerated shoots in a flask exhibit a normal phenotype.

27. Two pairs of PCR primers are designed to verify the presence of the *rolc* and *GUS* genes, and removal of the R/RS cassette.

    The primer sequences in Figure are as follows:

    rolC-P1 :5'-ggtcacgaggtcatagtagtgg-3 ;

    rolC-P2:5'-gttagcaaagtaggaaataata-3 ;

    GUS 1: 5'-gtggaattgatcagcgttgg-3';

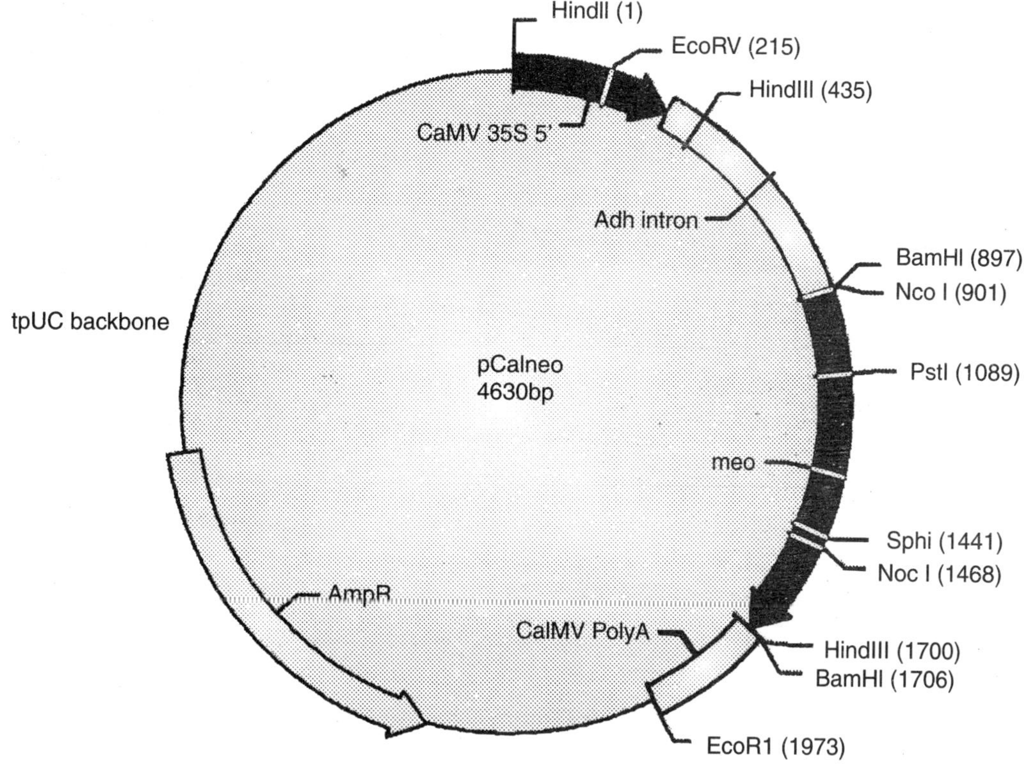

Figure 17.3: Schematic diagram of pCalneo.

GUS2: 5'-gcaccgaagttcatgccagt-3';

EX1 : 5'-ttgtcaagaccgacctgtcc-3';

EX2: 5'-tgcatcggcgaactgatcgt-3'.

28. In marker-free transgenic plants, the predicted 3.0-kb excision fragment and 1.7-kb *GUS* fragment are amplified by the primers EX1-EX2 and GUS1GUS2, respectively, whereas the predicted 1.0-kb *rolc* fragment is not amplified by *rolC-P1-rolC-P2*. The chimeric transgenic plants contain transgenic cells in which excision events do and do not occur. The predicted 3.0-kb excision fragment, 1.7-kb *GUS* fragment and 1.0-kb *rolc* fragment are amplified by the primers EX1-EX2, GUS1-GUS2, and *rolC-P1-rolC-P2*, respectively.
29. Self-crossing is difficult for several chimeric transgenic plants and outcrossing with nontransgenic plants is necessary to produce seeds.

SELECTABLE MARKERS

In the generation of *transgenic* plants, selection systems permit the *preferential* growth of transformed cells; *selectable* marker genes based on negative selection are *commonly* delivered alongside genes of interest. These marker genes encode proteins that confer *resistance* to a selection agent that inhibits growth or kills *nontransgenic* cells.

Genes encoding resistance to specific antibiotics or herbicides have proved *particularly* effective for selection and provide a means of rapidly identifying transformed cells, tissues, and *regenerated* shoots that have integrated foreign DNA and that express the selectable gene product and, by inference, the gene(s) of interest. For example, the *aminoglyco-side* antibiotics, such as *kanamycin*, neomycin, and G418 kill cells by inhibiting protein translation.

The *Eschericia coli nptII* gene, encoding neomycin phosphotransferase, inactivates these antibiotics by phosphorylation, thus allowing preferential growth of plant cells transformed with this gene on media containing these selection agents.

The herbicide phosphinothricin (PPT) is an analog of glutamine and acts by irreversibly inhibiting glutamine synthetase, a key enzyme for ammonium *assimilation* and the regulation of nitrogen assimilation in plants.

The *bar* gene, cloned from the bacterium *Streptomyces hygroscopicus*, encodes *phosphinothricin* acetyltransferase (PAT), which converts PPT into the nontoxic acetylated form and allows growth of transformed plant cells in the presence of PPT, or commercial *glufosinate* ammonium-based herbicides.

Although recent concerns relating to potential spread of selectable marker genes from genetically modified organisms released to the environment are driving *techniques* that avoid the use of such genes or remove them, these selection regimes remain an important tool for laboratory-based *transformation* research.

This chapter uses the *transformation* of bread wheat *(Triticum aestivum L.)* and pasta wheat *(T. turgidum ssp.* durum Desf.) with the *nptII (neo)* and *bar* genes to illustrate the application of antibiotic and herbicide selection systems, aspects of which have been reviewed in several publications.

MATERIALS

1. Plasmid constructs (pAHC20, pCalNeo).
2. Donor plants of *T. aestivum*.
3. Petri dishes (9 cm in diameter, triple-vented).
4. Biolistic transformation equipment.
5. Induction medium: Murashige and Skoog (MS) basal salts (12), 0.5 mg/L of nicotinic acid, 0.1 mg/L of thiamine-HCl, 0.5 mg/L of pyridoxine-HCl, 100 mg/L of myo-inositol, 375 mg/L of L-glutamine, 75 mg/L of L-proline, 50 mg/L of L-asparagine, 90 g/L of sucrose, 0.5 mg/L of 2,4-dichlorophenoxyacetic acid (2,4-D), and 10 mg/L of $AgNO_3$.
6. Regeneration medium: MS basal salts (12), 200 mg/L of thiamine-HCl, 1 mg/L of pyridoxine-HCl, 1 mg/L of nicotinic acid, I mg/1L of Ca-pantothenate, 1 mg/L of L-ascorbic acid and 30 g/L of maltose.
7. Agargel (Sigma Aldrich, Poole, UK).
8. 2,4-D.
9. $AgNO_3$.

10. Zeatin.
11. Glufosinate ammonium.
12. G418.
13. DNA extraction reagents and equipment.
14. Polymerase chain reaction (PCR) and electrophoresis solutions and equipment.
15. 25-Multiwell plat
16. 1.5-mL plastic cuvets.
17. Ammonium assay incubation medium: 50 mM potassium phosphate buffer, pH 5.8, 2% sucrose, 1.0 mg/L of 2,4-D, 25 mg/L of gluphosinate ammonium, and 0.1% Tween-20.
18. Ammonium assay reagent 1: 34 g/L of sodium salicylate, 25 g/L of trisodium cit rate, 25 g/L of sodium tartrate, and 0.12 g/L of sodium nitroprusside.
19. Ammonium assay reagent 2: 30 g/L of sodium hydroxide and 0.52 g/L of sodium dichloroisocyanurate.
20. Ammonium chloride.
21. Glutosinate ammonium-based herbicide.

METHODS

The methods described in the following subheadings are applicable to both spring- and winter-sown commercial UK bread wheat *(T. aestivum)* varieties (e.g., Canon, Cadenza, Imp, and Buster). Variations in the protocol for tetraploid wheat *(T. turgidum ssp.* durum) varieties (e.g., Ofanto and Venusia) are included in the Notes *subheading* The wheat tissue culture and transformation procedures are based on the method described by Barcelo and Lazzeri (1995) as modified subsequently by Rasco-Gaunt et al. (1999), Pastori et al. (2001), and Rasco-Gaunt et al. (2001).

This method allows the production of apparently *phenotypically* normal *transgenic* wheat plants in 15–18 wk, from the isolation of scutella through all tissue culture stages until plants are ready to be transferred to compost and evaluated for the presence of the *transgene*(s). *Immature* scutella are isolated and *cotransformed* with the marker gene and gene of interest using biolistics.

Two extra Petri dishes, each containing 10 explants, are prepared per experiment, one for *nonbombarded* controls and the other for scutella bombarded only with gold. After *bombardment,* explants are spread to 10/plate and callus induction from bombarded and nonbombarded explants is carried out on induction medium for 4–5 wk in the dark.

Plasmid Constructs

Typical *configurations* for the *bar* and nptII gene expression cassettes for wheat transformation are shown in Figures elsewhere in this chapter.

Herbicide Resistance

The construct pAHC20 contains the *bar* gene (se selectable marker under the control of the maize ubiquitin I promoter. The *bar* gene encodes the enzyme PAT which confers *resistance* to

PPT and glufosinate ammonium herbicides.

Antibiotic Resistance

The construct pCalNeo encodes neomycin *phosphotransferase* and confers *resistance* to *aminoglycoside* antibiotics such as kanamycin.

Regeneration and Selection

The regeneration of shoots from *embryogenic* calli is performed at 26°C under a 12-h photoperiod with 10 calli/Petri dish. The regeneration response is evaluated in each culture cycle by scoring *regenerants* with only shoots, only roots, or shoots and roots. When choosing a selection agent, it is important to test for natural resistance of the target plant material by first *performing* a kill curve *experiment* and establishing the optimum concentration.

Selection Using bar

1. Culture calli in Petri dishes of *regeneration* medium supplemented with 0.1 mg/L of 2,4-D, 10 mg/L of $AgNO_3$ and 5 mg/L of zeatin for 4 wk.
2. Evaluate the regeneration response.
3. Transfer *regenerating* calli to *regeneration* medium *supplemented* with 4 mg/L of the selection agent glufosinate ammonium and culture for 4 wk. Half of the tissues from each control plate should be cultured on *regeneration* medium with selection and the other half without selection to provide selected and *nonselected* controls controls.
4. Evaluate the *regeneration* and selection responses.
5. To ensure a low percentage of escapes, transfer only the healthy *regenerating* calli to regeneration medium in Magenta™ M vessels (Sigma Aldrich) supplemented with 4 mg/L of *glufosinate* ammonium and culture for a further 4 wk.
6. Repeat **steps** 4 and 5 until the plants are of sufficient size to transfer to compost.
7. Transfer putative transgenic plants to compost and grow to maturity in a glasshouse.

Selection Using nptII

1. Culture calli in Petri dishes of *regeneration* medium supplemented with 0.1 mg/L of 2,4-D, 10 mg/L of $AgNO_3$, and 5 mg/L of zeatin for 4 wk.
2. Evaluate the regeneration response.
3. Transfer regenerating calli to *regeneration* medium supplemented with 50 mg/L of G418 and culture for 4 wk. One control plate should be cultured on regeneration medium with selection and the other without se selected and *nonselected* controls.
4. Evaluate the regeneration and selection responses.
5. To ensure a low percentage of escapes, transfer only the healthy regenerating calli to *regeneration* medium in Magenta™ M vessels supplemented with 50 mg/L of G418 and culture for a further 4 wk.
6. Repeat steps 4 and 5 until the plants are of sufficient size to transfer to compost.
7. Transfer putative transgenic plants to compost and grow to maturity in a glass house.

Confirmation of Transformation by PCR

When plants are large enough for leaf material to be collected, DNA may extracted for PCR using the *hexadecyltrimethylammonium* bromide (CTAB) method, or by using a *commercial extraction* kit. Both the *bar* and the *nptll* genes can be detected by PCR using the primers and conditions detailed below.

bar

Forward primer: 5' GTCTGCACCATCGTCAACC 3'

Reverse primer: 5' GAAGTCCAGCTGCCAGAAAC 3'

Annealing temperature: 57°C Number of cycles: 30

Product size: 444 by

nptll

Forward primer: 5' GAGGCTATTCGGCTATGACTG 3'

Reverse primer: 5' ATCGGGAGCGGCGATACCGTA 3'

Annealing temperature: 57°C Number of cycles: 30

Product size: 679 by

Marker Gene Expression Assays

The next step, after confirming the presence of the marker gene by PCR in DNA from selected antibiotic- or herbicide-resistant plants, is to analyze its *expression*. Resistance to antibiotics and herbicides can be evaluated in established primary transgenic plants (T_0 generation) and their progeny (T_1 and subsequent generations). Two methods commonly used for testing resistance to PPT are described in the following *subheadings*. In addition, enzyme-linked *immunosorbent* assay (ELISA) based kits for *assessing* expression of the *nptll* gene are commercially available.

Ammonium Assay

Stable expression of the *bar* gene can be analyzed by the ammonium assay, which allows

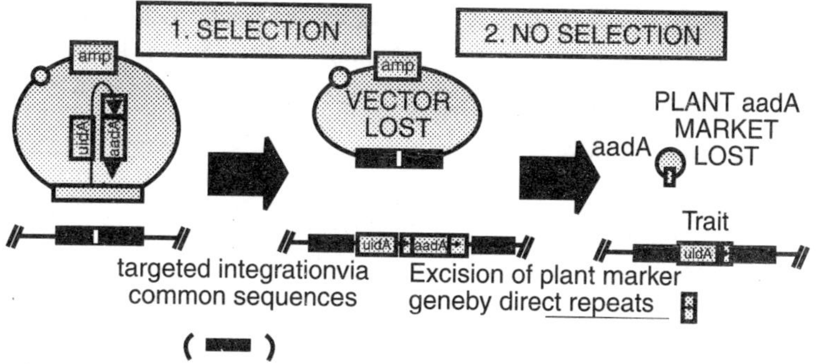

Figure 17.4: Scheme showing targeted integration and excision of marker genes by homologous recombination. Vector sequences are excluded at integration. Integration of foreign genes is driven by selection for the plant marker gene. Once selection is removed the plant marker gene is excised by homologous recombination between flanking direct repeats.

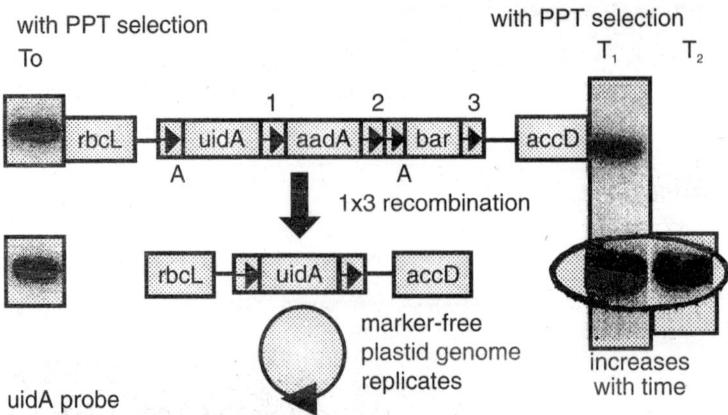

Figure 17.5: DNA blot analysis showing loss of marker genes once PPT selection is removed. The construct contains three 418-bp direct repeats (labe two 174-bp repeats (labeled 1, 2, and 3) and two 174-bp repeats (labeled A). Recombination between 418-bp repeats 1 and 3 excises the aadA *and* bar *gene resulting in a smaller band size. Note that excision takes place even in the presence of PPT. Excision is a unidirectional process, ensuring the rapid isolation of marker-free plants.*

the qualitative and quantitative detection of PAT activity in leaf tissue.

Qualitative Assay

1. Place 4 × 8 mm leaf pieces in 25-multiwell plates containing 1 medium per well, leaving one or two wells without tissue as.
2. Incubate for 5 h at 24°C under a photosynthetic photon flux density of 250 tmol/ m^2/s.
3. For each sample, take 200 μL of the incubation medium and add to 1 mL of reagent 1.
4. Add 1 mL of reagent 2 and mix by vortexing.
5. Incubate for 15 min at 37°C, followed by 15 min at room temperature.

The incubation medium with plant samples not expressing the *bar* gene and the negative controls will develop an emerald green to dark-blue color because of the presence of *ammonium* ions. The medium of explants from transgenic plants expressing the *bar* gene will develop a light green or yellow color that occurs in the absence of *ammonium* ions.

Quantitative Assay

1. Proceed as for the qualitative assay.
2. Prepare a standard curve with increasing *concentrations* of ammonium chloride by adding 200 μL of standard solutions of ammonium (0–10 mg/L) to 1 mL of reagent 1 and 1 mL of reagent 2.
3. Measure the absorbance of each solution at 655 nm.
4. Calculate the concentration of ammonium in each sample using the standard curve.

Leaf Painting Bioassay

Qualitative expression of the *bar* gene can also be scored using a herbicide leaf painting bioassay. This approach is simple and *inexpensive* and can be carried out on plants *in situ*. Application of herbicides based on glufosinate *ammonium*, such as Basta™, cause *desiccation* and *browning* in control plants, whereas plants expressing the *bar* gene are resistant and remain green.

1. Prepare dilutions of glufosinate *ammonium-based* herbicide using 0.1% Tween to give final concentrations of PPT of 0.2 g/L and 2 g/L.
2. Select healthy wheat plants at the tillering phase of growth. For each plant to be tested, select three *approximately* equal sized, healthy leaves, avoiding the flag leaf. Water the plants before herbicide application.
3. Label the chosen leaves on the stem *immediately* below the leaf to be painted (Tween only, 0.2 g/L of PPT or 2 g/L of PPT).
4. Mark each leaf with a ballpoint pen halfway along its length and paint the upper surface of the distal half of the leaf with the *appropriate* solution using a cotton bud. The application should be quite firm to ensure coating and some penetration of the solution into the leaf. All the control leaves should be painted first, followed by the lower *concentration*, then the higher concentration of herbicide to minimize carryover of the herbicide to other leaves.
5. The herbicide resistance of each plant is assessed 7 d after application by scoring each treated leaf according to the *percentage* desiccation/browning over the painted area and the percentage of the proximal region of the leaf that has been affected by the spread of the herbicide.

NOTES

1. Glufosinate *ammonium* is *synthetically* produced PPT bound is the active *component* in herbicides such as Basta™ M (Bayer Cropscience AG, Monheim am Rhein, Germany). Glufosinate ammonium can be dissolved in distilled water (10 mg/mL), filter sterilized, and stored in aliquots at -20°C.
2. Donor material is grown under controlled conditions. The age and condition of donor material for *transformation* is crucial; full details can be found in Pastori et al. (2001).
3. Induction medium should be made up at a 2X *concentration*, filter sterilized, and stored at 4°C. Induction medium for *T. turgidum ssp. durum is* the same as that for *T. aestivum* except with 30 g/L of sucrose (instead of 90 g/L) and 1.0 mg/L of picloram instead of 0.5 mg/L of 2,4-D.
4. The *regeneration* medium should be made up at a 2X *concentration*, filter sterilized and stored at 4°C. The *regeneration* medium for *T. turgidum ssp.* durum is the same as that for *T. aestivum.*
5. Agargel™ M is made up at a 2X concentration of 10 g/L and autoclaved before use.
6. A working solution of 2,4-D (1.0 mg/mL) can be prepared by dissolving 100 mg in 70 mL of ethanol, adding 30 mL of distilled water, *vortexizing*, and storing 1 mL aliquots at –20°C.

7. $AgNO_3$ can be dissolved in distilled water (20 mg/mL), filter sterilized, and stored in aliquots at –20°C.
8. A working solution (10 mg/mL) of zeatin can be prepared by dissolving 100 mg in 1 mL of 1 M HCl, adding 9 mL of distilled water, vortexing to mix, filter sterilizing, and storing in 1-mL aliquots at –20°C.
9. G418 can be dissolved in sterile distilled water (50 mg/mL) and stored in aliquots at –20°C.
10. Reagent 1 can be stored at 4°C in the dark.
11. Reagent 2 can be stored at 4°C for 2 mo.
12. Several *glufosinate ammonium* based herbicides are *commercially* available, any of which are suitable.
13. Bombarded and nonbombarded controls are included to determine whether the process of *bombardment* has a detrimental effect on callus induction and *regeneration.*
14. The methods described are for use with the specific constructs shown. *Protocolsusing* the nptII or *bar* genes with different promoter/intron/terminator *configurations*, or different marker genes, may require *optimization* for specific species/varieties.
15. The *bar* gene from S. *hygroscopicus* and the *pat* gene from *S. viridiochromogenes* both code for PAT; either of these genes can be used as selectable markers.
16. Agargel is melted in a microwave oven and added to an equal volume of medium. The *supplementary components* are added before the mixture is poured into Petri dishes. The tissue culture response is *improved* if the medium in the dishes is *relatively* deep (approx 30 mL/dish).
17. If the *regeneration* response is poor, repeat one round of *regeneration* (up to 4 wk) on Petri dishes of fresh medium without the *selection* agent.
18. The selected control is used to confirm that selection is effective (i.e., the *controls* should all die in the presence of the selection agent); the *nonselected* control is used to *monitor* the response of the *donor* material (i.e., the *nonselected controls* should survive).
19. Nontransgenic *material* should show typical symptoms of selection pressure, *including* slow growth, yellow-brown shoots, and poor root development.
20. Prepare the medium for Magenta™ M vessels in the same way as for Petri dishes with 50 mL of medium per Magenta™ M vessel. Magenta™ vessels should each contain a *maximum* of five plants.
21. Escapes are defined as plants that survive exposure to the selection agent, but which lack the transgene. The *percentage* of escapes depen pressure. If the *percentage* of escapes is high, greater selection pressure can be applied by increasing the *concentration* of the selection age selection pressure is *increased* too much, *transgenic* plants may also be lost. This may not be a problem if transformation frequency is high. However, if the *transformation frequency* is low, it is preferable to accept a higher *percentage* of escapes to avoid loss of transgenic plants.

22. Usually three rounds of selection are adequate.
23. Plants that survive the selection pressure with a good root system are *considered* putative *transgenic* individuals.
24. The nptII gene confers resistance to several *aminoglycoside antibiotics* including *neomycin,* kanamycin, G418, and *paromomycin.* In the majority of plant species, kanamycin is used as the selection agent, but it is not effective for use with wheat (and other cereals) as *nontransformed* cells exhibit some natural resistance. Kanamycin can also inhibit shoot regeneration, although G418 and *paramomycin* have been used *successfully.*
25. To extract DNA for PCR, kits such as Wizard™ M Genomic DNA Purification Kit (Promega, Madison, WI) or Extract'n'Amp (Sigma Aldrich) may be used. If the DNA is also to be used for Southern blot analysis, it is preferable to use the CTAB method.
26. Young, green leaves are preferable for this assay. Set incubations up in a laminar flow hood to avoid contamination. Ensure leaf *pieces* are fully *immersed* in the *incubation* medium; this can be achieved by briefly shaking the plates by hand.
27. Tissue culture rooms are often adequate for this purpose.
28. The various *commercially* available *glufosinate-ammonium* herbicide *formulations* contain different *concentrations* of the active ingredient PPT. Therefore, the volume of herbicide must be adjusted *accordingly* to give 0.2 g/L and 2 g/L concentrations of the PPT.

SIMPLE AND EFFICIENT REMOVAL OF MARKER GENES

Marker genes facilitate the identification of transformed cells and are important components of most plant transformation methods. Once transformed plants have been isolated, marker genes serve no useful purpose in a transgenic crop.

Only foreign trait genes add value to a crop, and all excess foreign DNA associated with the *transformation* process, such as marker genes and bacterial vector sequences, are *increasingly* viewed as undesirable. Removing excess DNA sim-plifies regulatory approval of a transgenic crop by limiting risk evaluation to the trait genes.

Selectable marker genes based on antibiotic resistance, which might impact on human health and the environment, are particularly controversial and European Union (EU) directive 2001/18/ EC requires their elimination from genetically *manipulated* organisms for *commercial* releases by 2004 and by 2008 for research purposes.

Increasing the precision of *transformation technologies* to exclude all excess DNA will play an important role in enhancing the value of the next generation of transgenic crops.

Exploitation of native *homologous recombination* pathways acting on DNA provides an attractive solution for increasing the precision of trait gene insertion into plant DNA and excluding vector and marker genes.

The strategy uses native plant enzymes and is simple because it avoids the need for foreign site-specific DNA recombinases. The overall scheme is shown in Figure elsewhere in this chapter.

Integration is based on homology between *transforming* DNA and its target site in plant DNA, allowing precise gene targeting.

Homologous DNA flanking trait and marker genes *promotes* integration and excludes vector sequences, which lie outside regions of homology. The integrated marker gene enables selection of *transformed* cells. Once transgenic cells have been isolated the marker gene has served its purpose and will be excised by spontaneous *homologous* recombination events between direct DNA repeats flanking the marker gene.

Excision of the marker gene can take place at any time during the *transformation* process but only cells that retain the marker will proliferate in the presence of selective agent. Once selection is removed, marker gene excision will lead to the accumulation of marker-free cells and eventually marker-free transgenic plants.

High rates of homologous *recombination* are required for efficient targeting and marker excision by flanking direct repeats. The procedure is not easily applied to foreign genes *integrated* into nuclear DNA owing to high rates of illegitimate recombination in the nucleus.

Excision of marker genes from transgenic plastids presents its own challenges because plastid DNA can be present in up to 10,000 copies per cell. High rates of marker excision are needed and this can be *achieved* by increasing the number and sizes of direct repeats.

This leads to the accumulation of marker-free plastid genomes and marker free plastids. At first cells will be heteroplasmic because they contain a mixed population of two plastid types; *marker-containing* plastids and marker-free plastids.

When two plastid types are found in the same cell, repeated cell divisions give rise to two populations of cells with a uniform content of either marker-containing plastids or marker-free plastids. Segregation of different plastid types during vegetative growth is known as cytoplasmic sorting.

Marker excision by *homologous recombination* is an effective procedure in tobacco plastids. Of the methods described to excise marker genes from plastid genomes homologous *recombination* is the simplest to use.

Unlike published methods based on herbicide resistance genes, plant selectable markers, and restoration of photosynthesis, homologous recombination has allowed the isolation of *transplastomic* plants with an unselected trait gene *(uidA)* that is free of all selectable marker genes.

Conservation of plastid DNA recombination pathways resulting in homology-based excision is likely given the procedure also works in *Chlamydomonas reinhardtii.* The procedure is likely to be applicable to all crops in which plastid transformation has been established. Plastid *transformation* vectors are constructed by standard cloning techniques. The minimum requirement is two direct repeats flanking the marker gene to be excised.

Both the length and number of direct repeats influence excision *frequency.* Two direct repeats of 418 bp are not sufficient to promote high levels of excision. Increasing the number of 418-bp direct repeats to three or *increasing* the length of two direct repeats to 650 by raises excision frequencies to the levels needed to isolate marker-free plants.

A variety of direct repeats promote excision indicating some flexibility in the choices of DNA sequences used to make direct repeats. The possibility that some DNA sequences might be more *recombinogenic* than others cannot be excluded because little is known on the substrate specificity of enzymes *mediating* homologous *recombination* in plastids.

Another factor that might influence excision frequency is distance between direct repeats. We have observed recombination between direct repeats located 1 kbp, 3.6 kbp, and 5.7 kbp apart. The overall size of a foreign insert in plastid DNA, might also be a factor.

If there are selective forces against large inserts in plastid DNA this would tend to favor marker gene *excisiomarker* gene excision. Duplicating the 5' or 3' regulatory elements flanking a marker gene provides a simple method for making direct repeats.

A *particularly* effective approach is to use two selectable marker genes and multiple direct repeats, which allows stepwise selection of transformed plants on two different selective agents. This strategy enables the use of weak selectable markers such as the *bar* gene to be used in *combination* with the efficient *aadA* marker gene to select plastid *transformants*.

Transplastomic plants containing *aadA* are first selected on *spectinomycin* plus *streptomycin* and then selected on (PPT). With high rates of excision, PPT selection is needed to retain the *bar* gene. Once selection stops excision of *aadA* and *bar* results in of high levels of marker-free genomes.

The use of two series of direct repeats in a single construct allows multiple excision events from a single insertion event in plastid DNA. Excision events were observed between two 418-bp direct repeats and two 174-bp direct repeats in a construct *containing* three 418-bp direct repeats and two 174-bp direct repeats.

Recombination between the 418-bp repeats excised *aadA* and *bar* to leave *uidA* in the plastid genome, whereas recombination between the 174-bp repeats excised *uidA* and *aadA leaving bar* in the plastid genome.

MATERIALS

Culture Media Components

1. Murashige and Skoog (MS) macrosalts (10X stock): 16.5 g °KNO_3, 4.4 g of CaCl2 · $2H_2O$ (or 3.3 g of $CaCl_2$), 3.7 g of $MgSO_4.7H_2O$, 1.7 g of KH_2PO_4. Dissolve salts separate in 100 mL of distilled water, mix solutions, and make up to 1 L. Store at 4°C.
2. MS microsalts (1000X stock): 22.30 g of $MnSO_4 \cdot 4H_2O$ (or 16.90 g of $MnSO_4\ H_2O$), 8.60 g of $ZnSO_4 \cdot 7H_2O$, 6.20 g of H_3BO_3, 0.83 g of KI, 0.250 g of $Na_2MoO_4 \cdot 2H_2O$, 0.025 g of $CuSO_4 \cdot 5H_2O$, 0.025 g of $CoC1_2 \cdot 6H_20$. Dissolve in 1 L of distilled water and store at 4°C.
3. Ferrous sulfate-chelate (200X stock): 7.45 g of Na_2EDTA, 5.57 g of $FeS0_4.7H_2O$. Place in distilled water separately, then mix slowly and heat to dissolve. Make up to 1 L with H_2O.
4. Spectinomycin dichloride pentahydrate (20 mg/mL stock): Check the purity of the powder, which can be as low as 60%. Dissolve in distilled water and make up to *concentration*, taking into account the purity of the powder. Sterilize through a 0.22-µm syringe filter unit (e.g., Millex GP, Millipore) and store as 10-mL aliquots at –20°C.

5. Streptomycin sulfate (20 mg/mL stock): Dissolve in distilled water to required concentration. Sterilize through a 0.22-μm syringe filter unit (e.g., Millex GP, Millipore) and store as 10-mL aliquots at –20°C.
6. DL-PPT (10 mg/mL stock): Dissolve in distilled water to required concentration. Sterilize through a 0.22-μm syringe filter unit (e.g., Millex GP, Millipore) and store as 10-mL aliquots at –20°C.
7. 6-Benzylaminopurine (1 mg/mL stock): Dissolve 50 mg in a few drops of *1 M* NaOH and make up to 50 mL with distilled H_2O. Store for 2 wk at 4°C. For longer periods store as 1-mL aliquots at –20°C.
8. α-Naphthyleneacetic acid (0.1 mg/mL stock). Dissolve 50 mg in a few drops of *1 M* NaOH and make up to 0.5 L with H_2O. Store for 2 wk at 4°C. For longer periods store as 1-mL aliquots at –20°C.

Culture Media

1. MS plant salt mixture with supplements: Fill a 1-L glass beaker with 700 mL of distilled water. Add 100 mL of 10X macrosalts, 1 mL of 1000X microsalts, 5 mL Fe-chelate, 0.1 g of myo-inositol, 1 mL of vitamin B_1 (1 mg/mL stock), 0.5 g of 2-(N-morpholino)ethanesulfonic acid (MES), 30 g of sucrose. Add 1 *M* KOH to pH 5.8. Make up to 1 L with distilled water. For solid media add 7.5 g of agar per liter of media or 2.5 g of Phytagel (Sigma, St. Louis, MO) per liter of media. Autoclave 0.5- to 0.7-L volumes in 1 L Duran (Schott) bottles.
2. RMOP medium: Make up MS plant salt mixture with supplements as described and add 1 mL of 6-benzylaminopurine (1 mg/mL s-Naphthyleneacetic acid (0.1 mg/mL stock) before autoclaving.

DNA Delivery and Selection

1. Gold particle suspension. Suspend 60 mg of gold powder in 1 mL of 100% ethanol in a 1.5-mL microtube and vortex-mix at maximum setting for 2 min. Centrifuge the particles at maximum setting in a microfuge for 10 s and discard the supernatant. Repeat ethanol wash twice. Dislodge the gold pellet from the side of the tube with a yellow tip before vortexing. Finally, suspend the gold in 1 mL of sterile distilled water. Place aliquots of 50 μL of gold mixture in 1.5 mL microfuge tubes, vortex-mixing between aliquots to ensure an even suspension of gold particles. Store the mixture frozen at –20°C or -80°C.
2. Calcium chloride (2.5 M stock): The solution is made from $CaCl_2$ $2H_2O$ and sterilized in an autoclave. Store aliquots of 1 m–80°C.
3. Spermidine solution (0.1 M stock): Dissolve spermidine (free base) in sterile water and store in 0.5-mL aliquots in 0.5 mL microfuge tubes. Store the tubes at -80°C for a maximum of 3 mo. Thaw each tube once and do not reuse.
4. Prepare plasmid DNA (1 mg/mL) using the Qiagen Purification Maxi Prep Kit and resuspend the DNA in sterile distilled water; store frozen at -20°C.

Histochemical (β-Glucuronidase (GUS) Assay

1. Prepare 0.5 M Sodium phosphate buffer, pH 7.0, with separate 1 M stocks of Na_2HPO_4

and NaH_2PO_4. Mix 58 mL of 1 M Na_2HPO_4 and 42 mL of 1 M NaH_2PO_4 and make up to 200 mL with distilled water.

2. Make up 50 mM Potassium ferricyanide in distilled water and store as 20 mL stocks at −20°C in 30-mL sterile universal containers.
3. Make up 50 mM potassium ferrocyanide in distilled water and store as 20-mL stocks at −20°C in 30-mL universal containers.
4. Prepare X-Gluc buffer by dissolving 50 mg of X-Gluc (5-bromo-4-chloro-3-indolyl-β-D-glucuronide, cyclohexylammonium salt) in 1 mL of dimethylformamide.

   To this, add 20 mL of 0.5 M sodium phosphate, pH 7.0, 1 mL of 50 *MM* potassium ferricyanide, 1 mL of 50 mM potassium ferrocyanide, and 77 mL of distilled water. Filter-sterilize the solution using a 0.2-µm syringe filter unit and store at −20°C in 5-mL aliquots.

Plant Material and Culture Conditions

1. Sterilize tobacco seeds (see **Note** 7) by placing in 100% ethanol for 30 s. Then replace the ethanol with sodium hypochlorite (5% active chlorine) for 10 min. Then wash seeds four times with sterile distilled water.
2. Germinate sterilized seeds on solid MS salts mixture (with myo-inositol, vitamin B_1, MES, and sucrose) in 9-cm Pet or in complete darkness by covering plates in aluminum foil.
3. In 3–7 d, transfer germinated seedlings to Magenta™ M jars (Sigma) containing the same MS salt mixture with supplements and grow at 25°C in a 12-h/12-h day/night regimen at 10–50 µmol/m²/s (µE) light intensity for 6–8 wk.
4. Plants with three to five leaves are suitable for transformation. The top unex panded leaf is not used for transformation.
5. Plants can be propagated in vitro by transfer of shoot tips to fresh Magenta jars. Cut each plant stem above the roots and excise all leaves below the apical meristem. Push the base of the bare stem into MS medium in a new

Magenta jar and grow the plants at 25°C in a 12-h/12-h day/night regimen at 10–50 tE light intensity. After 4–8 wk, three to five leaves appear on the plants at which stage the leaves below the unexpanded top leaf are suitable for transformation.

METHODS

Preparation of Leaf Explants and Particle Bombardment

Excise leaves from tobacco plants grown in vitro, and remove the midrib and petiole. Cut the *remaining* leaf sections into appropriate shapes to fit into a 4-cm *diameter* circle in the center of a 9-cm plate containing RMOP medium. Place leaf explants abaxial (bottom) side up on the medium.

Place pieces from a single leaf on several plates such that each plate contains leaves from several different plants. Typically, 10–20 plates are prepared at a time. Once prepared, use the plates immediately or leave in dim light overnight at 25°C.

Particle Bombardment

DNA–Gold Precipitation

1. Allow 50-µL aliquot of gold mixture to thaw and place on a vortex mixer at *maximum* setting for 1 min.
2. Make sure the gold is evenly suspended before adding 5 µL of plasmid DNA. Add the plasmid DNA (1 mg/mL) slowly while moving the tip of the pipet in the gold mixture and finger-tapping the base of the microtube.
3. Add 50 µL of 2.5 *M* CaCl2 quickly while moving the tip through the liquid and agitating the bottom of the tube with a finger to ensure good mixing.
4. Add 20 µL of 0.1 *M spermidine* quickly as the pipet tip moves through the liquid and finger-tap the bottom of the tube simultaneously to ensure good mixing. As soon as all the spermidine is added, vortex-mix at the maximum setting for 1 min.
5. Centrifuge the DNA-coated gold particles for 5 min at maximum setting in a microfuge. Discard the supernatant and add 250 µL of 100% ethanol. Dislodge and break up the pellet with a sterile pipet tip and suspend the particles by vortex mixing briefly.
6. Centrifuge the DNA-coated gold particles for 2 min at *maximum* setting. Discard the *supernatant* and add 70 µL of 100% ethanol. The tube is kept on ice without disturbing the pellet until it is needed. Just before use, the pellet is broken up with a micropipet tip and vortex-mixed very briefly by touching a mixer (about 1 s or less).

DNA Delivery

1. Set up Bio-Rad PDS 1000/He particle delivery system by placing the microcarrier launch assembly into the top groove (shelf position 1). This produces a 1-cm gap distance between rupture disk (1100 psi) and macrocarrier holder.
2. Two spacer rings separate the *macrocarrier* holder from the stopping screen, making a macrocarrier flight distance of 1.5 cm.
3. Place a 9-cm Petri dish *containing* the leaves placed on RMOP media in a Bio Rad PDS 1000/He gun in the third groove from the top (shelf position 1). This results in a 6-cm target distance (distance from stopping screen to target plate).
4. Pipet 5 µL of the plasmid-coated gold suspension onto the center of a *macrocarrier* and allowed to dry in a laminar airflow hood.
5. Operate the device according to the *instructions* supplied with the Bio-Rad PDS 1000 He Particle Delivery system using a vacuum of 28 in. Hg. Leave the vacuum pump on for 2 min once it has reached 28 in. Hg. Then turn off vacuum pump and fire the device.
6. After the leaf explants have been bombarded, store them in dim light for 48 h at 25°C.
7. We routinely carry out ten *bombardments* per plasmid construct to ensure the isolation of 5–50 *transplastomic* plants for each plasmid.

Selection of Plastid Transformants

1. Cut microprojectile-bombarded leaves into 2- to 5-mm-long edges and place on RMOP

solid medium containing *spectinomycin* (0.5 mg/L) and streptomycin (0.5 mg/L) in a 9 cm petridish. Use new scalpel blades and change them before each set of plates. Sterilize scalpels and Waugh's forceps (15 cm, 20 cm) by rinsing in 70% (v/v) ethanol and placing in a dry bead sterilizer (STERI 350) for 30 s. Place the cut leaf sections from one bombarded plate abaxial side up on two RMOP selection plates. Change the scalpel blade after cutting leaf pieces from four bombarded plates.

2. Seal plates with two strips of Parafilm and stack in groups of up to 10 plates. Incubate them at 25°C in a 12-h day/12-h dark cycle growth cabinet.
3. Green resistant shoots or clumps of cells appear after 8 wk and continue to appear after 20 wk postbombardment on RMOP medium *containing spectinomycin* and streptomycin. When selection is based on *spectinomycin* alone, green resistant cells are visible after 4–10 wk.
4. Transfer green tissue to RMOP medium containing 5 mg/L of PPT for shoot regeneration. Any shoots appearing on spectinomyin/streptomycin plates are cut into small pieces before placing on the RMOP-PPT (5 mg/L) plates. Unselected marker genes such as *aadA* flanked by direct repeats are excis propagated serially on PPT medium to maintain the *bar* gene.
5. Place regenerated shoots on MS medium containing 1 mg/L of PPT for rooting.
6. Combined *spectinomycin* plus streptomycin selection followed by PPT selection is very effective in driving homoplasmy of plastid *transformants*. Southern blots are used to verify *homoplasmy* using a plastid DNA probe.

GUS Expression Assay

1. Cut leaves or place whole seedlings in X-Gluc buffer with 0.1% (v/v) Triton X-100.
2. Incubate at 37°C for 16–40 h or until deep blue staining is apparent in the positive control, which contans *a uidA* transgene.
3. Remove X-Gluc buffer with a Pasteur pipet and replace with 70% (v/v) ethanol. Leave overnight and replace the liquid several times with 70% ethanol until all the chlorophyll has been removed from the explants.

Isolation of Marker-Free Transplastomic Shoots and Seedlings

1. Transfer transplastomic plants with roots to soil and grow without selection. Flowers can be self-pollinated or pollinated with pollen from *untransformed* wild-type plants *following* excision of anthers.
2. For each plant, collect seeds from all the flower pods and store these separately.
3. Sterilize (100–200 seeds) from each flower pod and germinate on MS medium containing *spectinomycin*.
4. Very soon after germination, screen the plates for seedlings with all white cotyledons to identify seedlings that have lost the *aadA* gene.
5. Transfer the white seedlings to MS medium and propagate in dim light.

6. After 2–4 wk move the seedlings with green true leaves to Magenta jars (Sigma).
7. Analyze the marker-free plants by DNA blot analysis and polymerase chain reaction (PCR).
8. The instability resulting from direct repeats is specific for the marker genes and once a direct repeat is excised with the marker genes (Fig foreign genes inserted into plastids should be inherited stably. All progeny from aadA-free plants contain the foreign trait gene, either *uidA* or *bar,* but are sensitive to *spectinomycin* because of excision of aad*A.*

Notes

1. Keep all glassware used to make media separate from those use. This avoids the *inadvertent* addition of *contaminants* such as detergents into media that might be deleterious to plant growth.
2. Autoclave solutions before storing at 4°C if kept longer than 2 wk. Autoclave settings are 121°C, 15 psi for 20 min.
3. The wetting agents used on some filters can be deleterious. Passing 10 mL of sterile water through a syringe filter unit before use will reduce the amount of wetting agent in a filter-sterilized solution.
4. *Streptomycin* stocks are usually discarded after 6 mo storage at -20°C.
5. We have not observed noticeable *differences* in our experiments when agar has been substituted with Phytagel. Leaf pieces placed on solid media are rarely flat and can curl with time. Leaf pieces placed on *phytagel* media tend to stay in closer contact with the solid surface for longer periods of time. Phytagel-medium tends to be better for rooting than agar solidified media.
6. We routinely use 1-μm gold for plastid transformation of tobacco. We have also obtained tobacco plastid transformants using 0.6-μm gold particles and 650 psi rupture discs.
7. Plastid *transformation* has been demonstrated in numerous of N. tabacum cultivars *including* Petit Havana, and Wisconsin 38, and N. plumbaginifolia.
8. To avoid possible loss of regeneration efficiency and fertility resulting from prolonged growth, discard in vitro plants after 18 mo and germinate new plants from seeds.
9. We normally house all plants and explants grown in vitro in a Sanyo MLR350 *illuminated* plant growth chamber at light setting 4.
10. Leave a small circle of 0.5 cm clear of leaves at the center of the 4-cm circle. Experiments with C. reinhardtii plastid *transformation* have shown that most *transformants* are found in a ring located between 0.5 and 4 cm from the centre of the plate. It is not important to cover the entire target area with leaves. Spread the leaf pieces onto as many plates as is feasible, leaving gaps between the pieces. We have found that more *bombardments* with fewer leaf pieces per plate is a better strategy than fewer bombardments with more leaf pieces per plate. This is because of the large *variation* in numbers of plastid *transformants* obtained between different bombardments.
11. Place plates in stacks in a Sanyo MLR350 illuminated growth chamber at light setting 3 at least 12–15 cm away from the lights in a Sanyo MLR350 chamber at light setting 4.

Place Petri dishes filled with 0.8% agar in 1 mM EDTA on top of the stacks to prevent condensation appearing on the top plate containing leaf explants.

12. Leaf pieces expand on RMOP solid medium. Make sure the leaf pieces are well separated. In some cases, it might be advisable to place the cut leaf pieces from one bombarded plate onto three 9-cm plates containing RMOP with antibiotics.
13. Resistant green clones appear later and grow more slowly with double selection using *spectinomycin* and streptomycin than with selection with spectinomycin alone. Resistant shoots appear 3–10 wk *post-bombardment* with spectinomycin selection. Including *streptomycin* eliminates spontaneous spectinomycin-resistant mutants and allows *aadA transformed* clones to grow. For more rapid isolation of plastid transformants, we select first on spectinomycin (0.5 mg/L) and then select the green resistant cells on *spectinomycin* and streptomycin (0.5 mg/L).
14. In rare cases, only one or two green resistant clumps of cells are observed after 12 wk. In these cases, it is advisable to cut the leaf pieces again and transfer to fresh RMOP medium with spectinomycin (0.5 mg/L) and *streptomycin* (0.5 mg/L). If no green clones are obtained at 12 wk, it is better to repeat the transformation experiments.
15. Two out of 42 clones were PPT resistant and had lost the *aadA* marker gene as a result of *recombination* between the 174-bp repeats marked A in Figure elsewhere in this chapter. The excision frequency would be expected to be higher if the sizes of the 174-bp direct repeats were increased.
16. The use of phytagel (0.25% w/v) rather than agar facilitates rooting.
17. To confirm integration into the plastid genome and the absence of wild-type plastid DNA, digest DNA from transplastomic plants with enzymes that cut outside the plastid DNA targeting regions in the plastid *transformation* vector. It is *important* that all wild-type plastid *genomes* have been replaced by recombinant plastid genomes before selection is stopped.
18. Retention of the *bar* gene in soil grown plants can be selected by spraying with a 1:1000 dilution of a herbicide such as Challenge (Hoescht) *containing* 15% (w/v) PPT.
19. Remove anthers from a transplastomic flower before pollen is shed and pollinate the flowers using a soft *paintbrush* loaded with pollen from a wild-type flower. Then cover the flower with a small waxed paper piece and tape it shut.
20. The segregation of marker-free plastids from *aadA* containing plastids gives rise to cells *containing* only marker free plastids. The spatial *distribution* of these marker free cells within a plant vary because cytoplasmic sorting is a stochastic process. This means the percentage of marker-free plants varies from flower to flower. It is *important* not to pool seeds from different flowers of an individual plant. Only egg cells need to contain marker-free plastids because pollen does not transmit plastid DNA to the zygote in tobacco. We have obtained 25% marker-free seedlings in tobacco. In species that inherit plastids from both parents, the frequency of marker-free plants is reduced. If 25% of eggs and pollen grains are marker-free, then 6% of *seedlings* ($0.25 \times 0.25 \times 100\%$) will be marker free. Any *bottlenecks* in sexual reproduction that reduce the number of copies of plastid DNA

in egg cells will *facilitate* the isolation of marker-free plants.

21. Spectinomycin selection is not lethal and shoots will recover after they are *placed* on antibiotic-free medium. In *tobacco, spectinomycin* stops shoot growth. In other species such as *Brassica napus,* shoots bleach but continue to grow in the presence of *spectinomycin*; this can result in the irreversible loss of plastid ribosomes. In these *species, screen* aadA-free *seedlings* by PCR using *aadA* primers.

18

Chapter

CHEMISTRY OF PESTICIDES

Pesticide residues in foods have been a matter of public interest since the *publication* of Rachel Carson's *Silent Spring* in 1962. The detection of trace amounts of organic pesticides in surface and *groundwater* has been a significant *environmental* issue since the early 1980s. The *simultaneous* detection of the nematicide 1,2-dibromo-3-chloropropane (DBCP) in *groundwater* in California and the insecticide aldicarb in well-water on Long Island, New York, in 1979 triggered the controversy over the safety of the U.S. water supply.

From a national perspective, particular concern was focused on the rural drinking water supplies for which *groundwater* is the principal source. Public debate about the safety of agricultural chemicals in drinking water has also involved nitrates from *fertilizers* and other sources.

The scope of the pesticide issue in water is so large and complex that this article can only address the more important classes of organic pest control chemicals.

Soils play a *significant* role in *modifying* the amounts and kinds of pesticides *ultimately* detected in water. Intensive research on the dynamic *interactions* between pesticides, soils, and water has led to an increase in *understanding* of the physical, chemical, and *biochemical* processes that impinge on all three systems.

PESTICIDE USAGE

There is a strong relationship between the amount of pesticide applied and the amount detected in soil and water. Some *background information* on pesticide usage and terminology is useful in *understanding* their impact on the *environment*. Pesticide is a generic name for *compounds* used in pest control. The three principal groups of pesticides, and the pests they control, are insecticides for insects, herbicides (qv) for weeds, and fungicides (qv) for plant diseases.

There is also a smaller group of *conventional* pesticide chemicals, including *rodenticides*, nematicides, fumigants, *molluscicides*, and plant growth regulators. This latter group of pesticides is of relatively low volume use compared to the three principal groups, but some have been involved in important episodes of water *contamination*.

There is also a group of *nonconventional* pesticides which include *important* industrial *compounds* that have pesticidal properties. This last group includes the wood *preservatives*, *disinfectants* (*excluding chlorine*), and sulfur. Pesticides are further subdivided into classes of compounds. Historically, insecticides included the *organochlorine*, methyl carbamate, and *organophosphate* classes of pesticides.

Herbicides comprise about 10–12 principal classes of compounds. Within each class of pesticide there may be several hundred active ingredients. Agriculture is the largest user of pesticides on a weight basis (77%), but *significant* amounts are also used by the industrial, *commercial*, and *government* sectors (16%) and for home and garden use (6%).

The last two categories are *significant* because each consumed 93 and 35 million kg of pesticides, respectively, in 1995. There has been a dramatic shift in the types of pesticides used in American *agriculture* since the 1950s.

In the late 1950s and early 1960s, the organic *insecticides dominated* the market. One of the largest classes of insecticides in use at that time were the organochlorines. The *environmental* era

Table 18.1: 1995 U.S. and World User Level Pesticide Sales

	U.S. Market		*World Market*		*U.S. Share of*
Group	***Quantity***	***%***	***Quantity***	***%***	***World Market, %***
		User expenditures, 10^6\$			
Herbicides	5,927	57	13,400	47	44
Insecticides	3,091	30	8,350	29	37
Fungicides	768	7	5,600	20	14
Other	635	6	1,350	5	36
Total	10,421	100	28,700	101	36
		Volume of active ingredient, 10^6 kg			
Herbicides	301	53	1,002	47	30
Insecticides	153	27	767	36	20
Fungicides	74	13	256	12	30
Other	40	7	107	5	36
Total	568	100	2,132	100	27

that started with the *publication* of *Silent Spring* and the following regulatory *legislation* led to the ultimate demise of these hard pesticides.

Most uses of the *organochlorine* insecticides, including aldrin [30900-2] and dieldrin [60-57-1], BHC [58-89-9] (1976), chlordane [59-74-9] and heptachlor [76-44-8] (1980), DDT [50-29-3] (1982), lindane [58-89-9], strobane [8001 50-1] (1976), and toxaphene [8001-35-2] (1982), have been canceled in the United States (see CHLOROCARBONS AND CHLOROHYDROCARBONS—TOXIC AROMATICS).

These persistent, nonpolar materials are extremely lipophilic and tend to *accumulate* in the fatty tissues of many wildlife species. As of 1996, the chlorinated *hydrocarbons* are used in certain countries. Despite being banned in the 1980s, the *chlorinated hydrocarbon* insecticides were still being detected in the 1990s, albeit at low levels, in air, sediment, and water samples.

Since the mid-1970s, organic *herbicides* have been the leading class of *pesticides* used in the United States from both a sales and tonnage basis. The total pesticide usage in the United States almost doubled between 1964 and 1977 and has been quite stable since that time, at about 500,000 t of active ingredient.

Most of the increase in usage has been for *agriculture*, increasing from 145,000 t in 1964 to 439,000 t in 1995. *Approximately* 21,000 *formulated* pesticide products are *registered* by the U.S. *Environmental* Protection Agency (EPA) for *marketing* and use in the United States.

This large number of products occurs because the same active *ingredient*, for example, 2,4-*dichlorophenoxyacetic* acid (2,4-D), may be *formulated, packaged*, and sold under a number of *different* brand names.

There are about 860 active *ingredients* registered under the Federal Insecticide, Fungicide, and Rodenticide Act (FIFRA), which was first enacted in 1947. FIFRA was amended in 1964 to add a cancellation process for those pesticides deemed to pose an unacceptable risk, in 1972 to establish the modern *registration* process by the newly *established* EPA, and in 1988 for the *reregistration* process.

Total sales of pesticides in 1995 were *estimated* at $10.4 billion. The *distribution* of sales among various classes of *pesticides* is shown in Table elsewhere in this chapter. The *herbicides* continue to dominate both the amount and total cash value of *pesticides* sold in the United States.

The leading *pesticides* used (by weight) in the United States are shown in Table elsewhere in this chapter. One reason for the extensive use of *herbicides* in the 1990s was the *significant* change in farming practices. No-till or *conservation* tillage is being used on larger and larger acreages of U.S. croplands.

Instead of plowing and *harrowing* fields prior to planting, seeds are drilled directly into the soil *containing* plant residues from the previous crop. Prior to drilling the seed, all weedy vegetation is killed using a contact herbicide such as paraquat, and full-season weed control is achieved with a *soil-applied* herbicide such as atrazine.

No-till generally requires more herbicide usage than *conventional* tillage, but reduces soil erosion, permits greater water *infiltration*, and is more *economical* from a labor *standpoint*. In addition to *conventional* pesticides such as insecticides, herbicides, and fungicides, there are other *chemicals* classified as pesticides and regulated under FIFRA.

Table 2. Quantities of Pesticides Most Commonly Used in U.S. Agricultural Crop Production in 1995[a]

Pesticide	CAS Registry Number	Type[b]	Rank	Usage, 10^6 kg ai[c]
Atrazine	[1912-24-9]	H	1	31–33
Sulfur	[7704-34-9]	F	2	27–29.5
Metolachlor	[51218-45-2]	H	3	27–29
Methyl bromide	[74-83-9]	N	4	25.5–28
Petroleum oil		I, H	5	23–25
Metam sodium	[137-42-8]	SF	6	22–24.5
Dichloropropene	[542-75-6]	N	7	17–19.5
2,4-D	[94-75-7]	H	8	14–16.4
Glyphosate	[1071-83-6]	H	9	11.4–13.6
Cyanazine	[21725-46-2]	H	10	11–13
Pendimethalin	[40487-42-1]	H	11	10.5–12.7
Trifluralin	[1582-09-8]	H	12	10.5–12.7
Acetochlor	[34256-82-1]	H	13	10–12.3
Alachlor	[15972-60-8]	H	14	8.6–11
EPTC	[759-94-4]	H	15	4.1–5.9
Chlorpyrifos	[2921-88-2]	I	16	4.1–5.9
Chlorothalonil	[1897-45-6]	F	17	3.6–5.5
Copper hydroxide	[20427-59-2]	F	18	3.2–5
Propanil	[709-98-8]	H	19	2.7–4.5
Dicamba	[1918-00-9]	H	20	2.7–4.5
Terbufos	[13071-79-9]	I	21	2.7–4.1

[b]Pesticide type: H = herbicide; I = insecticide; SF = soil fumigate; F = fungicide; and N = nematicide.

[c]ai • = active ingredient.

These chemicals include wood *preservatives, disinfectants* (excluding chlorine), and sulfur. In the United States these chemicals have annual usage of about 500,000 t, which is equal to *conventional* pesticides.

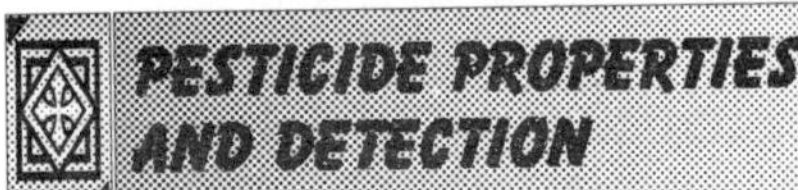

PESTICIDE PROPERTIES AND DETECTION

One of the first problems encountered by scientists attempting to get a national *perspective* on the potential *magnitude* of the groundwater pollution problem was the large number of soil types and *pesticides* involved.

It is estimated that there are about 10,000 soil types in the United States and about 860 active ingredients *registered* under FIFRA. The use of models to predict the potential movement of pesticides in soils under a variety of *conditions* began in earnest about 1980. An integral *component* of these models deals with chemical and physical properties of the pesticides.

An extensive pesticide *properties* database was compiled, which includes six *physical* properties, i.e., solubility, half-life, soil sorption, vapor pressure, acid pK_c, and base pK_b, for about 240 compounds. Because not all of the *properties* have been *measured* for all *pesticides*, some values had to be estimated. By early 1995, the Agricultural

Research Service (ARS) had developed a *computerized* pesticide property database containing 17 physical properties for 330 pesticide *compounds* (See USDA-ARS PROPERTIES DATABASE). The primary user of this data has been the USDA's Natural Resources *Conservation* Service (*formerly* the Soil *Conservation Service*) for leaching models to advise farmers on any combination of soil and pesticide properties that could *potentially* lead to substantial *groundwater contamination*.

Limits of Detection

One reason for the concern about pesticides in *groundwater* has been the ability to detect trace amounts of these *compounds* by more sophisticated analytical *methodology*. Based on the past usage rates and levels of *production*, pesticides must have occurred in *groundwater* prior to the 1980s, when significant efforts were made to detect, quantity, and rectify the drinking water problem. Limits of residue detection have increased *progressively* from parts per million (ppm), parts per billion (ppb), to parts per trillion (ppt). For an excellent review on pesticide analysis.

Monitoring Studies

The highly effective *nematicide*, 1,2-dibromo-3-chloroprpane [76-12-8] (DBCP), has aided in the past growers of citrus, peaches, grapes, cotton, and numerous other fruit and vegetable crops with no apparent *environmental* or *toxicological consequences*.

In 1977, however, *DBCP* was discovered to cause *temporary* sterility among male *production* plant workers and, at about the same time, the chemical was identified as a potential carcinogen. Use of DBCP in California was suspended in 1977.

A *monitoring* study conducted in May of 1979 revealed that 59 of 119 wells tested in the San Joaquin Valley contained *DBCP* residues at levels of 0.1–39 ppb and averaged 5 ppb. DBCP had been used on these sandy soils from ca 1960 to 1977. Although *residues* were highest (0.3 ppb) in *shallower* wells, DBCP was reported in two wells at 180-m deep.

DBCP use was *subsequently* suspended throughout the United States *following* these findings. Residues of the *insecticide/nematicide* aldicarb were detected in a domestic well located close to irrigated potato fields in Suffolk County on Long Island, New York in August 1979.

This discovery was followed by extensive survey of other wells in the vicinity and *regulatory* actions that canceled the use of aldicarb on Long Island. A number of *agronomic* and *geological* conditions on Long Island led to the *penetration* of aldicarb into local *groundwater* aquifers.

First, *application* rates of aldicarb [116-06-3*]* were high, 5.6–7.9 kg/ha (5–7 lb/acre), to ensure adequate control of two pests, the Colorado potato beetle and the Golden *nematode*. Second, potatoes were grown on irrigated sandy soils with high water tables on Long Island.

Finally, the *contaminated* Long Island aquifer is largely a shallow confined aquifer and the pH and alkalinity of the water are low. The DBCP and aldicarb episodes sparked intensive *monitoring* activity on a national level. Aldicarb fiel studies were *conducted* in 16 states over a period of six years involving *approximately* 20,000 soil and water samples.

National surveys showed *evidence* that other pesticides were being detected in wellwater samples. A 1984 review of leaching and monitoring data found 12 different pesticides in groundwater in 18 states as a result of *agricultural* activities; two years later a similar survey found at least 17 different *pesticides* in 23 states.

A chronology of selected monitoring studies in various states has been *summarized* in Table elsewhere in this chapter. The various surveys reported between 1979 and 1988 gave some valuable clues about the *magnitude* and extent of *groundwater contamination* on a national basis; taken together, they presented a challenge to policy makers on developing *regulations* to reduce pesticide residues in *groundwater.*

There were variations in sampling *techniques, statistical* design, and analytical methodology among studies. Problems also arose in defining the source of pesticides, i.e., nonpoint (*normal agricultural* use) vs point sources (spills), and the integrity of the wells sampled.

The most *comprehensive* national survey on pesticide in public and private wells has been conducted by the U.S. *Environmental* Protection Agency beginning in 1985. The purpose of the National Pesticide Survey was both to determine the frequency and concentration of pesticides in drinking water wells *nationwide,* and to improve *understanding* of the *association* of the patterns of pesticide use and the *vulnerability* of *groundwater* to *contamination.*

Table 18.3: Pesticides in Groundwater from Normal Agricultural Use.

Year	*Number of Pesticides Found*	*Number of States Where Pesticides Found*
1979	Aldicarb	New York
1979	DBCP	California
1984	12	18
1985	17	23
1985	56	Californiab
1988	67	33
1988	46	26

Extensive planning went into the *statistical* design for the selection of sampling sites and *analytical* methods for this national survey. Samples were taken from 540 *community* water wells in all 50 states and from 752 rural domestic wells in 38 states.

One hundred and twenty six pesticides and degradation/metabolic products were *analyzed* in this survey. The most *frequently* detected analyte was *tetrachlorotere-phthalate*, a *degradation* product from the herbicide dacthal [1861-32-1] or dimethyl *tetrachloroterephthalate* [1861-32-1] (DCPA).

This product was detected in 6.4% of the *community* wells and in 2.5% of the rural wells at *concentrations* well below the health advisory levels of 4000 mg/L. Health *advisory* levels (HAs) are defined as contaminate *concentrations* in drinking water that would have no adverse health effects over specified exposure periods.

Dacthal has been used as a herbicide on lawns, turf, and golf courses, but finds greatest use in fruit and *vegetable production*. The second most widely detected pesticide was the herbicide atrazine, used widely in corn and sorghum production.

Atrazine was detected in 1.7 and 0.7% of the 1292 *community* and rural wells, respectively. Other pesticides detected included simazine [122-349], prometon [1610-18-0], *hexachlorobenzene* [118-74-11, DBCP, dinoseb [88-85-7], ethylene dibromide [106-93-41, lindane, bentazon [25057-89-0], ethylene thiourea [96-457] (a product of the *ethylenebisdithiocarbamate* (EBDC) fungicides), alachlor [15972-60-8], chlordane [12789-03-61, and 4-nitrophenol [100-02-7] (a degradation product of parathion).

Table 18.4: Groundwater Database, Atrazine.

Wells	General Areas	Sensitive Areas	Total Wells
Number	10,200	5,300	15,500
Above maximum contaminant level	78	103	181
Above maximum contaminant level, %	0.76	1.94	1.17

A large database has been compiled from *groundwater* samples collected by industry (Ciba, Monsanto), EPA, and three *Midwestern* states (*Minnesota, Iowa,* and *Wisconsin*). Atrazine was the product of *significant* interest in the database on account of its *extensive* use.

The database includes wells in general areas, which were randomly picked, independent of herbicide use, and wells from sensitive areas of high atrazine use or where *groundwater* was *particularly vulnerable* to pesticide transport.

Eight years of collective *monitoring* have shown relatively few atrazine *detections* above the *maximum* contaminant level (MCL) of 3.0 ppb, which is a Federal Safe Drinking Water Act calculation that sets the annual average level of a chemical allowed in water.

PESTICIDE METABOLISM AND CHEMICAL DEGRADATION

Pesticides are *susceptible* to a variety of *transformations* in the *environment*, including both chemical degradation and microbial metabolism. Microbial *transformations* are catalyzed *exclusively* by enzymes, whereas chemical *transformations* are *mediated* by a variety of organic and inorganic compounds.

Many pesticide *transformations* can occur either *chemically* or *biologically*. *Consequently*, most pesticide dissipation studies include sterile treatments to *distinguish* between chemical degradation vs microbial *metabolism*.

Common *sterilization* treatments include *autoclaving*; *fumigation*, e.g., with ethylene oxide;

addition of *microbial* inhibitors, e.g., azide, mercuric chloride, and *antibiotics*; and gamma irradiation.

Microbial Metabolism

Studies indicate that, for many pesticides, metabolism by *microorganisms* is the most important *environmental* fate. Pesticide-degrading *microorganisms* are found in soils, aquatic *environments*, and wastewater treatment plants, although the greatest number and variety of *microorganisms* are probably in *agricultural* soils. A wide variety of pesticide-degrading *microorganisms* have been identified, including over 100 genera of bacteria and fungi. This is indicative of the *extraordinary* metabolic diversity of *microorganisms* as well as the extreme variety in pesticide *structural* chemistry.

The rate and extent of pesticide *metabolism* can vary *dramatically*, depending on chemical structure, the number of specific *pesticide-degrading microorganisms* present and their affinity for the pesticide, and *environmental* parameters. The extent of metabolism can vary from relatively minor *transformations* which do not *significantly* alter the chemical or *toxicological* properties of the pesticide, to *mineralization*, i.e., degradation to CO_2, H_2O, NH_4^+, Cl^-, etc.

The rate of *metabolism* can vary from *extremely* slow (half-life of years) to rapid (half-life of days). The majority of pesticides used, although generally susceptible to enzymatic *transformations*, are not utilized as growth substrates by *microorganisms*, i.e., as sources of carbon, nitrogen, and/or energy; this *phenomenon* is termed *cometabolism*.

Consequently, *population* densities of most pesticide degraders are stable, or fluctuate in response to variables other than pesticide *applications*. In some instances, however, *microorganisms* are able to utilize pesticides as growth substrates.

In the case of foliar-applied pesticides this may be desirable; however, in the case of soil-applied pesticides this typically leads to enhanced or *accelerated* rates of *biodegradation*, resulting in losses of efficacy.

It should be noted that only a portion of the pesticide molecule needs to be *mineralized* in order to observe enhanced rates of biodegradation. In addition, pesticides may also be utilized as growth substrates by consortia (two or more distinct strains) of *microorganisms*.

Transformations/Metabolic Pathways

The initial *enzymatic* transformation of most pesticides can be *generically characterized* as oxidative, reductive, or hydrolytic. In general, oxidative and hydrolytic *reactions* are typical of both fungi and bacteria, whereas *reductive* reactions are most typical of bacteria.

Oxidative reactions occur only under aerobic *conditions*, i.e., in the presence of oxygen; reductive reactions typically occur under anaerobic conditions, i.e., in the absence of oxygen; hydrolytic reactions occur under both.

The extent and/or pathway of pesticide metabolism can be highly variable, depending on the mix of pesticide-degrading *microorganisms* present at a *particular* site.

Many, if not most, pesticides are susceptible to several kinds of *transformations* and some are *susceptible* to complete *mineralization*. Consequently, it is difficult to predict the fate of any given *pesticide* at any given site.

Oxidative Reactions

The majority of pesticides, or pesticide products, are *susceptible* to some form of attack by oxidative enzymes. For more persistent pesticides, oxidation is frequently the primary mode of *metabolism*, although there are important *exceptions*, e.g., DDT. For less *persistent* pesticides, *oxidation* may play a relatively minor role, or be the first reaction in a *metabolic* pathway.

Oxidation generally results in *degradation* of the parent molecule. However, attack by certain oxidative enzymes (phenol oxidases) can result in the *condensation* or *polymerization* of the parent molecules; this *phenomenon* is referred to as oxidative coupling.

Examples of some important oxidative reactions are ether cleavage, alkyl-hydroxylation, *aryl-hydroxylation*, *N-dealkylation*, and *sulfoxidation*.Ether Cleavage. This is commonly observed as the initial step in the metabolism of the phenoxy herbicides 2,4-D, (2,4,5-*trichlorophenoxy*)acetic acid (2,4,5-T), and mecprop.

A wide variety of bacteria have been isolated which are able to catalyze this reaction (eq. 1), including *Alcaligenes, Azotobacter, Pseudomonas, Acinetobacter, Xanthobacter, Flavobacterium,* and *Arthrobacter.*

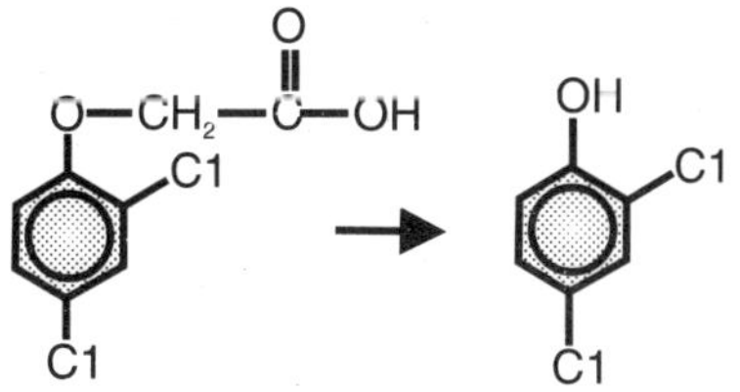

O—CH₂—C(=O)—OH, C1, C1 → OH, C1, C1 (1)

(1)

Alkyl-Hydroxylation. This is commonly observed as the initial *transformation* of alkyl-substituted aromatic *pesticides* such as alachlor [15972-60-8] and *metolachlor* [51218-45-2] (eq. 2). These reactions are typically catalyzed by *relatively* nonspecific oxidases found in fungi and *actinomycetes*.

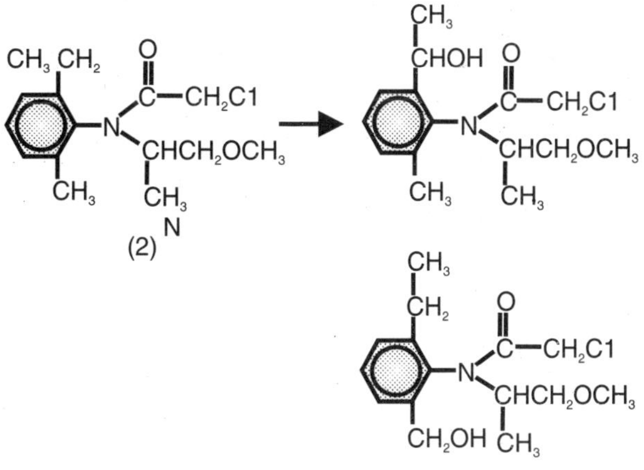

CH_3CH_2, $C(=O)-CH_2C1$, N, $CHCH_2OCH_3$, CH_3, CH_3 → CH_3, CHOH, $C(=O)-CH_2C1$, N, $CHCH_2OCH_3$, CH_3, CH_3

(2) N

CH_3, CH_2, $C(=O)-CH_2C1$, N, $CHCH_2OCH_3$, CH_2OH, CH_3

(2)

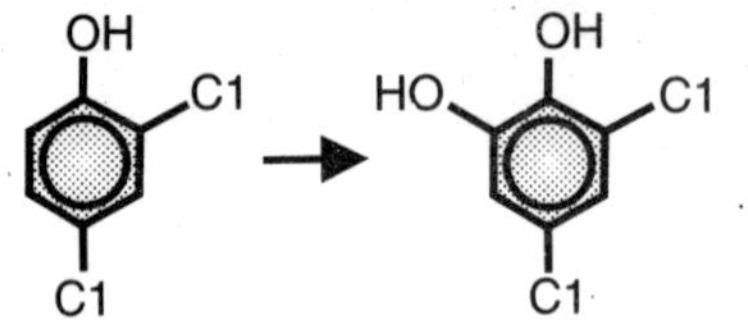

(3)

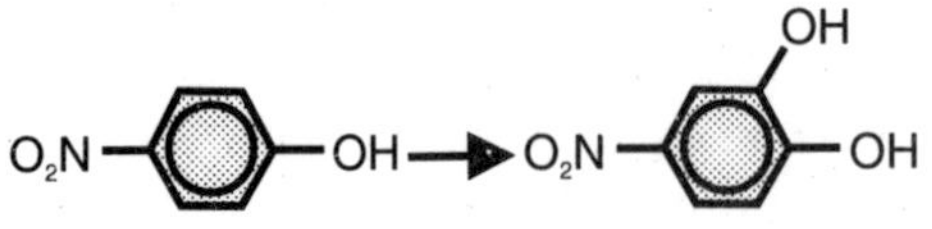

(4)

Aryl-Hydroxylation. This is *occasionally* observed as the initial *transformation* of aromatic pesticides. The vast majority of aromatic pesticide *degradation* products are susceptible to aryl-hydroxylation, representing either cometabolism or the initial step in *mineralization*. Numerous genera of bacteria and fung possess the *monooxygenases* and dioxygenases responsible for hydroxylation of aromatic products. Examples of aromatic products susceptible to aryl-hydroxylation include 2,4-dichlorophenol [120-83-2] (from 2,4-D) (eq. 3) 4-nitrophenol (from parathion) (eq. 4), 3,4-dichloroaniline, [95-76-1] (from propanil), and 3,6-dichlorosalicylic acid [3401-80-7] (from dicamba).

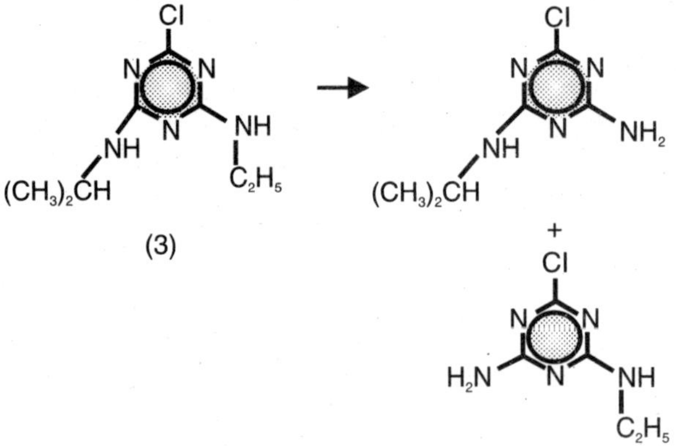

(3)

(5)

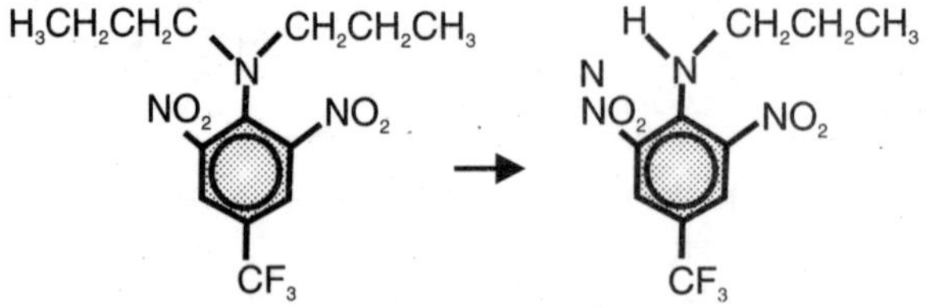

(4)

(6)

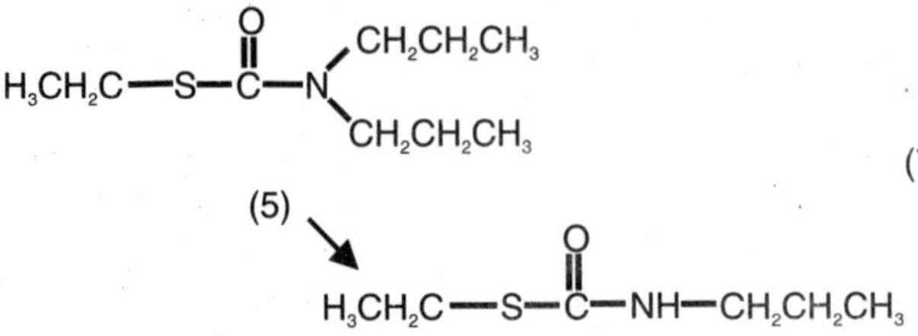

(5)

(7)

-N-Dealkylation. This is commonly observed as a pri$_d$ mary *transformation* of pesticides with N-alkyl substituents, such as atrazine [1912-24-9] (eq. 5) trifluralin [1582-09-8] (eq. 6), and S-ethyl *dipropylthiocarbamate* [759-94-4] (EPTC) (eq. 7). These reactions are catalyzed by a variety of bacterial strains, including *Nocardia, Pseudomonas, Rhodococcus,* and *Streptomyces.*

Sulfoxidation. This is a fairly common transformation of sulfur-containing pesticides such as aldicarb (eq. 8) and EPTC.

$$CH_3S-C(CH_3)_2-CH=N-O-C(=O)-NH-CH_3 \quad (6)$$

$$\downarrow \qquad (8)$$

$$CH3-S(=O)_2-C(CH_3)_2-CH=N-O-C(=O)-NHCH_3$$

Reductive Reactions

A number of pesticides are susceptible to reductive reactions under anaerobic conditions, depending on the substituents present on the molecule. Reductive reactions can be either chemically or enzymatically mediated.

Because biologically generated reductants, e.g., cysteine and porphyrins, are frequently the electron donors for both chemical and enzymatic reactions, results from sterile controls are not necessarily conclusive in distinguishing between the two mechanisms.

The only definitive means of *distinguishing* between chemical vs biological (*enzymatic*) reactions is to determine whether the reaction rate is consistent with enzyme kinetics. The most common reductive reactions are the reduction of nitro *substituents* and reductive dechlorination.

Reduction of Nitro Substituents

These reactions are very common in anaerobic *environments* and result in amine-substituted pesticides; anaerobic bacteria capable of reducing nitrate to ammonia appear to be primarily responsible. All nitro-substituted pesticides appear to be susceptible to this *transformation*, e.g., methyl parathion (eq. 9), trifluralin, and *pendimethalin*.

$$O_2N-C_6H_4-O-P(=S)(O-CH_3)_2 \quad (7)$$

$$\searrow$$

$$H_2N-C_6H_4-O-P(=S)(O-CH_3)_2 \quad (9)$$

Reductive Dechlorination

Such reduction of chlorinated aliphatic *hydrocarbons*, e.g., lindane, has been known since the 1960s. More recently, the *dechlorination* of aromatic pesticides, e.g., 2,4,5-T, or pesticide products,

$$\text{2,4-dichlorophenol} \rightarrow \text{4-chlorophenol} \rightarrow \text{phenol} \qquad (10)$$

e.g., *chlorophenols,* has also been documented (eq. 10). These reactions are of particular interest because chlorinated compounds are generally persistent under aerobic conditions.

Hydrolytic Reactions

Many pesticides possess bonds that are susceptible to hydrolytic attack. These reactions are most easily *characterized* according to the type of bond *hydrolyzed*: carboxylic acid ester, carbamate, *organophosphate*, urea, or chlorine (*hydrodechlorination*).

In many instances the specific hydrolytic enzymes have been purified and *characterized* and the genes encoding for the enzymes isolated and cloned. It is commonly observed that there are multiple forms of the enzymes *catalyzing* a particular *hydrolytic* reaction, which suggests that these catalytic functions have evolved *independently* in different bacteria.

Carboxylic acid ester hydrolysis is frequently observed as the initial reaction for pesticides with ester bonds, such as 2,4-D esters, pyrethroids, and DCPA (dacthal) (8) (eq. 11).

$$C_6Cl_4(COOCH_3)_2 \rightarrow C_6Cl_4(COOH)_2 \qquad (11)$$

(8)

Carbamate hydrolysis is frequently observed as the initial reaction for pesticides having *carbamate* bonds, such as aldicarb, carbofuran, carbaryl, and benomyl (eq. 12). Numerous genera of *carbamate-hydrolyzing* bacteria have been identified, including *Pseudomonas, Arthrobacter, Bacillus,* Nocardia$_n$ Achromobacter, Flavobacterium, *Streptomyces,* Alcali$_e$ *genes, Azospirillum, Micrococcus,* and *Rhodococcus.*

$$CH_3S-C(CH_3)_2-CH{=}N-O-C({=}O)-NH-CH_3 \rightarrow CH_3-S-C(CH_3)_2-CH{=}N-OH + NH_2CH_3$$

(12)

Organophosphate hydrolysis is frequently observed as the initial reaction for pesticides having *organophosphate* bonds, such as methyl parathion, chlorpyrifos (eq. 13), diazinon, and coumaphos. Several genera of *organophosphate-hydrolyzing* bacteria have been identified, including *Pseudomonas, Arthrobacter, Bacillus,* and Flavobacterium.

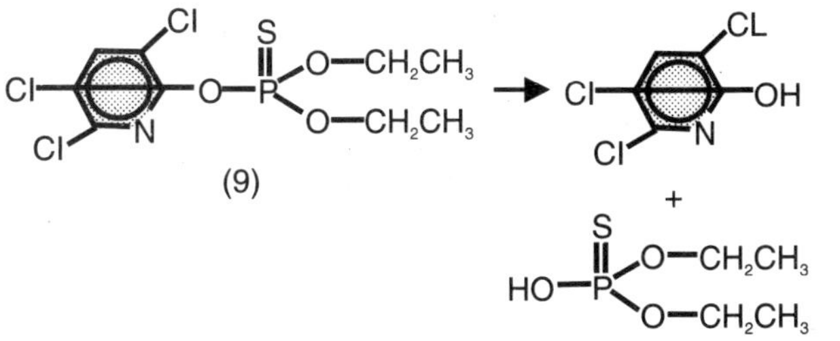

Cl, S, O—CH_2CH_3, Cl, O—P, O—CH_2CH_3, Cl, N (9) → CL, Cl, OH, Cl, N + S, O—CH_2CH_3, HO—P, O—CH_2CH_3 (13)

Urea hydrolysis is frequently observed as the initial reaction for pesticides having urea bonds, such as linuron, diuron, and chlorsulfuron (eq. 14).

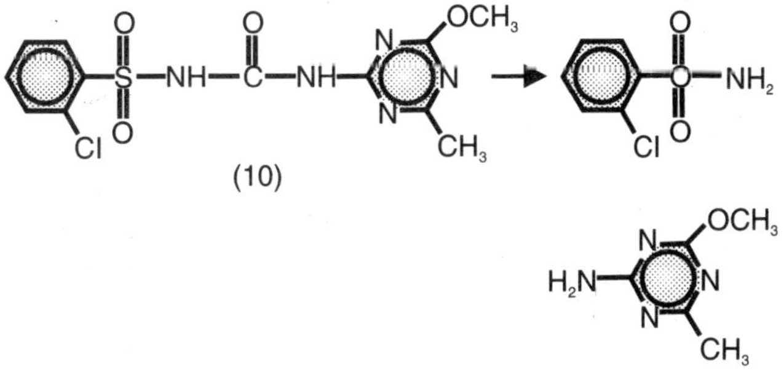

O, O, OCH_3, N, S—NH—C—NH, N, N, Cl, O, CH_3 (10) → O, NH_2, Cl, O; OCH_3, N, H_2N, N, N, CH_3 (14)

Hydrodechlorination has long been recognized as an important chemical transformation. However, the enzymatic *hydrodechlorination* of atrazine by soil *microorganisms* has also been demonstrated (eq. 15).

(3) 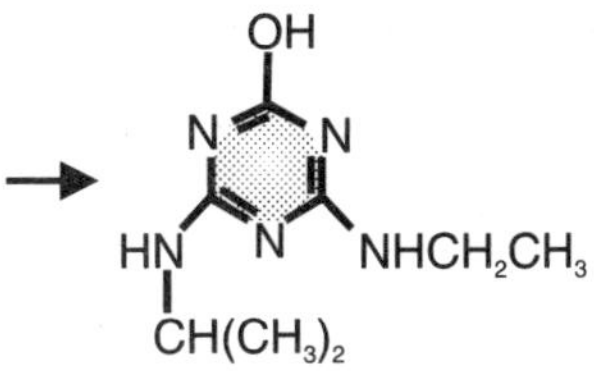 → OH, N, N, HN, N, $NHCH_2CH_3$, $CH(CH_3)_2$ (15)

Metabolic Pathways

Some pesticides are susceptible to complete degradation, i.e., *mineralization.* This typically requires a sequence of enzymatic *transformations,* i.e., metabolic pathway in which the product(s) are utilized as growth substrates by *microorganisms* or consortia of microorganisms.

The *mineralization* of pesticides by the white rot fungi, e.g., Phanerochaete *chrysosporium,* is apparently an exception to this scenario; these fungi mineralize pesticides via *extracellular* peroxidases without *necessarily* utilizing the products as growth substrates.

Most pesticides are susceptible to *mineralization* only under aerobic conditions, although a few, e.g., dinoseb, can also be *mineralized* under anaerobic conditions. One of the first pesticides *demonstrated* to be *mineralized* by soil *microorganisms* was 2,4-D. The metabolic pathway of 2,4-D biodegradation has been elucidated and shown to consist of the steps shown in Figure elsewhere in this chapter.

Other representative pesticides that have also been shown to be mineralized include glyphosate, parathion, carbaryl, EPTC, isofenphos, and propachlor. Pesticides that are susceptible to *mineralization* are not typically found in, or considered to be a threat to, *groundwater* supplies because of their rapid degradation, i.e., non-persistence.

Microorganisms can evolve, that is, develop metabolic pathways for the *mineralization* of previously persistent compounds. For example, there have been several reports documenting the existence of *atrazinmineralizing microorganisms.*

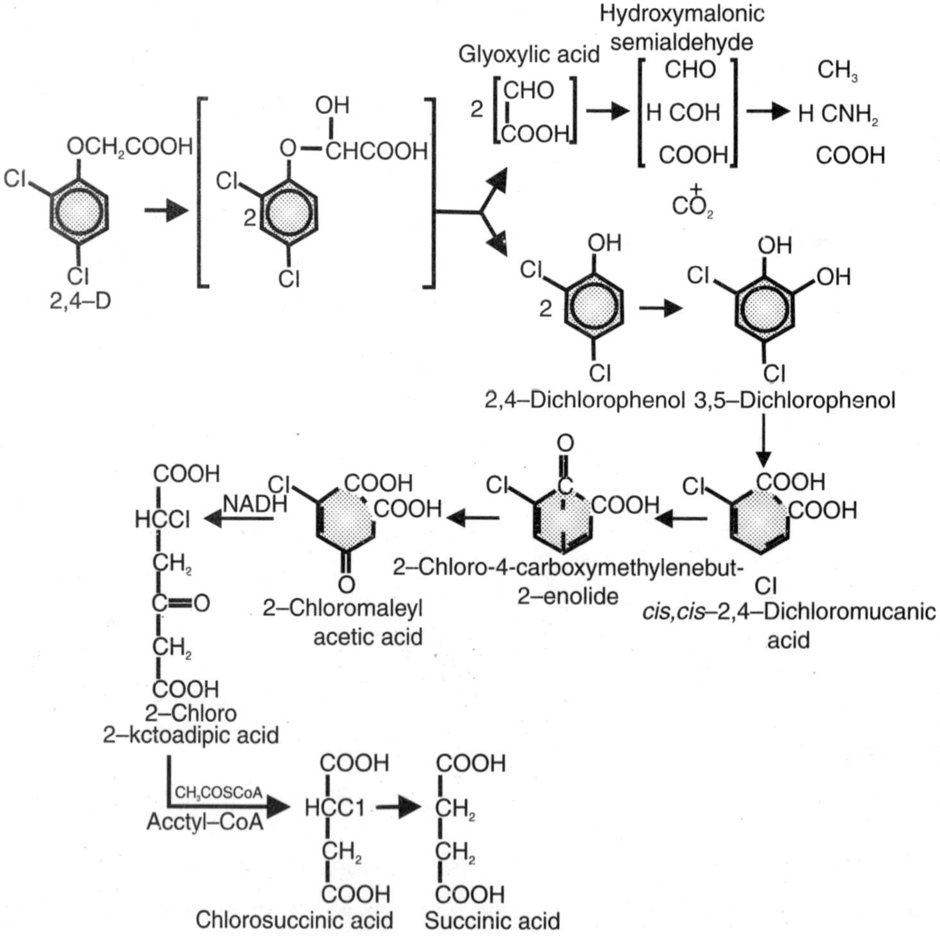

Figure 18.1: Metabolic pathway of 2,4-D biodegradation.

Kinetics of Pesticide Biodegradation

Rates of pesticide biodegradation are important because they dictate the potential for carryover between growing seasons, *contamination* of surface and *groundwaters, bioaccumulation* in macrobiota, and losses of efficacy. Pesticides are typically considered to be biodegraded via first-order kinetics, where the rate is *proportional* to the *concentration.*

Figure elsewhere in this chapter shows a typical first-order dissipation curve. For those pesticides that are *cometabolized,* i.e., not utilized as a growth substrate, the assumption of first order kinetics is appropriate.

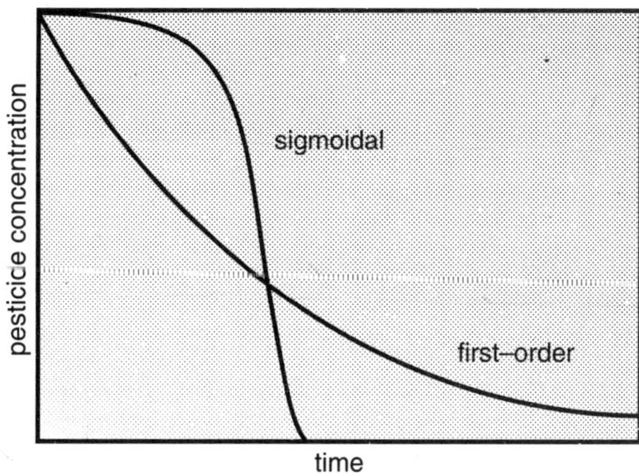

Figure 18.2: Kinetics of pesticide biodegradation.

The more accurate kinetic expression is actually pseudo-first-order kinetics, where the rate is dependent on both the pesticide concentration and the numbers of pesticide-degrading *microorganisms.* However, because of the difficulties in *enumerating* pesticide-transforming *microorganisms,* first-order rate constants, or half-lives, are typically reported.

Based on kinetic constants, it is possible to rank the relative *persistence* of pesticides. Pesticides with half-lives of <10 days are considered to be relatively *nonpersistent;* pesticides with half-lives of >100 days are considered to be relatively persistent. For those pesticides which are utilized as microbial growth substrates, sigmoidal rates of *biodegradation* are frequently observed.

Sigmoidal data are more difficult to *summarize* than *exponential* (first-order) data because of their inherent *nonlinearity.* Sigmoidal rates of pesticide metabolism can be described using microbial growth kinetics (Monod); however, four kinetics constants are required. *Consequently,* it is more difficult to predict the *persistence* of these pesticides in the environment.

Variability (*spatial* and *temporal*) in the rate of biodegradation of specific pesticides is *frequently* observed. Rates of *biodegradation* tend to be site-specific because of the differences in the numbers of specific pesticide degraders, pesticide *bioavailability,* and soil parameters such as temperature, moisture, and pH.

Rates of metabolism are directly *proportional* to the population densities of pesticide degraders as well as the bioavailable, i.e., soluble, *concentrations*. Studies indicate that *pesticides* sorbed to soil/sediment particles are not readily available for *biodegradation*; they must desorb into the solution phase before being metabolized.

Within certain boundary conditions, there is a positive *correlation* between rates of *metabolism* and soil temperature, moisture, and pH, although there are exceptions, e.g., *oxidative* reactions are less likely to occur in water-logged soils as a result of the slow rates of oxygen diffusion, whereas *transformations* catalyzed by fungi are more likely to occur at lower pH and/or soil moistures.

CHEMICAL DEGRADATION

Chemical, or abiotic, *transformations* are an important fate of many pesticides. Such *transformations* are ubiquitous, occurring in either aqueous solution or sorbed to surfaces. Rates can vary dramatically depending on the reaction *mechanism*, chemical structure, and relative *concentrations* of such catalysts as protons, hydroxyl ions, transition metals, and clay particles. Chemical *transformations* can be generically classified as hydrolyti,, photolytic, or redox reactions (transfer of electrons).

Hydrolytic and Substitution Reactions

A variety of functional groups common to many pesticides are *susceptible* to hydrolysis. Hydrolysis reactions are catalyzed by acids (low pH), bases (high pH), and/or transition metals (Cu^{2+}, Fe^{3+}, Mn^{2+}). Consequently, *environmental* parameters such as pH, mineral *composition* and concentration, and clay content can have dramatic effects on rates of hydrolysis.

In addition, the reaction *mechanism* in conjunction with chemical structure is of critical *importance* in dictating the rate of reaction. For instance, if the case of aromatic pesticides, if the reaction mechanism involves attack by a nucleophile (OH^-), then the presence of *electron-withdrawing* substituents such as NO_2^- and Cl^- causes the bond to be more electron-poor (more positive), resulting in faster rates of *hydrolysis*, whereas the presence of electron-donating *substituents* such as NH_2 and CH_3 causes the bond to be more electron-rich (more negative), resulting in slower rates of hydrolysis.

If the reaction *mechanism* involves attack by an electrophile (OH·), then electron-withdrawing *substituents* cause the rate of hydrolysis to be slower, whereas electron-donating substituents cause the rate of hydrolysis to be faster. Pesticides possessing bonds that are susceptible to chemical *hydrolysis* include carboxylic acid esters, *carbamates*, *organophosphates*, and ureas.

Chlorinated compounds are susceptible to substitution (*hydrodechlorination*). Carboxylic acid ester, carbamate, *organophosphate*, and urea hydrolysis are important acid/base-catalyzed reactions. Typically, pesticides that are susceptible to chemical hydrolysis are also susceptible to *biological hydrolysis*; the products of chemical vs *biological* hydrolysis are generally identical.

Consequently, the two types of reactions can only be *distinguished* based on sterile controls or kinetic studies. As a general rule, carboxylic acid esters, carbamates, and *organophosphates* are more susceptible to alkaline hydroysis, whereas *sulfonylureas* are more susceptible to acid hydrolysis.

Hydrodechlorination is a common reaction of chlorinated pesticides such as atrazine (eq. 15), alachlor, and metolachlor (eq. 16). These reactions are *catalyzed* primarily by transition metals or by soil surfaces (clays or humic substances).

$$(2) \rightarrow \quad 2\text{-}(CH_3CH_2)\text{-}6\text{-}(CH_3)C_6H_3\text{-}N(C(=O)\text{-}CH_2OH)(CH(CH_3)CH_2OCH_3) \qquad (16)$$

The kinetics of hydrolysis reactions may be first-order or *second-order, depending* on the reaction *mechanism*. However, second-order reactions may appear to be first order, i.e., pseudo-first-order, if one of the reactants is not consumed in the reaction, e.g., OH^-, or if the *concentration* of active catalyst, e.g., reduced transition metal, is a small fraction of the total catalyst concentration.

Photolytic Reactions

Much of the early research on photolysis of pesticides was conducted in organic solvents at high *concentrations* using powerful light sources. Both high and low pressure mercury vapor arcs, which emit uv light in sharp spectral lines, were *frequently* employed in these studies.

These earlier studies yielded useful data on the mechanisms and products of pesticide *photodegradation*. More recently, there has been considerable interest in photolysis in natural systems; an *excellent* review of this research has appeared.

Extensive pesticide *photodegradation* in soil is problematic for many compounds because light *penetration* into soils is extremely limited, often to depths of only 0.5 mm or less. The most likely candidate pesticides for soil photolysis are those that are water-soluble, weakly sorbed to soil surfaces, and have low vapor pressure; such *compounds* are most likely to rise with capillary water to the soil–atmospheric interface where photodegradation can occur. *Napropamide* and imazaquin are two pesticides that have been *demonstrated* to exhibit this behaviour.

Studies have appeared where *photolysis* in natural bodies of water under normal sunlight conditions has been examined. For example, metolachlor was slowly *photodegraded* by sunlight in lake water, with a half life of 22 days in summer and 205 days in winter. Addition of a 5% solution of dissolved organic matter to the water *extended* the half-lives two to three times longer, depending on the season.

Redox Reactions

Oxidative reactions typically occur as a *consequence* of the light-mediated *production* of singlet oxygen or hydroxyl radical, which are both potent oxidants. This process, termed indirect photolysis, involves the initial absorption of light energy by organic molecules, e.g., humic substances, which either is directly transferred to oxygen (*sensitization*) or results in a chain reaction leading to the *formation* of oxidants.

In contrast, soil organic matter has also been shown to quench *photolysis* of certain sorbed molecules. Chemical oxidative reactions in soil are generally of less *environmental importance* than biological oxidative reactions because observed reaction rates are slower on account of competition for oxidants by organic matter.

Although these may appear to be pseudo-first-order, the kinetics of redox reactions are typically second-order because either an *oxidizing* or a reducing species is required. *S-oxidation* of sulfur-containing pesticides such as aldicarb, parathion, and malathion can be of importance in the absence of microbial activity. The products of chemical vs biological *oxidation* are generally identical (eq. 8).

Reductive reactions typically occur in anaerobic environments where there is an abundant supply of electron donors. Electron donors are typically of biological origin, e.g., porphyrins or cysteine, which sometimes leads to confusion regarding the nature, i.e., chemical vs enzymatic, of the reductive reaction.

By definition, all reductive reactions which are not enzymatically catalyzed are chemical. The most significant chemical reductive reaction is reductive dechlorination.

Reductive dechlorination of chlorinated aliphatic *hydrocarbons*, e.g., lindane (eq. 17) is extremely facile and occurs almost exclusively via chemical *mechanisms*, although *microorganisms* are typically the source of electron donors.

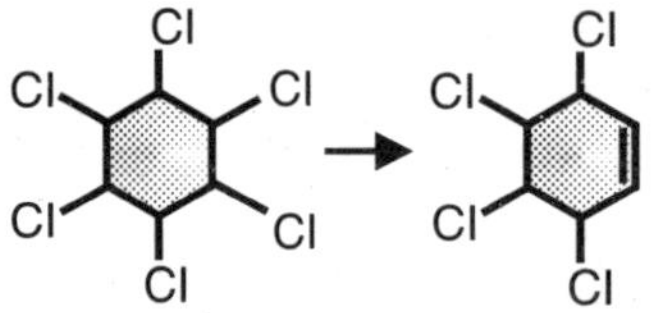

Cl Cl Cl Cl Cl Cl → Cl Cl Cl Cl (17)

(11)

The reductive *dechlorination* of chlorinated aromatics is more complicated in that the initial dechlorination of more highly chlorinated compounds may be either chemical or enzymatic, e.g., PCP, whereas the *dechlorination* of less chlorinated compounds or dechlorinated products is typically enzymatic. For example, the first *dechlorination* of 2,4-dichlorophenol (ortho position) can occur either chemically or enzymatically; the second dechlorination (para position) is enzymatic (eq. 10).

PHYSICAL PROCESSES AFFECTING PESTICIDES IN SOIL AND WATER

Persistence of pesticides in the *environment* is controlled by retention, degradation, and transport processes and their interaction. Retention refers to the ability of the soil to bind a pesticide, *preventing* its movement either within or outside of the soil matrix.

Retention primarily refers to the sorption process, but also includes absorption into the soil matrix and soil organisms, both plants and microorganisms. In contrast to *degradation* that decreases the absolute amount of the pesticide in the *environment,* sorption processes do not affect the total amount of pesticide present in the soil but can decrease the amount available for *transformation* or transport.

Transport processes describe movement of the pesticide from one location to another or from one phase to another. Transport processes include both downward leaching, surface runoff, *volatilization* from the soil to the atmosphere, as well as upward movement by capillary water to the soil surface.

Transport processes do not affect the total amount of pesticide in the *environment*; however, they can move the pesticide to sites that have different potentials for degradation. Transport processes also redistribute the pesticide in the environment, possibly *contaminating* sites away from the site of application such as surface and *groundwater* and the atmosphere.

Transport of pesticides is a function of both retention and transport processes. Many factors affect the mechanisms and kinetics of sorption and transport processes. For instance, differences in the chemical structure and properties, i.e., *ionizability*, solubility in water, vapor pressure, and polarity, between pesticides affect their behaviour in the *environment* through effects on sorption and transport processes.

Differences in soil properties, i.e., pH and percentage of organic carbon and clay contents, and soil conditions, i.e., moisture content and landscape position; climatic *conditions*, i.e., *temperature*, *precipitation*, and radiation; and cultural practices, i.e., crop and tillage, can all modify the behaviour of the pesticide in soils. Persistence of a pesticide in soil is a consequence of a complex interaction of processes.

Because the persistence of a pesticide can govern its availability and efficacy for pest control, as well as its potential for adverse *environmental* impacts, knowledge of the basic processes is necessary if the benefits of the pesticide are to be *maximized*.

Sorption and Desorption Processes

Sorption is a *generalized* term that refers to surface induced removal of the pesticide from solution; it is the attraction and *accumulation* of pesticide at the soil–water or soil–air interface, resulting in molecular layers on the surface of soil particles.

Experimentally, sorption is *characterized* by the loss of pesticide from the soil solution, making it almost impossible to *distinguish* between sorption in which molecular layers form on soil particle surfaces, *precipitation* in which either a separate solid phase forms on solid surfaces, covalent bonding with the soil particle surface, or absorption into soil particles or organisms.

Sorption is generally *considered* a reversible equilibrium process. Desorption is the reverse of the sorption process. If the pesticide is removed from solution that is in *equilibrium* with the sorbed pesticide, pesticide desorbs from the soil surface to *reestablish* the initial equilibrium.

Desorption replenishes pesticide in the soil solution as it *dissipates* by degradation or transport processes. Sorption/desorption therefore is the process that controls the overall fate of a pesticide in the *environment*. It accomplishes this by *controlling* the amount of pesticide in solution at any one time that is available for plant uptake, degradation or *decomposition*, volatilization, and leaching.

A number of reviews are *available* that describe in detail the sorption process; desorption, however, has been much les studied. Pesticides are sorbed on both *inorganic* and organic soil constituents. The sorptive reactivity of soil organic and inorganic surfaces to pesticides is dependent on the number and type of functional groups at accessible surfaces.

When a pesticide reacts with the surface functional groups, either an inner- or an *outersphere* surface complex is formed. Although *functional* groups account for much of the reactivity of soil to pesticide retention, accessibility of the functional groups to the pesticide is also an important

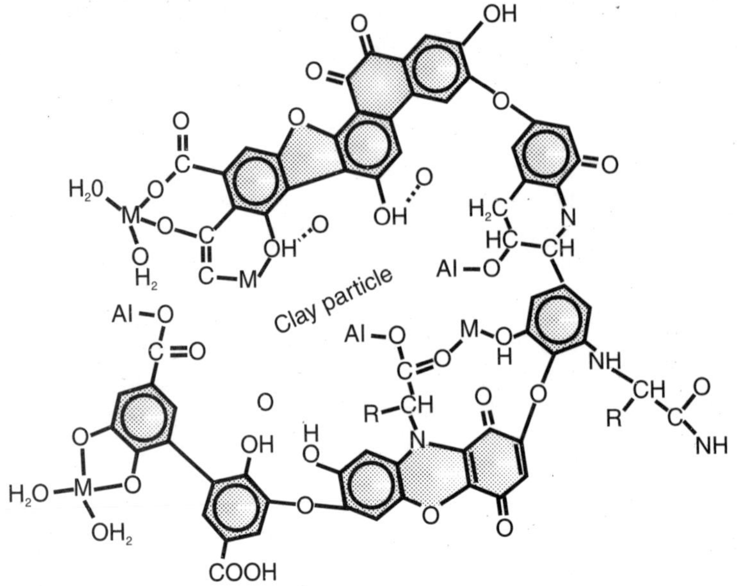

Figure 18.3: Association of clay particles and the functional groups of organic matter.

factor. For instance, steric *hindrance* caused by a large *neighboring substituent* or *chemical* may preclude the pesticide from interacting with the functional group.

The intimate *association* among different soil minerals and between soil minerals and organic matter makes many functional groups *inaccessible* to pesticide molecules, although some functional groups are accessible to molecules that move through tiny soil pores, clay interlayers, or polymeric soil organic matrix.

Inorganic solids are composed of crystalline and *noncrystalline amorphous* minerals. The key features of clay minerals in relation to clays as sorbents for pesticides have been described. The principal functional groups on inorganic surfaces contributing to the sorptive capacity are siloxane ditrigonal cavities in phyllosilicate clays and inorganic hydroxyl groups generally *associated* with metal (hydrous) oxides.

Organic components of the solid phase include polymeric organic solids, decomposing plant residues, and soil organisms. The exact structure of humic materials in soil is largely unknown, but it is suggested that humic materials may contain a variety of *functional* groups, including carboxyl, carbonyl, *phenylhydroxyl*, amino, imdazole, sulfhydryl, and sulfonic groups.

The variety of functional groups in soil organic matter and the steric interactions between functional groups lead to a continuous range of reactivities in soil organic matter. The relative *importance* of organic vs inorganic *constituents* on pesticide sorption depends on the amount, distribution, and properties of these constituents, and the *chemical* properties of the pesticide.

Soil organic matter is the principal sorbent for many organic *compounds* such as the unionized weak acid pesticides 2,4-D, chlorsulfuron, and picloram; the *nonionizable* pesticides linuron and trifluralin; and the *unionized* weak base pesticide metribuzin.

It has been suggested that the retention *mechanism* of nonionic organic chemicals in soil is a *partitioning* of the chemical between the aqueous phase and the hydrophobic organic matter. However, the *mechanism* may not be that simple.

For example, some clays have hydrophobic sites and many nonionic organic chemicals sorb *extensively* on the clay mineral fraction of soil. Of the various inorganic soil constituents, smectites (*montmorillonite clays*) have the greatest potential for sorption of pesticides on account of their large surface area and abundance in soils.

Weak base pesticides, both *protonated* and neutral species, have been shown to be sorbed as interlayer complexes. Sorption of atrazine on smectites ranges from 0 to 100% of added atrazine, depending on the surface charge density of the smectite.

The intramolecular forces that can attract molecules to the interface and retain them on the surface have been classified according to the *mechanism* involved. Organic compounds can be sorbed with varying degrees of strengths of interactions by physical/chemical bonding such as van der Waals forces, *hydrogen bonding*, dipole–dipole interactions, ion exchange, and covalent bonding.

For any given compound, there is likely a continuum of *mechanisms* with differing energy *relationships* that is responsible for sorption onto soil. For example, an organic molecule may be sorbed initially by sites that provide the strongest *mechanism*, followed by *progressively* weaker sites as the stronger sorption sites become filled.

London and van der Waals forces are short-range interactions resulting from a correlation in electron movement between two molecules to produce a small net electrostatic attraction. These interactions are *particularly* important for neutral high molecular weight compounds.

Hydrogen bonds are dipole–dipole interactions involving an electrostatic attraction between an *electropositive* hydrogen nucleus on *functional* groups such as –OH and –NH and exposed electron pairs on electronegative atoms such a_O and –N.

Hydrogen bonding is probably most prevalent in the bonding of pesticides to organic surfaces

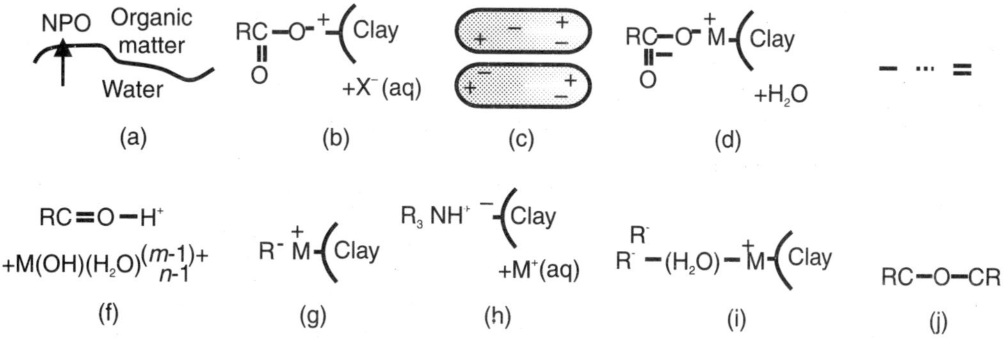

NPO Organic matter Water (a)

RC(=O)–O⁻ +(Clay +X⁻(aq) (b)

(c)

RC(=O)–O⁻ M⁺(Clay +H_2O (d)

– ··· =

RC=O–H⁺ +$M(OH)(H_2O)^{(m-1)+}_{n-1}$ (f)

R⁻ M⁺(Clay (g)

R_3NH^+ ⁻(Clay +M^+(aq) (h)

R⁻ R⁻ –(H_2O)–M⁺(Clay (i)

RC–O–CR (j)

Figure 18.4: Sorption mechanisms for pesticides on soil, where R =H or side-chain, M = exchangeable cation, X = exchangeable inorganic anion, and NPO = nonpolar organic compound: (a) hydrophobic bonding; (b) anion exchange; (c) London–van der Waals; (d) ligand exchange; (e) hydrogen bonding; (f) protonation; (g) cation bridging; (h) cation exchange; (i) water bridging; and (j) covalent bonding (37).

in the soil. For instance, hydrogen bonding has been proposed to be a *significant* soil binding mechanism for *chlorsulfuron*, fluazifop, and triazines such as atrazine.

Cation and water bridging involve complex formation between an *exchangeable* cation and an anionic or polar functional group on the pesticide. Cation and water bridging have been proposed as sorption mechanisms for fluazifop-butyl, picloram, *glyphosate*, and *chlorthiamid*. Protonation of a pesticide, or formation of charge-transfer complexes, at a mineral surface occurs when an organic functional group forms a complex with a surface proton.

This retention *mechanism* is particularly important for basic functional groups at acidic mineral surfaces at low pH and low water content, particularly in the presence of aluminum or other metal cations. *Protonation* may be a mechanism for sorption of some s-triazines, *chlorthiamid*, fluazifop and fluazifop-butyl, and *chlorsulfuron* on various substrates.

Anion-exchange *mechanisms* involve a nonspecific electrostatic attraction of an anion to a positively charged site on the soil surface, involving the exchange on one anion for another at the binding site. Ligand exchange is a sorption *mechanism* that involves *displacement* of an inorganic hydroxyl or water molecule from a metal ion at a hydrous oxide surface by a carboxylate or hydroxyl on an organic molecule.

For instance, this has been proposed as a mechanism for *chlorsulfuron* sorption on iron oxides. Cation exchange is an *electrostatic* attraction that involves the exchange of a cation for a cation sorbed at a *negatively* charged site on the soil surface.

Herbicides can be *permanently* cationic, such as paraquat and diquat; however, weakly basic herbicides that have functional groups such as amines and heterocyclic nitrogen compounds may also protonate to form the cationic form. Cation *exchange* has been *observed* with paraquat and diquat, fluridone, and s-triazines.

Hydrophobic interactions and trapping of molecules in a molecular sieve formed by humic materials have been *hypothesized* as retention *mechanisms* for prometryn. It has been shown that fluridone, fluazifop, and *bipyridylium* herbicides penetrate into *interlamellar* spaces of smectites and can become trapped.

A variety of *mechanisms* or forces can attract organic chemicals to a soil surface and retain them there. For a given chemical, or family of chemicals, several of these mechanisms may operate in the bonding of the chemical to the soil.

For any given chemical, an increase in polarity, number of functional groups, and ionic nature of the chemical can increase the number of potential sorption *mechanisms* for the chemical. Ionizable compounds such as basic compounds (trazines and *pyridinones*) and acidic compounds (carboxylic acids and phenols) can sorb by ionic mechanisms when they are ionized.

Weakly basic *compounds* may sorb by cation exchange; weakly acidic compounds may sorb by anion exchange. For these chemicals ion exchange is not the sole sorption mechanism. For instance, sorption of *bipyridylium* cations, i.e., diquat and paraquat, is primarily the result of cation exchange.

Other physicochemical forces, such as *charge-transfer* interactions, hydrogen bonding, and van der Waals forces, can also be involved in the sorption process. Triazines are weakly basic

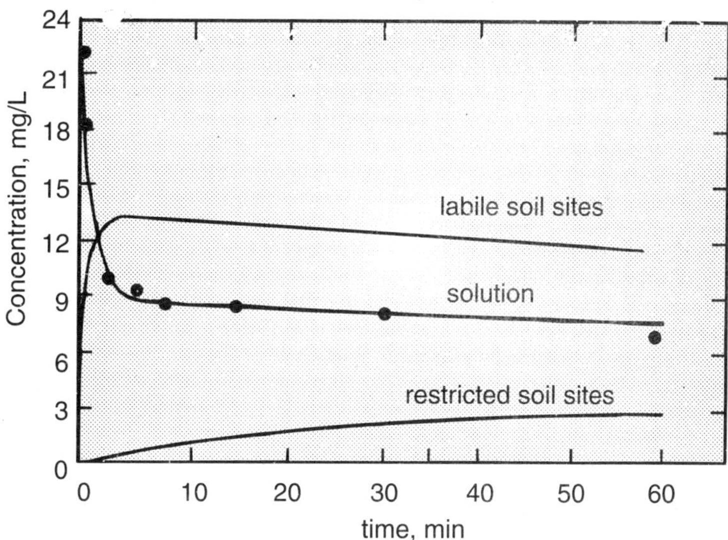

Figure 18.5. Sorption and desorption of atrazine and linuron on soil sediments (39).

chemicals that can be easily protonated at low soil pH levels.

The pK_a values for triazines range from about 1.7 for atrazine to 4.3 for prometon. There is abundant evidence for cation exchange as the bonding mechanism for triazines to soil. On the other hand, at soil pH values greater than two pH units above the pK_a, triazines are not protonated to a great extent and other mechanisms become more important, such as hydrogen bonding and *hydrophobic* attractions.

Pyridinones, such as fluridone, are also weakly basic compounds. With a pK_a of 1.7, fluridone sorption can involve cation exchange only in low pH soils. Sorption on soil at pH 5 to 6 is suggested to be by the same *mechanisms* for sorption on both soil organic matter and montmorillonite, i.e., charge-transfer interactions, *hydrogen* bonding, and van der Waals forces.

Depending on the pH of the system, weakly acidic organic chemicals (*carboxylic* acids and phenols) exist either as the undissociated molecule or the *corresponding* anion. Numerous studies have shown that the anion of such herbicides as 2,4-D is readily sorbed by anion exchange resins, but sorption of organic anions by soils via anion exchange is not likely because clays and organic matter are generally either *noncharged* or negatively charged.

Sorption of weakly acidic organics probably involves physical adsorption of the *undissociated* molecule and is not site-specific. Other sorption *mechanisms* for weakly acidic organics are also possible. Charge-transfer and hydrogen bonding were postulated as the sorption *mechanisms* for the weak acid *chlorsulfuron.*

Sorption of nonionic, nonpolar *hydrophobic* compounds occurs by weak attractive interactions such as van der Waals forces. Net attraction is the result of *dispersion* forces; the strength of these weak forces is about 4 to 8 kJ/mol (-1–2 kcal/mol). Electrostatic *interactions* can also be important, especially when a molecule is polar in nature. Attraction potential can develop between polar molecules and the *heterogeneous* soil surface that has ionic and polar sites, resulting in stronger

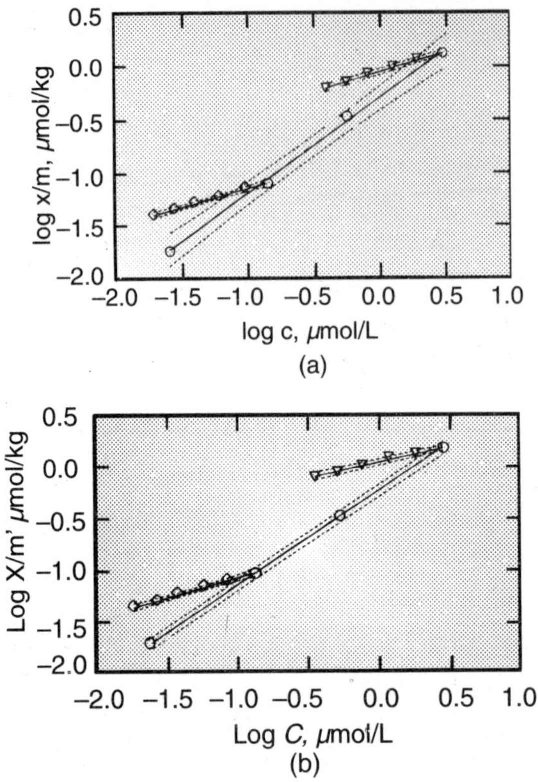

Figure 18.6: Sorption and desorption of imazethapyr on (a) Sassfras sandy loam and (b) Webster clay loam (45): 0 = sorption isotherm, 0 = desorption isotherm at 0.1728 μmol/L, and p = desorption isotherm at 3.4561 μmol/L.

sorption. Although most nonionic organic chemicals are subject to low energy bonding *mechanisms*, sorption of phenyl- and other substituted-urea pesticides such as diuron to soil or soil *components* has been attributed to a variety of *mechanisms*, depending on the sorbent.

The mechanisms include hydrophobic interactions, cation bridging, van der Waals forces, and *charge-transfer* complexes. Sorption in the soil is generally *controlled* by the rate of molecular diffusion into soil *aggregates* and the rate of reaction (rate of sorption) at the soil–water interface.

Diffusion has been found to be the rate-limiting step. Solute moves from mobile pore water to the sorbent surface *surrounded* by immobile pore water limiting the initial rate of sorption as sorption slows down.

The actual retention reactions tend to be relatively rapid, *particularly* the exchange-type reactions however, it has been proposed that two types of sorption sites may be involved that are *controlled* by the kinetics othe sorption process. In one report, sorption and desorption of atrazine and linuron on *sediments* reached 75% of the *equilibrium* value within 3 to 60 min; labile sites filled before restricted sites.

A pesticide may be retained on the soil surface sorption site initially by a rapid low energy binding *mechanism* and over time may bind to more stable high energy sites.

Sorption Modeling

Pesticide sorption is characterized by *describing* sorption isotherms using the Freundlich equation, $S = K_f C^N$, where S is the pesticide sorbed concentration, C is the pesticide solution *concentration* after equilibration, and K_f and N are constants. Although other *equations* have been used the Freundlich has satisfactorily described experimenta absorption results for a wide range of pesticides in a variety of soils.

The value of N is usually <1 and between 0.75 and 0.95, which indicates that pesticides are *proportionally* more sorbed at low solution *concentration* than at high solution *concentration*. For many modeling purposes, N has been assumed to be 1, resulting in a simplified equation, $S = K_d C$, where K_d is the linear distribution coefficient.

This assumption usually works for *hydrophobic* polycyclic aromatic *compounds* sorbed on sediments, if the *equilibrium* solution concentration is $<10^{-5}$ M. For many pesticides, the error introduced by the assumption of linearity depends on the deviation from linearity.

Because many studies have shown a direct relationship between pesticide sorption and organic carbon content of soil, attempts have been made to develop a *universal* sorption *coefficient* based on sorption of the pesticide to soil organic carbon. Sorption based on soil organic carbon is expressed as $S_{oc} = K_{oc} C$, where S_{oc} is pesticide sorbed per unit mass soil organic carbon, and C is pesticide solution *concentration* after equilibration.

If foc is the fraction of organic carbon, K_{oc} can be obtained from K_d in the equation $K_{oc} = K_d f_{oc}$. Assumptions in the use of this approach include sorption–desorption equilibrium, linearity of sorption isotherm, reversible sorption, sorption limited to the organic *component* of soil, and soil organic carbon having the same sorption capacity for different soils.

Because none of the *assumptions* is valid in the strict sense, the *magnitude* of error introduced in using this approach depends on how severely the assumptions are violated. For instance, imazethapyr is a weak acid herbicide and has both carboxylic acid and basic *quinolinnand* pyridine functional groups.

Imazethapyr is weakly sorbed. For four soils with different pH, % organic carbon and % clay, K_f ranged from 0.53 to 1.4; however, the range in K_{oc} was from 14 to 79, thus indicating that sorption is not limited to the organic component. Once sorbed, imazethapyr was only partially desorbable from all soils (N - desorption << $\hat{N}$ - sorption).

The hysteresis observed in desorption may be responsible for the difference between mobility estimations made from laboratory sorption studies and the limited mobility observed in the field.

Sorption coefficients are used in a variety of *applications*, ranging from *sophisticated* pesticide transport models to simplistic mobility screening models. The degree of rigor required in the *characterization* of sorption depend on the accuracy required of the intended use. In general, the greater the sorption coefficient, the greater the retardation of the pesticide while leaching through soil.

For instance, in mobility screening models, a Koc < 50 indicates that the pesticide is a leacher; a Koc > 500 indicates a nonleacher.

Indirect methods of *estimating* sorption have been used when actual *measurement* of sorption isotherm is impossible. For instance, sorption *coefficients* have been estimated from soil organic carbon and a specific surface of soil, and from *semiempirical* equations using pesticide properties.

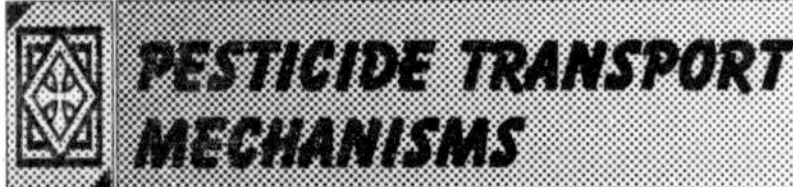

PESTICIDE TRANSPORT MECHANISMS

Pesticides can be transported away from the site of application either in the atmosphere or in water. The process of *volatilization* that transfers the pesticide from the site of application to the *atmosphere* has been discussed in detail. The off site *transport* and deposition can be at scales ranging from local to global.

Once the pesticide is in the atmosphere, it is subject to chemical and *photochemical* processes, wet deposition in rain or fog, and dry deposition. Water leaves the field either as surface runoff, carrying pesticides dissolved in the water or sorbed to soil particles *suspended* in water, or as water draining through the soil profile, carrying dissolved pesticides to deeper depths.

The distribution of water between drainage and runoff is dependent on the amount of water applied to the field, the physical and chemical properties of the soil, and the cultural *practices* imposed on the field. These factors also impact the retention and *transformation* processes affecting the pesticide. The documented occurrence of pesticides in surface water is indicative that runoff is an important *pathway* for transport of pesticide away from the site of application.d

An estimated 160 t of atrazine, 71 t of simazine, 56 t of metolachlor, and 18 t of alachlor enter the Gulf Mexico from the Mississippi River annually as the result of runoff. Field application of pesticides inevitably leads to pesticide *contamination* of surface runoff water unless runoff does not occur while pesticide residues remain on the surface of the soil.

The amount of pesticides *transported* in a field in runoff varies from site to site. It is controlled by the timing of runoff events, pesticide *formulation*, physical–chemical *properties* of the pesticide, and properties of the soil surface.

Under worst-case conditions, 10% or more of the applied pesticide can leave the edge of the field where it was applied. It appears that pesticides with solubilities greater than 10 mg/L are mainly *transported* in the aqueous phase as a result of the *interaction* of solution/sediment ratio in the runoff and the pesticide sorption coefficient.

For instance, on a silt loam soil with a steep slope (>12%), >80% of *atrazine* transport occurs in the aqueous phase. In contrast, it has been found that total *metolachlor* losses in runoff from plots with medium ground slopes (2–9%) were <1% of applied chemical. Of the metolachlor in the runoff, sediment carried 20 to 46% of the total transported pesticide over the *monitoring* period.

There are three basic strategies to control the amount of pesticide in runoff: reduce the amount of runoff of soil and water; lower the amount of pesticide in the runof; and retard the field-to-stream delivery of pesticide. Cultural practices can reduce the pesticide in runof. For instance, pesticide incorporation and contour plowing can lead to *significant* reductions in dissolved and sorbed pesticide *concentrations*, and in total metolachlor loss in runoff, relative to *application* as a *pre-emergence* spray with cross-contour plowing. Pesticide runoff is also affected by timing of *application*. For example, twice as much atrazine-applied pre-emergent was in the runoff water and sediment compared to that of applied post emergent.

Tillage practices have also been shown to have a dramatic impact on soil erosion and water runof. Conservation tillage systems and contouring have been shown in numerous studies to reduce sediment los in runoff, but water runoff is not necessarily affected.

The percentage of applied alachlor lost from up-and down slope moldboard plow, strip-till, and no-till were 6, <1, and 2%, respectively. Total loss from *contoured* moldboard plow, strip-till, and no-till were 2, <0.1, and 1%, respectively. The greater amounts of alachlor transported in no-till compared to strip-till were the result of pesticide washoff from plant foliage and residue. It was also found that alachlor and *carbofuran* were transported from plots largely in moving water, but terbufos and metabolites were recovered mainly in eroded sediment.

Conservation tillage increased atrazine and metolachlor surface runoff by 42% and decreased tile discharge by 15% compared with *conventional* tillage, but total field runoff was the same from all treatments. Runoff events shortly after herbicide application produced the greatest herbicide *concentrations* and losses in both surface runoff and subsurface drainage.

The influence of *conventional* and soil-specific management on leaching and runoff losses of soil-applied alachlof was studied across a soil catena (landscape) with varied slope and drainage characteristics. Averaged across soils and events, the *concentrations* of alachlor in runoff (water, sediments, and water) were less for soil-specific applcation rates than for the uniform application rate.

There is little information on the removal of pesticide from field runoff. However, water containing pesticide moving through a vegetative filter strip resulted in *reductions* of up to 70% for 2,4-D and up to 96% for trifluralin.

Pesticide Runoff Modeling

Obtaining the field data necessary to understand the potential runoff of pesticides under a variety of conditions and soils would be an expensive and time-consuming process. As a result, a variety of simulation models that vary in their conceptual approach and degree of complexity have been developed. Models are influenced by their *intended* purpose, the biases of the developer, and the scale at which they are used.

One of the first complete, *continuous simulation* models was the pesticide runoff transport model (PRT). Improvements in the PRT model led to the hydrologic simulation program–Fortran model. A number of other models have been developed. These models represent a *compromise* between the available data and the ability to *encompass* a wide range in soils, climates, and pesticides.

These models have had mixed succes when extended beyond the data with which they were calibrated. No model has yet been developed that can be proven to give accurate predictions of pesticide runoff on an absolute basis, i.e., predicting pesticide *concentrations* in runoff consistently to within a few percent.

Leaching

Numerous studies of pesticides in *groundwater* have indicated that *pesticides* are present as the result of agricultural practices and may be the product of both point source and nonpoint source pollution. The movement of pesticides in soil water depends on rainfall or irrigation water, the macroscopic and *microscopic* structure of the soil, and the sorption–desorption *characteristics* of the pesticide on the soil.

Water moves through the soil under both saturated and *unsaturated* conditions. When the soil is saturated with water, the pores are filled with water and transport occurs at the maximal rate. Movement of water and pesticide occurs at much slower rates under *unsaturated* conditions because only the smaller pores are filled and water moves in response to water potential gradients.

Generally, coarse-textured soils have greater rates of water *movement* than fine-textured soils when saturated. However, under *unsaturated* conditions, fintextured soils may have greater transport rates. In water, herbicides are transported by mass flow.

Highly soluble pesticides have a greater initial potential for *movement* than insoluble pesticides, assuming that sorption of both chemicals to soil is similar. *Simutaneously*, the chemical process of *diffusion* affects the distribution of herbicide in the water.

Dispersion resuling from *differential* flow rates within pores and sorption to soil retards the movement of *pesticides* relative to that of water, or a *noninteracting* tracer such as bromide. Soil pores have a wide range of sizes and lengths, and are highly *interconnected.*

A portion of the pore space usually is not part of the continuous flow path or flows at much slower than average rates. Pesticides can enter and exit these spaces through diffusion. Pesticide diffusion coefficients are inversely related to sorption, except for peticides of high vapor pressure, such as trifluralin, which have a high degree of movement as a volatile *compound* through air-filled pore space.

Because many pesticides are applied to the soil surface, the transport of pesticide during water infiltration is important. Water infiltration is *characterized* by high initial *infiltration* rates which decrease rapidly to a nearly constant rate.

Dry soils have greater rates of *infiltration* than wet soils during the initial application of water. Thus, *perfluridone* movement after application of 3.8 cm of water was *considerably* greater in soil at a water content of $<1\%$ of field capacity than at 50% of field capacity.

Fluometuron moved deeper into the soil in response to greater rainfall intensity or after rainfall onto a dry rather than a moist soil. Sorbed pesticides are not available for transport, but if water having lower pesticide *concentration* moves throug the soil layer, pesticide is desorbed from the soil surfac until a new equilibrium is reached.

Thus, the kinetics o sorption and desorption relative to the water *conductivit* rates determine the actual rate of pesticide transport. At high rates of water flow, chances are greater that sorption and desorption reactions may not reach equilibrium.

Nonequilibrium models may describe sorption and desorption better under these *circumstances.* The prediction of herbicide *concentration* in the soil solution is further complicated by hysteresis in the sorption–desorption isotherms.

Both sorption and dispersion contribute to the substantial retention of herbicide found behind the intial front in typical *breakthrough* curves and to the depth distribution of residues.

Pesticide Leaching Modeling

Modeling of pesticide movement through soil has received considerable attention beginning

Table 18.5: Application Rates of Sulfonylurea and Imidazoline Herbicides.

Name	*CAS Registry Number*	*Structure*	*Application Rate, g/ha*
Chlorsulfuron; 2-chloro-N-(4-methoxy-1,3,5-triazin-2-yl)-aminocarbonyl)benzenesulfonamide O O 0 CH_3	[64902-72-3]		4-26
Chlorimuron ethyl; ethyl 2-(((4-chloro-6-methoxy-pyrimidin-2–yl)aminocarbonyl)aminosulfonyl)-benzoate 1	[90982-32-4]		8-13
Imazapyr; 2-(4,5-dihydro-4-methyl-4-(1-methylethyl)-5-oxo-1H-imidazol-2-yl)-3-pyridinecarboxylic CH3	[81335-77-5]		150-200
Imazaquin; 2-(4,5-dihydro-4-methyl-4-(1-methylethyl)-5-oxo-1H-imidazol-2-yl)-3-quinolinecarboxylic acid	[81335-37-7]		70-140

about the time when groundwater *contamination* in numerous locations wad found. Simulation models can provide assessment of potential contamination of *groundwater* and alternative cultural practices; they can be used in lieu of expensive monitoring studies.

Numerous pesticide transport simulation models have been developed, including PRZM, LEACHM, CMLS, GLEAMS, and Opus. These models have met with varying degrees of successas a result of several factors. Spatial variability in soil properties and climatic conditions cause problems in characterizing pesticide leaching as well as limitations in the model's *characterization* of the soil/crop system.

Fo. instance, most models assume *homogeneous unsaturategfields*. However, many field studies have shown the existence of macropores resulting from soil aggregated structure, earthworm burrows, wetting and drying cracks, and decaying plant roots. Models are being developenin the 1990s to include preferential flow through the macropores. For pesticides to leach to *groundwater*, it may be neces dsary for preferential flow through *macropores* to dominate the sorption processes that control pesticide leaching to groundwater.

Several studies have demonstrated that large continuous macropores exist in soil and provied pathways for rapid movement of water solutes. Increased *permeability*, percolation, and solute transport can resu-from increased porosity, especially in no-tillage systems where pore structure is still intact at the soil surface.

Plant roots are important in creation and stabilization of soil macropores. Preferential flow through root-mediated soil pores has been *demonstrated* for chloride, nitrate, and other ions that are not sorbed onto soil organic matter and clays.

However, pesticide sorption onto soil affects both mobility of the pesticide as well as its residual life in the soi. Pesticide sorption onto root organic matter or organic linings of worm burrows may also slow transport of pesticides relative to water, thus countering the effects of increased *permeability* caused by roots.

Sorption and transport processes are directly or indrectly affected by soil *properties* such as soil moisture, temperature, pH, and organic carbon content. Tillage systems affect these same soil properties.

Conventional tillage systems can decrease moisture compared to *consevation* tillage systems, resulting in decreased degradation, *volatilization*, and leaching of the pesticide. Different tillage systems have different effects on soil temperature.

In general, increased tillage increases soil temperature in the spring and summer. Rates of chemical and micrbiological reactions and *volatilization* are temperaturdependent. Continuous application of *ammonium* fertilize in conservation tillage systems decreases pH substantially.

Tillage dramatically affects organic carbon content of soil. Once a soil is plowed for the first time, the organic carbon content begins to decrease. Leqving a residue on the surface, as in conservation tillage, increases the organic carbon content of the soil.

Soil microbial *populations* can be substantially greater in *conservation* tillage systems. The interaction of all these factors makes it difficult to predict an overall effect of conservation tillage on the potential leaching of a pesticide compared to that in a conventionally tilled field.

However, it was found that a prolonged rain *immediately* after application resulted in short-term levels of pesticide in groundwater to be greater under no-till than under conventional till plots, which *suggested* that preferential transport in no-till had occurred.

In contrast, it was suggested that there can be greater leaching losses of surface-applied pesticides to *groundwater* under plow-tillage than under no-till.

FUTURE TRENDS

The year-to-year *variation* in pesticide usage depends on weather, area planted, farm income, interest rates, previous year's inventory, extended labeling of existing products, deleted registrations, crop prices, strength of the U.S. dollar (exports), patent *expirations*, lawsuits, levels of pest infestation, and federal legislation and enforcement.

In addition, there are several important trends that influence the production and sales of pesticides and in turn have a *significant* impact on the detection of pesticides in the U.S. surface and groundwater supply.

New Herbicides

There arc also several *significant* developments that will have longer-term impact on pesticide usage and residues in water. There has been a steady decrease in the amount of herbicide needed to control weeds since the 1940s. Extensive use of two more recently developed classes of *herbicides* will further dramatically reduce the amount of applied to control weeds.

The *sulfonylurea herbicides* are extremely active compounds first *discovered* in the mid-1970s at DuPont; they have been discussed extensively. Sulfonylurea herbicides have *experienced* a rapid and widespread success since their *commercial* introduction in 1982 with chlorsulfuron.

The sulfonylureas are applied at rates of 2–75 g/ha. The chemistry of the *sulfonylurea* molecule permits the synthesis of a very large number of useful analogues, *consequently* many new herbicides are *anticipated* for crop production.

As of this writing (1996), over 350 patents have been issued to about 27 *agricultural* companies covering tens of millions of structures known or expected to be herbicidally active. Another class of herbicides, the imidazolines, was discovered at American Cyanamid in the early 1980s.

Extensive research has led to the development of four *commercial* compounds: imazapyr, *imazamethabenzmethyl*, imazethapyr, and imazaquin. Like the sulfonylureas, the imidazolines are extremely active at low rates.

Biotechnology

A second factor that will affect the future of the pesticide market are the advances made in biotechnology. Although *biotechnology* has played a *significant* role in medical technology, it has yet to make an important impact in pest control programs.

One of the most widely researched genetic engineering approaches involves inserting an insecticidal gene from *Bacillus thuringiensis* (Bt) into plants. Bt is a common gram-positive soil microorganism that produces insecticidal protein crystals, called ^{delta}endotoxins, that control a number of lepidopteran (caterpillar), dipteran (fly and mosquitos), and coleopteran (beetle) pests.

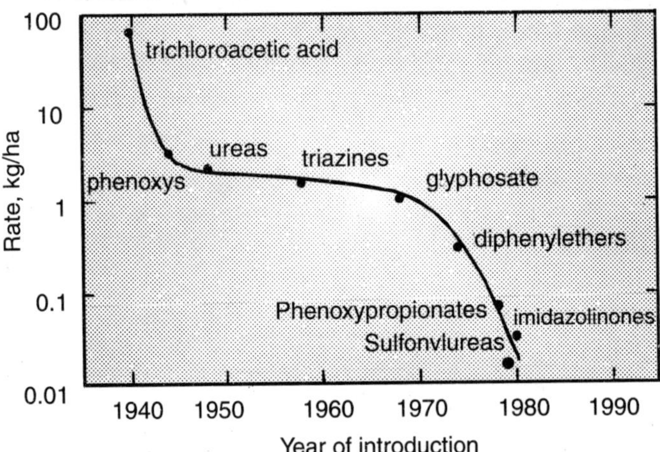

Figure 18.7: Historical trends in recommended herbicide applcation rates, by chemical class.

The crystals are highly condensed, high *molecular* weight proteins (typically 75–150 Kd in mass). The genes that encode the toxic protein are found on *plasmids* in the *Bacillus, i.e.,* small, *extrachromosomal,* self-replicating, circular pieces of DNA. By the use of plant vector systems, Bt genes have been inserted into tomato, potato, and tobacco plants.

These transgenic plants express (produce) enough of the endotoxin to be protected from feeding damage by insect larva. Insect resistance is stably inherited in *subsequent* plant generations. The Bt genetic approach is particularly attractive because the toxin is *extremely* safe to humans, fish, animals, and other nontarget organisms.

Genetic engineering (qv) research is also underway on soybeans to make them tolerant to the herbicide glyphosate, a broad-spectrum weed control agent generally considered extremely safe from an *environmental* standpoint.

Sustainable Agriculture

The third factor that will influence the future of pesticide sales is the emphasis on sustainable agriculture systems that rely on more natural pest control methods and reduced pesticide usage. These are integrated systems that require nutrients and crop protection chemicals from on-farm natural sources and cultural methods.

Many current sustainable farms are site-specific systems that may depend on the soils in a particular region and the *availability* of large volume, cheap *nutrient* sources, i.e., cover crops or manure. Composting is under renewed interest in the 1990s as a source of nutrients and natural pesticides.

In part the success of sustainable agriculture will depend on how well useful genes can be manipulated in economic crops via biotechnology.

New Legislation

A fourth factor that should reduce pesticide usage on a global basis are the regulations being passed in the 1990s in many countries, which are to limit the use of agricultural *chemicals* by specific deadlines. This trend is most apparent among the European Community (EC) of nations in Western Europe.

Pesticide usage is very high in the EC countries; Western Europe is the largest agrochemical sales market in the world. In 1991, for example, the EC held a 31% share of global agrochemical sales. Per hectare annually, Dutch farmers use about 20 kg of pesticides, considerably more than the *Belgian* producer, at 12.4 kg.

French and Swiss farmers use 6 kg; German farmers, 4 kg; and U.S. growers, 2.2 kg (2 lb/ acre). Holland has used pesticides intensively because of climatic *conditions* that are conducive to fungal and bacterial diseases, limited diversity in their crop rotations that would otherwise disrupt the life cycle of pests, and large exports of *propagated* materials, e.g., bulbs, that require high plant sanitary standards.

In 1991, the Dutch *government* instituted a plan to decrease pollution *pressures* from agrochemicals. One goal of the Dutch program is to reduce pesticide use by 50% by the year 2000. Another objective is to reduce the input of soil sterilization products to control insects, nematodes, and fungal pathogens by making purchase of the chemicals on a prescription basis with the *stipulation* that they can only be applied every four years to a particular field.

Denmark has passed similar *regulations* that would reduce pesticide use by 50% by 1995. The interim goal of 25% reduction by 1990 was reached in 1988. The French *government* is beginning to enact legislation that would protect water.

In April 1991, the French *Environmental* Ministry introduced a water plan to better manage water resources and decrease both point and nonpoint sources. Germany is working with individual growers to reduce agricultural production by reducing pesticide usage.

Local German *authorities* are prohibiting pesticide usage on *nonagricultural* fields. Biotechnology, use of highly active chemicals at lower rates, wide adoption of sustainable agriculture, and enactment of more restrictive use *regulations* will lower the pesticide burden in the *environment* and improve water quality.

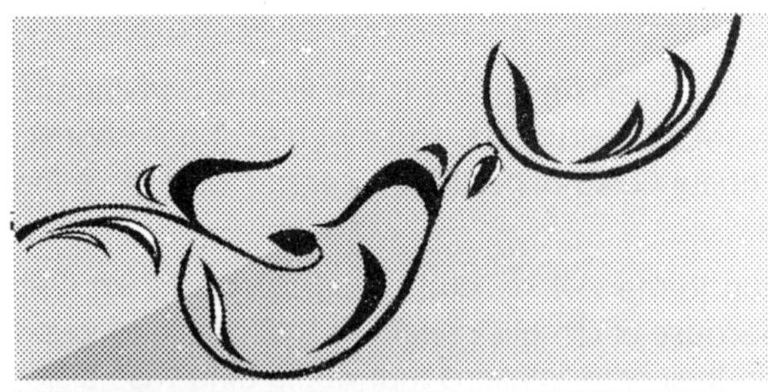

INDEX

A

B

C

D

E

F

G

H

I

J

K

L

M

N

O

P

Q

R

S

T

U

V

W

X

Y

Z